PFIESTERIA

Crossing Dark Water

The True Story Behind the Public
Health Menace That Now Threatens
the Nation's Tidal Waters

By the Maryland "Family Doc"
Who Blew the Whistle....

Ritchie C. Shoemaker, M.D.

 GATEWAY PRESS, INC.
Baltimore, MD   1998

Please direct all correspondence and book orders to:
Ritchie C. Shoemaker, M.D.
1604 Market St.
Pocomoke City, MD 21851

ISBN 0-9665535-0-0

Cover photographs by Robert L. Huey
Cover design by Janet Kratfel

Published for the author by
Gateway Press, Inc.
1001 N. Calvert Street
Baltimore, MD 21202

Printed in the United States of America

Dedication

This book is nonfiction. The events are described as they happened, and the watermen and their families—Ray Maddox, Tommy East, Jack Howard and Ray's wife, Lori —are quoted in their own words.

For the watermen of Maryland's Eastern Shore, the pfiesteria invasion of 1997 was much more than just another "science story." By taking away their health, pfiesteria took away their livelihoods, since these hard-working fishermen and crabbers depend on their ability to fish the waters in order to survive.

Dr. Shoemaker's work in diagnosis, treatment and prevention of acute pfiesteria-related illness, along with his analysis of the environmental problems that trigger pfiesteria outbreaks, is measurable in human health benefits. No longer do the watermen fear chronic disease from the river. No longer do the protests of the watermen go unheeded. No longer will others deny the importance of truth in the politics, economics and science of environmental study of pfiesteria.

This story is dedicated to the watermen, their families and those who share their love for the beauty of the Pocomoke River, a pristine and scenic jewel among Maryland's rivers.

Special thanks go to Debbie Hudson and JoAnn Shoemaker, whose efforts have made this book possible.

Table of Contents

Foreword

What if ...

What if you were a dedicated, hard-working family doctor ... and then one day, your neighbors began to tell you they'd "gotten sick" while swimming or fishing in the local river?

What if you examined them—and discovered they were right?

What if you quickly sounded the alert ... but the public health authorities refused to admit that the illness existed, or that it was being caused by a pollution-linked biological invader that had crept into the nearby watershed?

Question: If you were the local "family doc," what would you do?

This book tells the gripping story of a medical doctor who was forced to answer these very questions.

Pfiesteria: Crossing Dark Water describes what happened when Ritchie Shoemaker, M.D.—a 45-year-old practicing physician in Pocomoke City, Maryland—discovered that people were being made sick by the "pfiesteria blooms" that began occurring in the Chesapeake Bay watershed in 1997 ... and that are now threatening other U.S. watersheds as well.

For Dr. Shoemaker, the year that followed his discovery was marked by continuing controversy and political struggle.

First, the Maryland State Department of Health and Department of Natural Resources denied that anyone was sick.

Then, they insisted that the obvious human illness was caused by "manure runoff" ... rather than by agricultural chemicals and pesticides that are routinely used in modern agriculture and animal feeds. Those substances are usually safe when used on land—but they can become highly toxic when they contaminate watersheds. And one-third of the Eastern Shore of Maryland is water.

Although the politicians labeled his theory as "improbable" and "irresponsible," Ritchie Shoemaker fought on—eventually becoming the first physician to prove that human illness is acquired from pfiesteria toxin, and that the illness can be treated.

At the same time, Dr. Shoemaker was working furiously to develop the first scientifically accurate model showing how the application of permanganate will stop pfiesteria dead in its tracks.

Ritchie Shoemaker challenged the government scientists and the health officials (including the Maryland governor's own hand-picked Commission on Pfiesteria) … and he won!

Part political history and part high-speed eco-thriller, *Pfiesteria: Crossing Dark Water* tells the amazing story of how a lone "country doc" proved that the little guy can stand up to City Hall.

Scientifically documented from start to finish, *Pfiesteria: Crossing Dark Water* reveals the hidden forces that produced one of Maryland's—and the nation's—most pressing environmental dangers. Yet the book ends on a note of hope.

According to the doctor from Pocomoke, it's still not too late to turn back the dark tide of pfiesteria—by implementing appropriate and effective public health and environmental policies, instead of relying on outdated "politics as usual" to stave off this growing national threat.

chapter 1

Autopsy

July 6

It began on a steamy July afternoon in 1997, when a man named Ray called my office to tell me about a dead fish.

"Dr. Shoemaker? Ray Maddox is on the line—he says it's important."

"Thanks, Joyce. Tell him I'll be right with him."

I had just taken some fluid from an arthritic patient's knee, and I was about to put it under the microscope. Like most smalltown doctors, I spend a lot of time helping folks manage chronic illnesses such as arthritis, diabetes and hypertension. I do my best to comfort them and relieve their pain. After a few years, I begin to know them not as "people with diseases"—but as living, breathing human beings who have become my friends.

After more than eighteen years as a "smalltown doc," that daily human interaction is the thing I've come to cherish most.

But Ray Maddox hadn't called to tell me about his aching lumbago or his nagging shin splints.

"Hiya, Doc! Say … I've got that fish for you."

"Hello, Ray. Thanks for the call. Did you find a fresh one?"

"Yessir, I sure did. A 14-inch trout. We pulled him out of the river just two hours ago. He's in real bad shape, Doc—a blood-burster, with fresh lesions all over him. This is definitely the fish you wanted to see. He looks like all the other dead fish we've been picking up for the past eight months now. The state keeps saying it's a natural thing, but I know it isn't."

"I've got him on ice, Doc, but he ain't gonna keep long before he starts stinking to high heaven!"

He chuckled once, deep in his throat, and I had a quick mental image of this ruddy-faced, Eastern Shore waterman. For a moment I could picture Ray leaning from the cab of his battered Ford pick-up, broad-shouldered and sun-burned and grinning hard, as he listened to a buddy brag about some monster-sized bass he'd just caught.

But the burly fisherman wasn't joking around now, as he described the massive "fish kills" that were taking place almost weekly in his beloved Pocomoke.

"We found at least 30 dead fish in the nets today, Doc. And we pulled up more yesterday, in a different spot. That last big rain just set the killing off. The dead fish were all bleedin' … and when I cut into 'em, it looked like the flesh had dissolved. Looked like something had been feeding on 'em. Whaddya think?"

Frowning, I paused to reflect for a moment. I was a family practitioner, not a fish specialist! But if the principles of biology applied to "both mice and men," perhaps they applied to fish as well. At any rate, I was eager to help, and for a very simple reason: As a self-educated naturalist and outdoorsman, I loved the Pocomoke River.

Alarmed by the scary stories I was hearing, I'd vowed to get to the truth about was happening to the fish and the fishermen in my neck of the Pocomoke woods. The ugly fish lesions and the "dissolved flesh" suggested a toxic agent. Had some kind of mysterious poison been attacking fish in our river? Was this a violent bacteria attack? Fertilizer runoff? Industrial pollution? Some lethal combination of the above? And what about those recent fish kills in coastal North Carolina, with millions wiped out since 1991 by an organism with the unlikely-sounding name of "pfiesteria"?

It was complicated, all right. "Sorry, Ray," I told the worried fisherman on the other end of the phone, "but I don't have any answers for you right now. I'm gonna have to put that fish of yours through an autopsy. Maybe even send him up to Dr. Taylor in the pathology lab at Peninsula Regional. I won't stop until I get some answers."

"Fair enough, Doc." I could hear the agitated Maddox breathing hard on his end of the line. "Listen, have you heard about what happened to some of the boys down here in Shelltown?"

"You mean the fellows working with you—the ones who keep getting sick all the time?"

"That's right," growled the veteran commercial fisherman and crabber. "Some of them guys around Shelltown have been mighty sick, the past few months. My father has worked these waters for sixty years, and he's never seen anything like it."

"So I've heard, Ray." I'd been listening to rumors about God-awful diarrhea, doubling-over cramps and blinding headaches suffered by fishermen for several months now. There were also one or two vague reports of people with "memory loss"—whatever that might mean. "Tell me something, Ray: How come none of these folks have come to me for medical care?"

"Well, you know, they stick with their old doctor, the one that birthed 'em and raised 'em. You know Tommy East, don't ya? He got pneumonia seven different times last winter, back when the dead fish first started turning up in the nets. And Jack Howard ... his skin lesions and his stomach cramps got so bad, last spring, he had to quit working on the water for two months!

"Something's wrong down here, Doc. Something's bad wrong

along the river, and we're hoping you can tell us what it is. Can you come on down here and pick up this fish?"

I shook my head. "Sorry, Ray. I've got a boatload of patients scheduled this afternoon. How about if I ask Jack Spurling to do it? Would that be all right with you?"

"Sounds good to me," said Ray. "Jack knows where to find me. But you better tell him to hurry. That trout's oozin' blood, and I don't know how much longer he'll last."

"I'll call him right now."

"Thanks, Doc. Give me a holler, as soon as you know something?"

"You bet I will, Ray."

I hung up, and went back to my microscope and my arthritis-test.

▼   ▼   ▼

A retired meteorologist from NASA, Jack Spurling was a devoted naturalist. He was also a dedicated volunteer—a gung-ho envionmentalist who'd spent the best part of a year helping me build a mile-long "Nature Trail" through the ecologically unique Pocomoke Swamp.

When I told Jack about Ray Maddox and the "blood-bursting trout," he headed straight for his car. And by five o'clock that same afternoon, I was striding into the medical lab that adjoins my office at 1604 Market Street in downtown Pocomoke City.

First I set the package that Spurling had given me down on the stainless steel table at the center of the lab. Then I pulled on a pair of latex surgical gloves. A moment later, I was unwrapping the dead trout that Ray Maddox had pulled from the river earlier that day.

I closed my eyes for a moment, as the unmistakeable aroma of dead fish assaulted my nostrils. Then I pulled away the last of the newspaper-wrapper and began my inspection of Ray Maddox's catch.

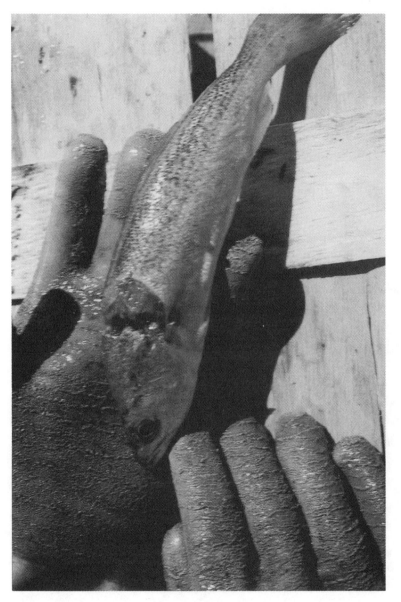

Blood bursting fresh lesioned trout.

Fish of all species had grotesque lesions.

At first glance, this 14-inch grey trout resembled any other member of the species "Salmonidae." Brown-speckled and narrow-mouthed, the graceful-looking creature came equipped with sleek fins and a tail powerful enough to send him zooming through the water at will. What a thing of beauty ...

But then I took a closer look, and caught my breath.

No slime.

Somehow, this trout had lost patches of protective slime—the transparent, mucous-like substance that protects fish from invasion by any number of different kinds of fish-eating germs.

Not good. And there was more: On the fish's ventral side, I quickly discovered a raw, circular area, about an inch in diameter, that appeared to be covered with small red bubbles. What the hell was going on here? Was the fish bleeding from inside, somehow bleeding right through his own skin and scales?

Intent on solving the mystery, I reached for the scalpel.

As soon as I made the first cut, I got a surprise. The bubbles were bursting, one by one, releasing waves of liquid, unclotted blood. Beneath the carnage, I soon discovered another grisly fact: The underlying muscle had been dissolved away!

There was no doubt about what was going on here.

I was looking at a classic example of "liquefaction necrosis," aka "death by dissolving." It was the kind of scenario that usually occurs in the presence of a toxin ... and in tissues that have been deprived of most of their oxygen.

As I snipped off several biopsy specimens for the microscope, I reviewed the morphology. What kinds of illnesses—or poisons—could cause this kind of devastation in living tissue? Was I looking at some kind of "gangrene-event," which might suggest an earlier trauma, followed by the dissolving of these cells? Had the "flesh-eating strep disease" left the pages of the National Enquirer ... only to turn up in the Pocomoke?

Or had my trout somehow ingested an organic poison, while feeding out there on the bottom of the tranquil river?

Not likely.

Utterly at a loss for an explanation, I began to carefully inspect the rest of the fish. But nothing struck me as particularly unusual ... nothing, that is, except for the marine creature's brain covering, the meninges, which seemed almost purple, rather than than normal pearly-white. Was this abnormality related to the necrosis? And what about the fact that the fish's spleen felt a bit thicker than it should? Did that matter, or not?

Increasingly mystified, I was forced to admit that I didn't know what the hell I was doing. At this point, only one thing seemed certain: The ruthless invader that had devoured this trout's muscles had entered the fish through a hole in the protective slime layer. How did I know this? It was simple. Other parts of the fish had lost some slime-layer, and only those areas displayed liquefaction.

Suddenly, the sequence of biological events seemed clear. The breach of the slime layer came first; after that, it was open season for any aggressive fish-flesh eater. One quick look at the dissolved flesh was enough to show that it had been destroyed long before the lesions made their ugly appearance on the fish's bleeding skin.

The killer-toxin—whatever it was—had blasted its way through the slime first, then chewed ruthlessly at the vulnerable tissue beneath.

I was looking at a first-class scientific mystery.

Nor did I have the faintest clue—on that humid July afternoon of '97—as to whether or not the toxic villain that had killed the trout might also have the ability to break through human defenses, and then ravage at will. Headaches ... cramps ... diarrhea. What had made the watermen of Shelltown so sick in recent months? What had caused Tommy East's recurring pneumonia, Jack Howard's terrible cramps?

It was time to get some help.

It was time to call in Robert Taylor, M.D., the crackerjack pathologist over at Peninsula Regional Hospital in Salisbury, located only 35 miles north on Rte. 13. Taylor was a veteran disease-analyst who had helped me more than once as I struggled to diagnose unusual cases involving my patients in the past.

Maybe Dr. Taylor had seen this kind of massive toxin-liquefaction at work before.

▼　　▼　　▼

The Pocomoke: If there's a more beautiful, more soul-stirring body of water on Planet Earth, I have yet to find it.

Drift along the Pocomoke River in a silent canoe—as I have so often during my 18 years of living on Maryland's bucolic Eastern Shore—and you'll soon begin to feel the magic of this sinuous, marshland stream. No more than 50 yards wide in many places, the Pocomoke snakes through farmland and swamp, past sleepy rural villages and immense cypress trees, as it meanders south from Delaware into the heart of Maryland's Eastern Shore coastal plain.

The mighty Algonquin were the first to feel the river's haunting power. They named her "Pocomoke," which means both "dark water" and "broken ground" (a reference to the cypress knees in the surrounding swamp)—and which captures in only two words the living mystery of this astonishing watercourse. *Dark Water ...*

Dip your paddle into the river's mahogany- and tannin-hued surface, and all at once you're watching a startled great blue heron boil up out of the shallows, before zooming away in upward soaring flight. Drift around that next looping bend, and the river opens onto a vista of sun-dappled water and black gum trees nodding their heads above the lapping current. *Pocomoke.* Lean back, take a deep breath, and the scent of wild rose and sweet bay magnolia tantalizes you with the promise of an unspoiled, unchanging Eden.

But this paradise also had a shadow-side. This black water had hidden dark mysteries before. More than once, the tidal flow and the downstream current had swept hapless youngsters into the depths, causing unforgettable tragedies that were also part of the river's haunting legacy.

During nearly 20 years of practicing family medicine in tiny Pocomoke City (three stoplights and 4,000 inhabitants), I had come to love the river like a part of my family. And why not? How many times had I paddled across her shadowy surface, accompanied by my wife JoAnn and our excited daughter, Sally?

How many times (not often enough!) had I whiled the afternoon away with a pal from the nearby town—or maybe one of my medical patients—while pursuing the river's elusive largemouth bass, or her crafty perch and bluegill?

As an enthusiastic, community-oriented naturalist, I had also worked long and hard with other like-minded folks for several years to build a mile-long "nature trail" alongside the river. Accompanied by a series of wetland gardens and ponds, the nature trail had been the heart of a three-year, $300,000 conservation project for which I'd done most of the fundraising. And what a thrill it was, these days, to stroll along the "floating boardwalk" we'd erected beneath the black gums and the swamp maples, so that people from all over the world could enjoy our wooded wetlands.

Imagine my shock, then, on a dismal and rainy morning in the fall of 1996, when I opened my morning newspaper to discover that there was trouble in paradise, and that my beloved Pocomoke had been poisoned by some mysterious alien that no one could identify.

The nightmare had begun in October of '96, when the "watermen" (professional fishermen, crabbers and oyster-tongers) who worked the river and the adjoining Pocomoke Sound began discovering dead fish not far from their home base of Shelltown, a tiny hamlet located 14 miles south of Pocomoke City.

Day after day, as the newspapers from Salisbury and Washington and Baltimore dramatically reported, these troubled watermen had been pulling scores of dead trout, perch, carp, mud shad, menhaden and eel from their nets.

But these marine victims weren't just dead. They were also horribly disfigured—covered with bloody lesions that showed where some marauding attacker had gnawed right through their scales and flesh, all the way down to their bones and spines. It was scary stuff … and the news media pushed the story for all it was worth. Had an "alien" microorganism invaded our peaceful Pocomoke, wreaking biological havoc and producing the kind of "toxic meltdown" that more properly belonged in the "X-Files" of television fame?

Or were these mysterious fish-deaths simply part of a mundane local story about fertilizer runoff and industrial pollution, or maybe a surging "algae bloom" that had briefly upset the ecological balance around the Pocomoke Swamp?

What was going on here? Even more troubling than the sudden fish-kills were the stories I was beginning to hear in my medical practice on Market Street—stories about fishermen who had come down with mysterious cramps and fever and diarrhea, and even with life-threatening pneumonia, on several occasions. Was the "alien" also beginning to attack the human beings who lived and worked along the river?

Also: Was there a link between the Pocomoke invasion and the devastating "pfiesteria" plague that had been killing fish by the millions in the coastal waters of North Carolina during the early 1990s?

Alarmed by these questions, Maryland Democratic Governor Parris N. Glendening—who would be facing a tough reelection battle in 1998—had already ordered four separate departments of the State of Maryland to investigate the source of the fish lesions.

Led by Department of Natural Resources Secretary John Griffin, investigators from Environment, Health, DNR and Agriculture were already swarming back and forth across the scene of the carnage, intent on scrutinizing the outbreak and its possible impact on the state's huge fishing and crabbing industry. So far, however, the biologists and the politicians had created more heat than light, as they debated furiously among themselves about both the cause of the plague and the remedies that might be used to combat it.

But the "Great Pfiesteria Debate" wasn't happening in a vacuum. While the scientists collected their endless water samples, the watermen who lived along the river were holding their collective breath. Their livelihoods were at stake, and they knew it. If they didn't get some help, and fast, they might very well end up losing their entire industry ... which was precisely what would happen, if the Gov decided to declare the Pocomoke "off limits" for an extended period of time.

For men like Ray Maddox and Jack Howard and Tommy East, the answers to these questions would determine nothing less than economic survival. The stakes were high.

And they were going to get much higher, very soon.

chapter 2

Background

July 6

On the morning after the fish autopsy, I made my call to Dr. Taylor, the pathology wizard at Peninsula Regional. I caught him in his huge lab on the fifth floor, and when he heard my voice on the line, he chuckled out loud.

"What do you want this time, Ritchie?"

Dr. Taylor was quite accustomed to fielding my eager questions about unusual maladies affecting my patients. But I wasn't talking about distorted auto-immune responses or the allergen-factor in triggering asthma attacks, today. Instead, I raced through a high-speed description of the mauled fish, the reports about pfiesteria, the growing concerns about the sick watermen.

As always, Dr. Taylor listened patiently. Then: "Sounds to me like you're sitting on a medical mystery, Ritchie. Will you send me that fish specimen [chemically preserved] in formalin? I'll be happy to take a look, no charge."

He paused for a moment, and I could hear the wheels turning over in Salisbury. "I'll do my best, Ritch—but I warn you that I'm not a fish pathologist!"

"That's all right," I said gratefully. "If the source of those lesions can be diagnosed under a microscope, I know you'll find it."

I thanked him, hung up, and went to work on my caseload for the day. Suddenly, it was a relief to be listening to complaints about lower back pain and sinus infections again, as I resumed the endless round of consultations and prescriptions that has been my professional life for the past two decades.

The truth was, I dearly loved the daily practice of medicine. As a "smalltown family doc," I got a terrific charge out of helping my patients enjoy healthier, more vigorous lives. Whether I was counseling a senior citizen with hypertension ("Let's talk about exercise!") or trying to convince an esophageal "reflux"-sufferer to quit smoking ("Listen, I know you can do it!"), I found huge amounts of satisfaction in my role as a rural physician.

Along with caring for my patients, I was also fascinated by the mysteries of medical science. How did an antibody attack an invading germ and kill it? How did the chemical base pairs in DNA send the "instructions" to developing cells, thus creating such human traits as blond hair, brown eyes, or the ability to run 100 yards in less than ten seconds?

Starting way back at Carlisle High School in Pennsylvania, those kinds of questions had inspired my continuing curiosity. As an enthusiastic high school science student, in fact, I'd been named "most likely to succeed"—partly on the basis of my frequent declaration that I was going to singlehandedly find the cure for cancer!

Looking back today on those adolescent years of feverish idealism and urgency, I've come to understand that my hard-charging attitude was probably a genetic inheritance. As the son of a chemical engineer and a schoolteaching mom, after all, I'd been encouraged every day of my life to look for the nearest intellectual challenge, and then immediately take it on.

Born in Charlotte, N.C., in 1951, I'd grown up in several American cities and towns (Charlotte; Wilbraham, Mass.; Princeton, N.J.; Hinsdale, Ill. and Carlisle, Pa.), as my father's engineering career took him through a number of job-transfers. More than once, in fact, I'd dreamed of becoming an engineer, myself. But I soon discovered, after enrolling at Duke University in the fall of 1969, that the fine arts of structural and mechanical engineering were rapidly becoming just another branch of computer science.

No thanks. I wanted something livelier ... something that would provide me with a few thrills and spills, while also preparing me for the kind of public service-oriented research career that I dreamed of.

After a few exhilarating semesters at Duke, I found the vocational rollercoaster that I'd been searching for, and its name was "physiology"—with a side order of molecular biology. Finding out how things biological worked at the fundamental levels turned me on. Enrolled in a challenging course on protozoology, I found myself squinting hard into a microscope, caught up in an endless pursuit of one-celled creatures who turned out to have lives every bit as exciting and unpredictable as those of their multi-celled cousins —if only you knew how to get down on their level and really scrutinize them.

Ask any medical or science student to tell you about that "magical moment" when the bright light of intellectual curiosity switches on, and you'll probably hear an exciting story like the story of what happened to me the first time I eyeballed a colony of Euglena.

I met Euglena one Saturday morning in a biology lab at Duke, after loading a fresh slide into a high-powered microscope. Tiny, one-celled animals (remember the "paramecium," from your own high school days?), these feisty critters came equipped with a whip-like tail (the "flagellum") and a keen sensitivity to any form of light.

Perched above my microscope, I realized that I was having the time of my life, as I ran some experiments designed to show how this minuscule organism responded to light by ratcheting up its reproduction rate, while zipping around its aquatic environment like a teenager sky-high on brand-new hormones.

As a one-celled "flagellate," Euglena was a cousin to the "dino-flagellate" pfiesteria organism that would invade our lovely Poco-moke 25 years later. But all I knew about the hyperactive Euglena then was that it gave me a marvelous opportunity to learn how nature operates, way down there on the micro-level where so many vitally important biological processes are actually carried out.

What a blast I was having in that biology lab! And yet my hours with the microscope were strictly limited by economic necessity. Since I was paying my own way through college (a personal choice), I found myself working four and five part-time jobs at once ... and without the luxury of being able to spend entire days huddled over a platoon of darting Euglena.

In spite of these constraints, however, my love of research was growing by the hour, and I felt certain that the laboratory life was the life for me. But when I finally began my experiments on DNA replication during my junior year, I also began to understand just how incredibly arduous, detailed and repetitive microbiological research really is.

My undergraduate research project at Duke had been an electron microscope study which focused on DNA replication in a one-celled protozoan called "tetrahymena." While trying to understand how the enzymes that triggered this reproduction process were regulated by metals, I read a ton of research materials that described how these often-studied protozoans had been used for years to monitor pollution and heavy metals in estuaries.

Although I didn't know it at the time, the stage was being set for my later discovery of the key role copper plays in unleashing the fish-eating form of pfiesteria. Deeply interested in the physiology of cancer, I spent hundreds of hours studying DNA replication, and for an obvious reason: Cells can't divide and cancers can't grow without it!

But the work was endlessly repetitive, and in the end, I had to face the facts: The drudgery of daily research on this incredibly complex, molecular level was simply too high a price for me to pay.

As a gregarious, fun-loving fellow who enjoys being with other people, I was also beginning to understand that the lonely life of the dedicated, solitary researcher would not be enough. I needed to be around other folks, day in and day out, in order to keep hitting on all eight cylinders.

Of course, it was also true that my undergraduate studies weren't taking place in a vacuum. The late 1960s and early 1970s were a period of political upheaval and social unrest, as the Vietnam War entered its final phase and an entire generation continued to question the assumptions and values that ruled America.

One of the most exciting initiatives to emerge from this youthful idealism was the growing "Family Practice" movement in American medicine. Led by the American Board of Family Practice (organized in 1969), the movement spoke urgently to many of us who wanted to see medicine return to its roots as a family-oriented service aimed at caring for ordinary people, day in and day out.

By 1972, as I prepared to head off to Duke Medical School, I understood one fact with compelling clarity: I no longer wanted to be a lab-based researcher, even though I loved the intellectual challenge of learning about life's processes. I wanted to concentrate now on helping patients.

I was going to work with people—not one-celled protozoans. Intent on becoming a "family-practice doctor" who would still make occasional house calls when required, I found the climate at the high-powered and high-tech Duke Medical School to be far less interested in providing "primary care" than I was.

And my response? As always, I decided to take the bull by the horns ... and quickly launched "First Contact," a small brochure in which I published articles on subjects related to primary care: accessibility, costs, quality, you name it.

That tiny publication soon grew into a national journal with more than 800 subscribers, and thus became the first medical student publication of its kind. Although "First Contact" didn't last very long, it succeeded beautifully in calling attention to the Family

Practice movement—while also strengthening me in my decision to become a practicing family physician.

With "First Contact," I had bucked the medical establishment, and I'd lived to tell about it. Energized as never before, I threw myself into my medical studies, and into my regular shifts at the Duke Medical Center in Durham, where I was being given more and more responsibility as a medical student who would soon have his degree in hand.

It was during these "on-call" shifts at Duke Medical that I began to discover the reverence—the deep-seated affection and respect—for patients that would later form the heart of my family practice, first as a resident in Williamsport, Pa., and then, starting in 1980, in the rural and easygoing world of Maryland's Eastern Shore.

During four years of medical training and then three years of residency at Williamsport, I would experience many moments in which both the sacredness of life and the inestimable value of human beings impressed themselves upon me with burning urgency.

I know I'll never forget the night at Duke Medical Center when I lost my first patient, a young man named "Billy Joe" who died of cancer. Only 21 years old, the kid had dreamed of a career as a musician, and had shared his hopes with me on many occasions. And he'd fought like a tiger against the lymphoma that would ultimately claim him. But he'd lost his battle, finally, and when the end came I was holding his hand.

It was the kind of moment that stays with most young doctors, and it certainly stayed with me. After that night, I redoubled my efforts to become the very best healer I could be ... and to go on getting to know every single one of my patients as much as possible, even though it meant confronting the grief of losing one of them every now and then.

As the years passed in Pocomoke, my life was enriched by my marriage to JoAnn. Soon our daughter Sally came along to charm and enchant us. I also found that I was delighting more and more in the house that JoAnn and I had built at the edge of the river.

More and more, I was finding spiritual peace, a saving joy in the thousands of trees that she and I were planting in our little corner next to the Pocomoke River.

Later still, after putting in those three years of volunteer work on the Nature Trail, I felt proud that I'd helped to build a kind of spiritual oasis for the entire community—a peaceable kingdom in which dozens of people shared and enjoyed the task of protecting this precious marshland.

When the plague arrived in 1996—the bleeding lesions, the dead and rotting fish—I took it personally. And when I kept on hearing the same mantra from the state—"The river is safe; humans can't get sick from the river!"—I took that personally, too.

I was determined to get to the bottom of the nightmare, and I was determined to go to war against whatever dark forces, biological or otherwise, had invaded our little corner of paradise.

▼   ▼   ▼

It took the Salisbury pathologist, Dr. Taylor, several days to analyze the lesioned trout I'd sent him. And when he called me back, there was a note of fascinated curiosity in his voice.

"The flesh of the specimen does show deep, penetrating ulcers," said Dr. Taylor, "but we weren't able to identify a definite cause."

I shook my head in frustration. "How about *clostridia*?" (The *clostridia* family of bacteria were famous for producing toxins that liquified muscle.)

"Nope, no *clostridia*," said the Salisbury-based pathologist. Then he went on to explain that the attack on the fish had, indeed, triggered a white blood cell response—the kind of reaction that you'd expect from an infection. A lining of regrowing cells was surrounding the destroyed tissue, in effect walling it off from the rest of the tissue of the fish ... which meant that by the time you saw the lesions in these unfortunate fish, it was too late. The physiological damage had already been done.

But what did all of these ugly symptoms actually mean? It was a real puzzle. Could the pfiesteria toxin have punched through the fish's slime layer, scales and skin, en route to attacking the muscle? Of did the one-celled bug simply open the door for something else —another microorganism that did the actual feeding on the fish-tissue?

Dr. Taylor was as intrigued by the biology problem as I was. "Good luck, Ritchie! Let me know if I can help ... and if I get some more time up ahead, I'll be happy to take a look at anything else you come up with."

I was delighted to hear it. Taylor was an outstanding microbiologist, and he'd already come to my rescue several times in the past ... starting way back in 1983, when he'd been instrumental in helping me to pinpoint an unusual case of "cat scratch fever" in one of my patients.

Is there any joy quite like the joy of solving a medical mystery? After carefully examining my 1983 patient's enlarged lymph nodes, I'd spent several days ransacking my medical library in search of answers, before discovering a provocative article by Dr. Andrew Margelith, a top researcher at the Armed Forces Institute of Pathology. Margelith had come up with a special staining technique that for the first time showed that a bacteria caused cat scratch fever.

Bingo! Convinced that my patient was afflicted with this malady, I'd quickly petitioned Taylor, whose staff had kindly forwarded the specimen to the Institute. Within a matter of days, Dr. Margelith was using the tissue sample I sent to try to grow the cat scratch germ in the lab—the first time that such an attempt had been made in the annals of research! (The formal study describing his breakthrough lab-culture would appear in 1988.)

Can you see why I was such a fan of Dr. Taylor and the Armed Forces Institute? But that wasn't the first time I'd relied on their shared expertise in order to help a patient. In 1981, while volunteering at a local migrant-worker camp on the Eastern Shore, I'd come across a Haitian vegetable picker with a bizarre lump. A local surgeon had removed the offending tissue—but what was it? Dr. Taylor?

Presto: Within weeks, he'd identified the source of the lump—a rare mycobacterium, "avium intracellulare," which was later confirmed at the Institute.

And what an eye-opener it was, four years later, when we began hearing about the links between this usually non-virulent bacterium and AIDS ... a connection that would soon join the growing body of knowledge about the growing AIDS outbreak of the mid-1980s.

In the end, avium intracellulare would be identified as an "AIDS-Defining Illness" ... and the world would learn that it most frequently occurred among three groups of people: homosexuals, IV-drug users and Haitians. Without knowing it (and before we knew anything about "universal precautions"), Dr. Taylor and the rest of us had been working at the frontier of the AIDS epidemic.

When it came to solving bacteriological puzzles, Dr. Taylor was simply invaluable. How I wished I'd called him during the pneumonia epidemic of 1987, over in Ocean City, when I found myself consulting with more than 30 previously healthy patients who'd come down with a severe, atypical pneumonia.

To my amazement, blood tests aimed at pinpointing acute reaction levels of immunity (IgM antibodies) turned up positive for a variant of Legionnaire's bacteria! Adding to my concern was the fact that the patients got better with antibiotics like erythromycin, but not with penicillins or cephalosporins. This was the same scenario that had unfolded back in Pennsylvania in 1976, when so many died of Legionnaire's that the story went front-page for several weeks.

After reading up on the problem for several days, I went to work on discovering the source of the infection. But I had no way of imagining that I was about to get my first, frightening look at how the State of Maryland's medical bureaucracy could slow down vitally important research by dragging its regulatory feet.

What happened was this: When I reported these cases of the unusual form of Legionnaire's Disease, the State Department of Health and Mental Hygiene responded not by issuing a health alert—but by simply changing the criteria that it used to identify a "positive case." And their motivation? As far as I was concerned, it seemed rather obvious: With 500,000 tourists swarming into the Ocean City resort beaches each weekend, the state wasn't about to issue any scary health-bulletins about the possible presence of Legionnaire's just before Memorial Day.

In this case, the medical foot-dragging at the state level seemed transparently obvious. First, the Health Department changed its criteria for "positive" by changing the "dilution requirements" in the lab tests. Up until that summer, you see, the Department had required blood-serum to test out positive after being diluted 16 times. But when I sent them four cases that met that criteria, the medical honchos quickly changed the guidelines. Suddenly, the test had to read positive after 32 times dilution.

Fair enough: I quickly sent them five cases of 32 times dilution. What happened next? You guessed it: Almost overnight, the Health Department decided that the dilution-standard should be raised to 64! Doing my best to shake off my disbelief, I packaged up reports on seven patients—each of whose blood-serums had been diluted 128 times.

The state response was quite interesting. Instead of confirming my diagnosis—on the basis of their own guidelines—the medical brass announced that the test they'd been using in previous years was "no longer diagnostic"—and that there was no discernible health risk!

Those Ocean City tourist-dollars would remain safe ... even if some of the tourists, themselves, would end up running the risk of contracting the dreaded Legionnaire's Disease.

End of story. Although I spent several weeks grinding my teeth in frustration during that episode, there was a bright side: This maddening encounter with the state's medical bureaucracy had prepared me well for the much larger brouhaha that would surround the pfiesteria outbreak, as the political and economic consequences of the infestation triggered a major public-policy showdown along the banks of the Pocomoke.

By the middle of July, then, I was knee-deep in research on the microbiological Frankenstein that had attacked our river. Encouraged by Dr. Taylor's analysis, I spent several days on the telephone, ringing up every expert I could find—starting with Dr. Eric May, a fish pathologist over at the combined federal and state biology labs in Oxford. Dr. May listened carefully to my analysis of the problem, then made a delightful suggestion: Did I want to join him at Ray Maddox's warehouse in Shelltown, where he planned to autopsy a few lesioned fish?

You bet I did. A world-class expert on marine life in the Chesapeake, Dr. May had performed more than 80,000 fish-autopsies in recent years, as he monitored the effects of industrial pollution and agricultural runoff on the Chesapeake.

I caught up with Dr. May and his research associate at Shelltown on the ninth of July. Wearing no more protection than an ordinary pair of surgical gloves, he was already hard at work cutting up a series of fish victims. Fascinated, I watched him dictate his findings to the research associate, who was carefully preserving samples of damaged organs and skin for later analysis.

"Take a look, Ritchie—the lesions are exactly the same on each fish."

I nodded. The sequence of disease-events seemed quite clear by now; in each of these attacks, the lesions had been preceded by a breakdown in the slime layer of the affected fish. But how did the scenario work, exactly? Dr. May wasn't convinced that pfiesteria had caused the lesions—although he did acknowledge that the invader was capable of eroding the slime layer.

His hypothesis was an interesting one: What if the pfiesteria first attacked the fish, weakening its defenses and its immune system ... so that "secondary invaders" could then mount an unstoppable assault? After the "shock troops" (the pfiesteria) did their work, such powerful marauders as the clostridia species of bacteria would be free to pump their toxins (gas gangrene, for example) into the defenseless fish.

Maybe. But it was also possible, suggested Dr. May, that the secondary invader was a fungus, or one of the vibrio species or gram negative rods (such as aeromonas) that roamed the estuary and its rivers in search of marine victims.

It was complicated, all right. Like the rest of us, Dr. May was also grappling with the murky problem of "fish stress"—whatever that was supposed to mean. Everyone knew that the Chesapeake was a "stressed environment," by the late 1990s, with ever-increasing amounts of fertilizer-runoff produced by the huge agricultural industry in Delaware, Maryland and Virginia flooding into the Bay. But what was the actual effect on its fish?

It was *terra incognita,* for the most part. Sure, we had a few "baseline" studies, done over time—but they mostly served to underline the obvious fact: As pollutants of one kind or another trickled into the watershed, its environment was becoming increasingly hostile to fish, crabs, oysters and most other denizens of the deep.

Another key factor in the equation, of course, was the amount of rainfall we were receiving—since increasing rain produced increasing runoff, and brought more ecologically upsetting "nutrients" into these fragile waters. And indeed, the spring and summer of 1996 had been extraordinarily wet, with the "average" rainfall for the period having been surpassed by 36 inches.

For the tidal marshlands around the Pocomoke, increased rainfall mean increased flooding of the "mudflats"—swampy regions where traces of heavy metals (copper, iron, mercury, etc.) tend to leach out of the water and sink into the muck ... only to be washed out and pushed into the churning river during seasons of flood. And since the same flooding caused "holes" to develop along the river bottom (some of them 40 and 50 feet deep), it seemed quite possible that large amounts of these heavy metals were being deposited on the riverbed and trapped in holes where they might eventually be ingested by fish.

Was there a link of some kind between the heavy rains, the heavy metals and the lesioned fish?

Dr. May thought the real problem began with fish stressed by low salinity and low pH. Lots of living things in the water attack stressed fish. Intrigued, I listened carefully while he outlined a theory suggesting that rainfall played a major part in the assault on the fish.

He showed me how many of the autopsied fish had developed enlarged spleens—a clear indicator that they had been stressed by infectious agents before their deaths. He also pointed to the reddened or dusky-colored brain-coverings of some of the victims, although some had managed to escape this deformity.

Was the unnatural coloring a sign of brain-inflammation? And could that have caused the erratic swimming and the breakdown in other defense mechanisms that the watermen had told me about?

Dr. May shook his head. "We simply don't know enough yet, Ritchie. We need more tests, more chemical analyses. I haven't autopsied fish I know were swimming erratically."

But he was interrupted by loud voices and sudden footsteps, as several of the watermen hurried into Ray Maddox's warehouse to ask urgent questions about Dr. May's autopsy. Watching quietly from the sidelines, I could see the anxiety in their faces, as Dr. May explained that more studies would be required, before we could hope for useful conclusions.

"Dr. May," said Lori Maddox, Ray's wife, at one point, "somebody's gotta do something, and fast! This thing is spreading up and down the river ... just take a look at our dog."

A moment later, Dr. May and I were bending over the Maddox family dog and looking carefully at the ugly red lesion that clung to the lower portion of his right side. But when I dared to suggest that the wound might simply be an infected flea bite, Lori glared hard at me.

"My dog doesn't *have* fleas, Doc!"

Well, maybe not. But I couldn't help wondering, at that moment, if the "pfiesteria hysteria" wasn't beginning to affect many of the good folks of Shelltown. ...

Imagine my reaction, a few seconds later, when a longtime waterman named Tommy East held up his right arm to display a nasty-looking, deeply inflamed patch of what appeared to be a skin-fungus. After inspecting the area carefully, I offered to write him a prescription for ointment, if he'd drop by my office the next day.

"Okay, Doc, but this thing looks more like a rash than a fungus to me! And it won't heal—I've tried everything on it, and no luck. And there's more. I been losing weight, forty pounds so far, and throwing up ... stomach pains, can't remember stuff like I used to. Feel like I'm losing my memory, Doc!"

We all stared at each other for a few seconds. Then Lori broke the silence. Wonderfully practical and down to earth, she quickly offered to bring me a "whole stack" of articles, letters and government information that she'd already collected about the problem.

"Somebody's gotta post this river, Doc—we gotta tell 'em it's not safe! These folks don't know what they're getting into, when they go out on that water. We've tried to warn some of 'em, but they tell us we're crazy."

She gave me a hard, searching look. "We're not crazy, Doc—and that river isn't safe!"

chapter 3

The Mystery Deepens

July 9

Driving home from Shelltown, I struggled to make sense of the complicated biology that lay behind the fish kills and the reports of illness among the frightened watermen. What the hell was actually taking *place* here? It now seemed obvious that the fish lesions hadn't been caused by a single toxin, germ or disease process.

No, there were simply too many unknowns in the equation to blame the outbreak entirely on pfiesteria. What if the invading microorganism merely served to breach the fish defenses, thus establishing a "beachhead" that opened the door for other organic invaders?

Another key question: How did the ailing fish in our threatened river compare to their sick cousins in the Neuse River, down in the coastal marshlands of North Carolina—where a pfiesteria plague had been wiping out millions of fish for the past five or six years? Was the pathology similar? If so, could the experts in the Tar Heel State help us pinpoint the cause of the outbreak, while also advising us on the best way to fight it?

It bothered me that Dr. May knew about a gag order issued by the DNR. Some scientists had been told to refer any questions about fish kills to the public relations department without answering them.

With so many questions facing us, what was the point of shutting down open discussion about the problem? Surely the first step in solving it would be to understand the geography and the physical characteristics of the endangered river and estuary. Right after dinner that evening, I retreated to my study, armed with half a dozen different topographical maps of the Eastern Shore. Bending over them in the lamplight, I carefully traced the course of the Pocomoke from its origins in neighboring Delaware, where it runs narrow and deep, to its eventual mouth along the Chesapeake coastline.

Lined by stately cypress trees, the Pocomoke flows with calm, measured elegance through the hardwood forests of the upper reaches of the Eastern Shore, providing a canoeing paradise. Described everywhere as "wild and beautiful," the placid stream curves through what appears to be pristine marshland dominated by the plant species that are usually found in cypress swamps: black gum trees, sweet bay magnolia, wild rose, sweet pepper bush and several types of viburnums.

Located at the border between southern and northern climatic zones, the Pocomoke and its surrounding swamp also provide temporary quarters for the millions of migratory birds who seasonally traverse the Atlantic Flyway. Beneath the surface, meanwhile, the famed large mouth bass remains a major regional attraction, even if their numbers have declined from the 1950s, when the Pocomoke hosted the annual National Bass Roundup.

Spend an afternoon paddling across the "Dark Water" of this coastal stream, and you're likely to spot a pileated woodpecker or a bright yellow prothonotary warbler ... or maybe even a majestic bald eagle soaring effortlessly over his section of the swamp. Watching a family of deer lap at the burbling current, it's hard to believe that the giant Ocean City beach resort lies only 45 miles to the northeast, or that Baltimore and Washington are less than three hours away by auto.

But they are. And there's no escaping the fact that this fragile watercourse and its surrounding marshlands exist in a complex, endlessly threatened relationship in which the stresses of urban development and agricultural runoff have become key factors in the ecological health of the entire region.

Even a brief look at the dynamics of the river is enough to show how those stresses daily affect it. As the stream reaches the Pocomoke Swamp, it begins to widen, and to good effect—since the surrounding marshes serve to reduce storm surges, while also retaining pollutants, filtering nutrients and storing heavy metals in a reduced state.

Make no mistake: These Pocomoke swamps are huge, and they hold inconceivably large amounts of water. That was one of the first lessons I'd absorbed, while building the Nature Trail ... an experience that had taught me more about wetlands than any textbook ever could. Here, scattered along the marshes and hidden deep in the last "old-growth loblolly forest" in Maryland, I'd gone eyeball to eyeball with a diverse community of insects, animals, birds, mosses, plants.

Until quite recently, of course, the traditionally low population of the remote and rural Eastern Shore had served to protect the river from most environmental stressors. But all of that had been changing rapidly in recent years, as yield-hungry farmers continued to load their fields with fertilizers—both organic and bought (chemical), and ambitious developers sent up an ever-increasing demand for roads, water and sewer systems throughout the nearby resort areas.

Wide and tidal, the Pocomoke flows slowly from Snow Hill to Pocomoke, a distance of only 13 miles. Because the elevation decreases so slowly, the water may take up to three weeks to reach Pocomoke City and environs. At the same time, however, the tidal flow from the neighboring Chesapeake Bay and Pocomoke Sound remains quite vigorous—creating a dynamic which forces large amounts of agricultural nutrients from nearby counties deep into the river's meandering course.

Below Pocomoke City, the river changes its character. In recent years, the shipbuilding industry that once thrived here (while relying on the abundant Atlantic white cedar) has been replaced by large-scale agriculture. Now chicken, soybean and tomato farms cover vast tracts of rural real estate—extending, in some cases, all the way to the banks of the Pocomoke. Today, most of these massive farming operations use the "no till" system, which means they rely mostly on herbicides to clear unwanted vegetation.

While employing this procedure for the past five to ten years under the "Best Management Practices" agricultural guidelines of the State of Maryland, the farmers had discovered that they could cut a shallow furrow, plant their seeds, then cover the future crop with an easily available fertilizer (chicken manure), and thus avoid costly tilling.

This strategy also dramatically reduced the wind- and water-driven erosion of their fields. By employing it, the farmer saves the time required for tilling, the cost of tilling, and the cost of fertilizer. Obviously, these hard-working farmers greatly appreciate the savings in labor and fertilizer costs. So effective is the "no-till" approach, in fact, that it can often turn marginal farmlands into viable money-makers.

Ecologically, however, the drawbacks of no-till seem obvious—starting with the crucially important fact that fertilizers, herbicides, and pesticides are left totally exposed to wind and rain, which means that many of them are rapidly flushed into the region's drainage system, and end up in fragile watercourses such as the Pocomoke.

Poring over my maps on this quiet evening in the summer of '97, I marveled all over again at the complex geography of the Pocomoke watershed, which reaches into five counties and three states. Below Shelltown, where watermen like Ray Maddox and Tommy East were at that moment worried sick about their professional futures in the fish and crab industry, it was easy to see how the river undergoes an abrupt change.

From this point on, the stream is mixed daily with tidal flow from the nearby Chesapeake, producing an entirely different biological habitat. In addition, this constant back-and-forth movement of the tidal flow continuously deposits nutrients and heavy metals and pesticides along the bottom of the estuary.

Instead of being flushed out of the watercourse, in other words, these potentially harmful substances (and especially the heavy metals) begin to form concentrated layers in the mud of the estuary.

Of course, the Chesapeake tidal flow also triggers some other dramatic changes along this stretch of the watershed. Suddenly, within the space of a mile or two, swamp plants begin to give way to brackish water species. As salt content and acidity shift rapidly with the changing tides and seasons, the local plants, grasses, fish and phytoplankton closely mirror that change, with the appearance of dozens of new marine-based organisms.

While studying the Pocomoke maps carefully, I couldn't help noticing the strong similarities between our wetlands and the huge "Great Dismal Swamp" sections of coastal North Carolina—a region that had been witnessing massive fish kills for more than five years now. More than once, a skilled botanist for the Nature Conservancy, Ron Wilson, had pointed out to me during our walks that such well known Pocomoke plants as the cross vine, the redbay, the pond pine and the crane fly orchid were also common inhabitants of the Great Dismal and its major river, the Neuse, which flows through the heart of the swamp before emptying into the estuary that is the Pamlico Sound.

Interesting! As I examined the similarities, I found myself grappling with a tantalizing question: If the Pocomoke and the Neuse were so much alike, was there any chance that the North Carolina "pfiesteria blooms"—reportedly the cause of the fish kills there—were also responsible for the biological mayhem that was taking place along the Pocomoke?

Maybe. But first, another key question about the North Carolina scourge would have to be answered. Had the devastating Carolina outbreak been triggered, as many analysts now believed, by huge amounts of hog waste spilling into local rivers? A product of the giant hog farms that dominated this region, the waste was thought to have somehow upset the delicate ecological balance of the Neuse. ...

As far as I could tell, however, there were no gigantic infusions of animal waste then taking place along the threatened Pocomoke —although the area certainly had its share of massive chicken farms, starting with the vast poultry empires run by "conglomerate integrators" (the industry term for poultry operators who control every aspect of poultry production) Frank Perdue and Tyson Farms, along with several other major producers.

Chicken manure-as-culprit? Perhaps. But the EPA had said that the Pocomoke was one of the cleanest rivers in the U.S.—and I certainly wasn't aware of any major spillage of manure into our limpid stream. On the other hand ... Lori Maddox's stack of files *had* contained a rather disturbing "Feed Report" from the U.S. Department of Agriculture, showing that there were huge amounts of copper in each of the feeds provided to chickens during the three stages of production: laying, starting, and finishing.

Copper?

If "large amounts" of copper had been placed in the feed—in order to kill fungus and prevent spoilage—would copper also turn up in the chicken manure that was being washed into the river, especially during periods of heavy rain?

Perhaps. What if the copper-heavy manure was somehow triggering off the pfiesteria feeding frenzy?

My brain whirling with the possibilities, I headed off for bed. But a new line of inquiry had now been opened, and I liked that. It was time to go back and take a look at some of the troubling talks I'd had recently with physicians who were trying to understand the pfiesteria outbreak in North Carolina.

Yeah, good luck, I told myself as I drifted toward sleep. The word from Carolina was that the state health department had been "stonewalling" bigtime. What if the docs who'd been at the center of the controversy had been muzzled, and wouldn't talk to me?

▼   ▼   ▼

"Dr. Morris? This is Ritchie Shoemaker, in Pocomoke City, Maryland. I'm a family physician, and I've been talking to some people here who think they might have gotten sick after fishing or swimming in the Pocomoke River. ..."

Dr. Chris Morris listened attentively. An obstetrician based in New Bern, North Carolina, she was "absolutely convinced" that some of her patients had been sickened by exposure to areas of fishkill along the Neuse River, located in the heart of the eastern North Carolina marshland.

Enthusiastic and energetic, Dr. Morris was the first physician I called in the Tar Heel State, as I struggled to find a link between the Neuse River version of pfiesteria and our own outbreak. And she was a terrific resource. Indeed, Dr. Morris had become so alarmed by the pfiesteria outbreak and its human health consequences that she'd "gone public" with a letter to Vice President Al Gore. (As a matter of fact, she was still quite miffed that he hadn't answered her!)

Although Dr. Morris had seen only a few cases of what she thought was human illness caused by pfiesteria, she'd had lengthy discussions with other physicians who were also tending victims of the river bug. After describing their growing concern, she gave me a clear warning—by pointing out that the "political and economic" problems triggered by the outbreak were as difficult to solve as the medical puzzles created by the dinoflagellate invasion itself.

Hers was a chilling warning. "I'd be careful, if I were you," said the Carolina investigator. "The doctors who have come forward with reports of this illness haven't exactly been greeted with open arms by the State of North Carolina!"

Dr. Morris was convinced that the human dimensions of the infestation were being ignored by state health officials, and she quickly suggested I call another New Bern physician, Dr. Chris Delaney. As a practicing physiatrist, Dr. Delaney treated musculoskeletal disorders on a daily basis. And like Dr. Morris, Dr. Delaney had seen patients with disturbing skin lesions.

He'd also run into a few folks with neurological problems—headaches, loss of memory—that seemed to be linked to exposure to the waters of the Neuse and nearby Pamlico Sound. Dr. Delaney was equally concerned about the tepid "official response" to the toxin-linked illness he'd observed in several patients. He pointed out that the U.S. Centers for Disease Control (CDC) had been investigating the estuarine-related illness problem.

But the huge federal health agency was insisting that the rivers were safe, and that no human illness was caused by exposure to the watershed.

Dr. Delaney also referred me to several articles in the local Raleigh News and Observer that described how doctors with concerns about pfiesteria were being labeled as "extremists." According to the newspaper, the North Carolina State Health Department had dragged its feet on the issue in order to protect both jobs and tourist dollars, in a frustrating scenario that would probably be repeated in any state where the bug started making headlines.

Not good. Increasingly alarmed by these reports from North Carolina, I called Dr. Donald Schmechel at Duke University, who confirmed that he had treated at least one case in which changes in mental status, liver function and intellectual performance were directly attributable to the pfiesteria organism. But Dr. Schmechel refused to identify the victim ... and seemed intent on downplaying the entire episode. He obviously knew a lot more than he was going to tell a stranger on the telephone who'd called him out of the blue from Maryland.

"We know there's a toxin, maybe several, linked to pfiesteria," said the Duke researcher, "but so far, we haven't been able to identify it successfully. You should know that researchers in Florida are also working very hard on this case."

Dr. Schmechel's report was disturbing—but not nearly as alarming as the story of what had happened to Dr. Howard Glasgow, an N.C. State researcher who'd been studying the pfiesteria organism for more than a year.

Dr. Glasgow's pfiesteria-experience read like something out of a lurid "eco-thriller." While working in an N.C. State lab directed by Dr. JoAnn Burkholder, the subject of an important book on the North Carolina pfiesteria attack, the researcher had at first managed to avoid the toxin-linked illness that struck down several of his co-investigators.

Later, however, after Dr. Burkholder reclassified the facility to "Hazard Level Three"—a security-boost that required heightened safety measures throughout the lab—the unfortunate Dr. Glasgow wound up stationed near an exhaust fan that swirled with aerosol-borne pfiesteria toxins night and day.

Dr. Glasgow breathed in large quantities of the toxin, and his health rapidly deteriorated. Soon he was struggling with unexplained memory loss, personality changes and impaired intellectual functioning.

I listened to this account with growing fascination. What did it mean ... the fact that Dr. Glasgow had been poisoned by "aerosol exposure" (rather than water or droplet exposure) to the bug's nasty toxin? Was the "aerosol factor" a potentially important clue to the mystery?

I had my work cut out for me, and I knew it. And the political problems were going to be even tougher than the public health problems. Without clearcut proof of the toxin's effect on human health, I knew that it would be impossible to get Maryland health officials to issue a warning about the toxic impact of pfiesteria on humans.

The political battle was about to be joined, and the good health of my friends and neighbors along the Pocomoke depended on getting the word out soon. These waters were not safe for humans, as long as high levels of pfiesteria lurked within them!

It was time to get to work in earnest. I was going to spend my summer vacation working on the Great Pfiesteria Mystery ... while also trying to increase public awareness about the human dimensions of the looming microorganism invasion.

chapter 4

On the Trail of the "Cell from Hell"

July 9

By midsummer of 1997, I was neck-deep in scientific data and eyewitness accounts of the biological predator that had invaded our once tranquil river.

Ask any professional epidemiologist to describe how he or she goes about the business of analyzing a disease outbreak, and you'll probably find yourself listening to the story of Dr. Robert Koch, a German scientist who developed a powerfully effective system for pinpointing the source of epidemics.

Koch had become famous in medical circles in the 19th Century, after showing physicians how to prove "disease causation" by an infectious agent. According to the German physician, the key step in understanding the "illness syndrome" was to first identify a group of people (a "cohort") who displayed similar symptoms after having undergone a similar exposure to a disease-causing agent. Isolate the same disease agent from each.

The next step in the Koch method is to expose an unaffected patient to the causative agent—thus triggering the target-illness. Next the investigator isolates from the newly sickened patient the same germ that caused the illness in the first cohort of patients.

The Koch method was a proven system for nailing down the triggering mechanism in any disease outbreak. But how could I use this powerful tool, I asked myself, when the pfiesteria toxin hadn't been isolated in a lab? I had sick patients—but there was no way I could prove that the illness was from a common-source exposure, and no one was lining up just to try a new toxin.

According to the public relations-obsessed Maryland Department of Natural Resources, in fact, the toxin simply wasn't a factor in the Pocomoke "epidemic" reported by the watermen. They kept saying it over and over again: The river was safe; no humans were made sick by the river!

I found myself confronting a chaotic series of scientific fragments and unable to get a clear focus on the epidemiology involved. But at least I had Lori Maddox's collection of articles and letters to work with … along with the reports on some water samples that had been gathered back in May by an enterprising TV reporter from Washington named Brad Bell.

Bell had sent his water samples to Dr. Burkholder, who had quickly determined that pfiesteria was present. Bell's lab tests had been conducted on samples taken from a backwater pool full of dead fish, and they had checked out as "positive" for pfiesteria.

Interestingly enough, however, Dr. Burkholder found samples taken by the Maryland DNR the same day—but from the middle of the river—to be negative for pfiesteria.

Predictably enough, the DNR continued to insist that the entire river was free of toxins produced by pfiesteria, and that humans faced no disease threat there. But my growing pile of "anecdotal" evidence from Shelltown suggested otherwise.

Based on what I was hearing from the professional watermen, the invading organism had already triggered a small epidemic among those who worked with fish and fish nets in this rural world.

There was no doubt, for example, that Tommy East had been getting sick over and over again since the fall of '96, and especially during periods when he was harvesting fish from the river.

Tommy was a tough-as-nails waterman, hardly a complainer—but everybody in Shelltown had heard his stories of painful belly aches, coughing attacks and runaway diarrhea.

Like Tommy East, fisherman Jack Howard had been sick off and on for the best part of a year. He'd come down with pneumonia repeatedly too ... and he'd also suffered with belly aches and painful rashes. And like Tommy, Jack had begun to develop some problems with his short-term memory, telling me on one occasion: "Every time I go into it [a pfiesteria bloom], I'm glad I wrote down where I left my car!"

In the end, Jack Howard had simply stopped fishing in the river ... and had launched a one-man campaign aimed at calling public attention to the plague. He talked to anyone who would listen: congressmen, local politicians, newspaper and TV reporters, you name it.

But nobody was really listening. Nobody wanted to face up to the truly frightening possibility that the disease agent in the Pocomoke might threaten human beings, along with millions of hapless fish.

By mid July, as I struggled to make sense of dozens of lab reports, newspaper stories, and personal accounts of the outbreak, I had managed to locate some extremely useful research on the toxins produced by pfiesteria.

Much of the work had been done during the early 1990's by Dr. JoAnn Burkholder, the aquatic botanist from N.C. state in whose lab Dr. Glasgow had become so ill. An outstanding scientist, Burkholder was probably the best-known researcher on pfiesteria in the United States, after being profiled in a powerfully written book on the subject, "And The Water Turned To Blood."

According to the savvy Dr. Burkholder, who had also been made ill by her exposure to the toxins, pfiesteria was nothing less than

"The Cell From Hell." For starters, she pointed out, this cunning organism knew how to "morph" itself into a large-celled, amoeba-like phase which made a nice living by engulfing blue-green algae and single-celled plankton—along with another important group of protozoans, known as the "cryptomonads."

Interesting enough, as Dr. Burkholder had noted, the energy-producing chloroplasts in the microorganisms ingested by the ballooning, amoeba-like pfiesteria continued to go right on synthesizing food (via photosynthesis) after being devoured by the Pocomoke invader.

As Dr. Burkholder's research made clear, the benign amoeba-form of pfiesteria was accustomed to gobbling up lots of cryptomonads, which contained the energy-producing chloroplasts, along with their starch granules, fatty acids and other tasty nutrients.

But the chloroplasts weren't the only significant organic molecules to be found in the protozoa being devoured by the amoeba-version of pfiesteria, which continued to feed contentedly and grew to huge sizes ... provided that its favorite prey—the blue-green algae —remained plentiful.

As far as I could see, the biological puzzle came down to this: Why didn't the pfiesteria remain content with the energy-producing chloroplasts they were taking in, each time they snarfed up another colony of blue-green algae?

Why did pfiesteria spontaneously turn into its much smaller—and exceedingly toxic—form? If the amoeba-phase was a "contented cow" grazing peacefully on the algae and their chloroplasts, why switch over to the toxic version?

I spent several days gnawing at this puzzle, before a possible answer suddenly jumped out at me: Reproduction!

Was pfiesteria changing its shape—and its feeding strategy—in order to breed?

With growing excitement I reread biology lessons on "cell fission," which is the reproductive method employed by the amoeba-phase of pfiesteria. Protozoans, I remembered (and that included the amoeba-phase of pfiesteria) could reproduce without sharing DNA with another partner. Known as "asexual reproduction," cell fission is basically a "splitting" of the cell into two halves, each of which then becomes an individual, without any sharing of gene-regulating DNA.

But that was the scenario in the *amoeba* phase.

What if pfiesteria somehow converted itself into a second "animal phase" … in which sexual reproduction would call for DNA-sharing, accomplished by the morphing into tiny zoospores?

As Dr. Burkholder had reported, the zoospores manufactured a toxic substance. But for what purpose? As I reviewed the evidence, it seemed clear that this particular toxin functioned exactly like the "pheromones" (powerful chemical signaling-devices) used for breeding purposes by many protozoans and other animals. A pheromone was a kind of "reproductive calling card," if you will, which summoned members of a species to gather for mating.

It wasn't Chanel No. 5, maybe, but it worked. Once released by the zoospores, the pungent chemical attracted many others for both feeding and breeding. But what if the pheromone just happened to be toxic to other species—such as fish?

Eureka! I knew from those high school biology courses that pheromones are powerful chemical agents, and especially in the insect world. My Japanese beetle traps employ them, for example; and if you've ever swatted a yellow jacket at a picnic and seen a dozen others arrive instantly, you've witnessed the "signaling power" of this biological agent.

After mulling the problem for days on end, I wound up asking myself another crucially important question: Was there a pfiesteria pheromone that not only summoned the zoospores for breeding, but also stimulated the "excystment" of quiescent cysts?

But let me back up for a moment, to explain: After the mating has taken places, the now-fertilized zoospores sink back into the muck, to become "cysts" (or seeds) which lie inert, just beneath the surface of the topmost muck-layer at the bottom of the estuary.

But as Dr. Burkholder had pointed out, something in the water was awakening these harmless sleepers, and then triggering off a violent feeding frenzy.

Normally, these hardy zoospore cysts will rest in the muck for five years or so, before becoming activated. And they're incredibly resilient: Researchers have pointed out that these hard-nosed swimmers can survive acid attacks, freezing temperatures, and heat up to 170 degrees Fahrenheit, without missing a beat.

My question was a simple one: What force had driven the "Cell From Hell" out of the Pocomoke muck? Was it a chemical agent? If so, was this same chemical agent the key mechanism in transforming the pfiesteria from the harmless amoeba-phase into its toxic form—the cannibal-like zoospores?

Dr. Eric May had shown in 1992 that pfiesteria was present in Jenkins Creek a tributary of the Choptank River. He suspected that it had been present for thousands of years but could not prove that. What he had proved was that pfiesteria—at least in its harmless amoeba phase—had been hanging around in the Chesapeake Bay for a very long time. But something had changed their habitat. Something had reduced their basic food supply—those chloroplast-loaded blue-green algae—and sent them racing off, like microscopic piranha, in search of other foodstuffs to attack.

What recent changes could I identify in the habitat?

How well I remember that warm summer evening on which the answer suddenly appeared to me!

I'd gone out for a leisurely stroll along the river ... when all at once the skies opened up, and yet another fleeting cloudburst began.

Hustling back toward the house, head down, I watched my soggy workboots splatting against the rain-drenched mud of the riverbank. Gushing and gurgling, the downpour swirled through the muck, washing it steadily toward the water's edge. ...

All at once I caught my breath.

The mud!

Why hadn't I thought of it?. Those heavy rains of the past winter ... *that* was the new factor, the key change in the "habitat"! What if the heavy rains were washing something into the watershed ... something that attacked pfiesteria's food supply of blue-green algae and cryptomonads?

Metals? Heavy metals in the fertilizer ... maybe even in the feed that millions of Eastern Shore chickens were devouring, 24 hours around the clock ... Copper! What about pesticides?

chapter 5

An Essay on the Nature Of Chicken Manure

July 9

With growing excitement, I went to work on the "copper problem." How could I learn more about this heavy metal and its possible impact on the Pocomoke watershed? Wait a minute ... I'd read about copper in Lori Maddox's stack of documents! Among several other interesting items, the waterman's wife had kindly loaned me a Maryland Department of Agriculture study that had found heavy levels of copper in both chicken feed and chicken manure.

Hurrying into my office, I quickly located the document I wanted. Yes ... now I remembered. Lori had been fighting-mad about chicken waste, the last time we'd talked. "That chicken manure is everywhere, doc! The farmers are supposed to store it right, which they don't. They're supposed to spread it on fields right, for fertilizer, which they don't. You can't tell me that a big pile of manure sitting next to a river is a good thing for the river!"

Of course, I'd also seen some manure practices that I didn't think were right. Spreading manure on top of snow, or on a field just before a big rain didn't seem to make a lot of sense. How could winter vegetation, if any, take up any nutrients—when the fertilizer seemed certain to run off whenever it rained hard?

Lori was also angry about nearby tomato farmers spraying their crops all the time. "I don't know what they're using, but they spray every week—more just after a rain. That's when we get the fish kills."

She had a point, and it became clear as soon as I did some research. It had been soon after the rains, during the past fall and winter, that the watermen of Shelltown had noticed a significant increase in fish with lesions. Later still, as the water temperatures warmed in May and June, the association of rain, tomato spraying and lesioned fish seemed very clear to Lori. Could she be right? Were there any hard scientific facts to back her up?

Maybe. For starters, everybody knew that the landscape upstream from Shelltown was dominated by chicken farms. They were the major industry, after all, throughout the Delmarva Peninsula. In this area, major chicken producers such as Tyson Foods and Perdue, along with several others, supply chicks for farmers to grow in long houses on the farmers' land. The feed is also supplied, and the feeding schedule is regulated. And it seemed that every time you turned around, there was one less independent chicken farmer and a larger Tyson. Here as elsewhere in the nation, the small farmer was rapidly becoming a thing of the past.

If you know anything at all about large-scale chicken-farming, you know that every phase of the process is carefully regulated by economics and the big companies. For best results, the farmer must carefully control such factors as the water supply, temperature and humidity. Then, provided that all goes well, the chickens will grow to selling size in just six to eight weeks. Flocks of to 50,000–100,000 birds are not unusual. The chickens are grown, collected, processed and sold, with the typical farmer earning about a dime on each chicken. And the farmer gets the manure for free. (He also gets to breathe the dusty, ammonia-filled air in his chicken house, gather up his dead chickens and do lots of other hard work for his ten-cent payoff.)

Bit by bit, I was beginning to understand how the industry

worked. Fact: The chicken-growing cycle is repeated six to eight times over the course of a year. Fact: Chicken farming is a main source of income for farmers on the Eastern Shore, and it's a very risky business. If a heat wave wipes out half his flock, the farmer takes the hit. If the heating costs in a cold winter turn his dime profit into a penny, he takes a second hit. The work is also repetitive, and endless, and one of the most onerous chores the farmer faces is disposing of the huge amounts of chicken manure that are produced along the way.

It's a tough way to make a living. But many of them do quite well at it, and as a group, they have enormous economic clout. That clout impacts on the farmers who sell feed-corn to the chicken-growers, and it affects the local economy in a thousand other ways as well. (Doctors in Pocomoke often don't get paid until the chicken check comes in.)

Over the years, the Maryland Department of Agriculture had responded to the ever-increasing use of land in this region for chicken farming by issuing advisories called "Best Management Practices." Make no mistake: Agriculture had always been quite concerned about the possibility that "runoff" from chicken manure might add to nutrient enrichment in ground water, producing harmful effects on the environment.

But the state and federal government had tried to help, over the years, by creating programs aimed at helping the farmers to build storage and composting barns where both dead chickens and manure could be organically recycled, especially during the winter season. The government had also been quick to point out that farmers could use new agriculture techniques in order to convert manure into useful fertilizer.

I hadn't expected a lesson in chicken manure—but that's what Lori Maddox's Department of Agriculture study was providing me. As I paged through the data on annual chicken and manure production, I could almost smell the reeking ammonia odor that clung to the various chicken farms I'd visited over my years around the Pocomoke. ...

There's no polite way to say it, folks: The houses in which chickens are grown just don't seem like healthy places to work. The ammonia smell and the dust—combined with the endless blizzard of chicken feathers—can be overpowering, especially if you're laboring with an allergy or two. (Come to think of it, I've often wondered why I don't see more evidence of lung disease in chicken farmers!)

It was a stinky business. But what happened to the manure after it was bundled off to the storage barns, supposedly to be rendered into harmless fertilizer? For one thing, as other ag experts had made clear, the ammonia evaporation from the chicken waste continues unchecked—until more than 80 percent of the available nitrogen in the manure has evaporated, by the time it's ready to be spread on fields.

So much for the aroma. But what about the nutrient-enriching phosphates? I was surprised to learn that the phosphates found in chicken manure do not evaporate. Indeed, they act like a kind of organic Velcro: Once spread on the farmer's field, they bind tightly to soil particles and are not easily moved.

As the experts at Agriculture were eager to point out, the normal values of phosphates in soil range from 150 to 250 ppm (parts per million) in areas without chicken farming. On the Eastern Shore, however, phosphate levels in and around the Pocomoke River and its watershed can reach 1200–1500 ppm in the areas of highest chicken manure disposal. These incredibly high values of phosphates seem alarming at first—but the leaching of phosphates out of the soil is quite limited, even at these high levels.

Happily, water quality measurements in the Pocomoke River have shown that nitrogen and phosphate levels have not been significantly increased in the last 15 years.

So although the soil phosphate levels were high, the effects of nitrogen and phosphates on Pocomoke River water had remained consistent for a long time. ...

So far so good. Yes, I was finally beginning to understand chicken manure! But then I turned another page, and my eyes nearly jumped out of my head. In this section of the Ag report, the numbers seemed incredible. What was all this copper (200 ppm) doing in chicken feed? In each of the three types of chicken feed (laying, starting, finishing), the copper levels appeared to be jumping off the page. Why were they using so much of it? Did copper stop water loss and diarrhea? No, arsenic did that.

Was copper being used as a mineral, like iron, cobalt and selenium? Maybe ... but the same analysis showed copper levels in the manure to be twice as high as in the feed! Puzzled, I called Rick Nelson, head of the Somerset County Farm Bureau and asked him a few questions about the contents of chicken manure.

The next day he sent me a copy of a different State Department of Agriculture analysis that showed copper in the Eastern Shore manure to be twice as high as the amount in feed. His charts showed more than 400 ppm of copper present in chicken manure —a value far greater than that registered by any of the other heavy metals!

I didn't understand, so I got on the horn and interviewed a couple of chicken feed manufacturers. One of them warned me: "Don't use my name, I'd lose my job." When I promised anonymity, he explained that copper is a fungicide. "You should see the stacks of copper sulfate they put in feed," muttered my source. "As soon as the Ag inspector is gone, they just load it up."

Obviously, saving a penny a pound by preventing spoilage of feed wasn't "chicken feed," when it came to the farmer's bottom line.

The feed manufacturer had a good point. All at once, I was remembering a useful analogy from my college days, when I worked testing concrete at building sites. Understand: Concrete must have the right amount of air, the right slump and the right compression strength, or else it won't pass specifications. But more than once, just after I'd gotten my sample of concrete from a truck for testing, I saw the construction boss adding water to the truck, as soon as I turned my back. Watered concrete saved money, too.

So far, so good. But now it was time to carry my copper-education further. The Delmarva Poultry Institute is a large conglomerate on the Eastern Shore, and after speaking with three or four secretaries, I again posed my unusual question: "What is the purpose of putting copper in chicken feed?"

I was quickly informed that copper is a necessary element added to chicken feed to prevent water loss in the chicken, and that it posed no threat to water quality or human health. Moreover, what was I doing asking questions about chicken feed—when I obviously didn't know what the hell I was talking about?

Mystified, I hung up the phone. Why had they bitten my head off? I didn't understand this aggressive defensiveness! But now I became more determined than ever to find out what the copper was doing in the chicken feed. And I soon learned that copper is a growth stimulant. The manufacturers say they don't fully understand the metabolic reactions, but they do understand the bottom line, which reads: "More copper equals faster growing chickens equals more profit."

It was time to pay a visit to an old pal, John Hughes, a recognized expert in the use of chemicals for agriculture. Luckily, he was willing to listen to some of my concerns about agriculture chemicals.

Copper is added to chicken feed as a fungicide, Hughes patiently explained, in the same way that it gets added to fields and seeds —including wheat and rye. Copper is added to fields where green leaf crops will be grown, including corn, tomatoes, soy beans, melons, peppers and sugar cane, in order to prevent fungi from killing the early seedlings. It does the same thing for the tobacco industry. The copper is added to the fields either as a sulfate or hydroxide, and ranges in amounts from four pounds per acre to twelve pounds per acre for specialized tomato farms using "black plastic culture."

Under the plastic culture tomato-growing technique, black plastic layers the ground, with irrigation hosing underneath. Rows of plants are then grown through holes in the plastic. The black plastic keeps the ground warmer and increases plant production, but it also poses the hazard of accentuating runoff of any chemicals used on the tomatoes. The fact that copper sulfate is sprayed on tobacco plants and orange trees further piqued my interest.

Okay, I asked myself: What about those fish kills in North Carolina and in the Indian River and St. John's River in Florida? Had copper been washed into these rivers after a rain from the tobacco fields, melon fields, sugar cane fields and orange groves? Also: If chicken feed used copper as a fungicide, what about hog feed? Those breaches of 25 million-gallon hog waste lagoons that had been making the news might have dumped more than just nitrates and phosphates into the Neuse River!

It was time to get on the phone again. Soon the North Carolina Department of Agriculture swine agent, W.G. Simmons, was explaining how hog feed is enriched with copper sulfate to prevent deterioration. Hog farms have been blamed for most of the nutrient enrichment of rivers in North Carolina, including the Neuse.

Iowa remains the leading producer of hogs in this country; North Carolina has moved into number two. But hog production in Iowa is spread throughout the State, whereas the production of hogs in North Carolina is concentrated in the area east of Route 95 in southeast North Carolina. Hog waste production in this area has received national attention. Researchers such as Dr. Burkholder, along with environmental activists, such as Rick Dove, have been concerned about the amount of hog manure on the surface and subsurface of waters in North Carolina's Coastal Plain. The hog manure, they suspect, contributes to the environmental degradation that led to the continuing pfiesteria problem in Pamlico Sound.

Interesting! But the case for sugar cane and citrus seemed less compelling. Environmentalists have been quite vocal about the problems caused by sugar cane growth adjacent to the Everglades, an area where pfiesteria has not been reported. There have been outbreaks of pfiesteria in rivers on the Atlantic coast of Florida, including the St. Johns and Indian Rivers.

There have also been local concerns that there may be nutrient enrichment from agriculture in these rivers, but the data are sketchy and certainly not convincing. It remained a nagging question for me, however, as to why pfiesteria grows so well in areas where copper is used widely, but not everywhere. Was copper used in citrus plantations? If so, that would complete the circle of evidence for causation. But at this point, I simply didn't know.

And the role of copper in the water continued to bother me. Farming, including no-till, puts manure, herbicides, fertilizers and copper right up to the edges of fields along the Pocomoke River. I'd written essays and presented ideas to river environmental groups about wetland buffers. In Worcester County, for example, there had been a movement to change some of the buffer regulations to allow developers to cut down trees and native vegetation on waterfront property, creating better water viewing for owners of expensive property. Several large development owners supported a turf grass proposal. The idea was that a 25-foot-wide turf grass boundary would be required along water edges to prevent runoff of chemicals that could potentially harm the bays, watersheds and wetlands of Worcester County.

Fortunately, the County Commissioners had been forced to table this attempt to weaken wetlands regulations.

Pressured by the environmental community, the commissioners had publicly admitted that there were fundamental flaws in the turf grass argument. Those flaws begin with the fact that a large amount of material deposited in our watersheds is airborne. Cutting down trees and windbreaks destroys the ability to retard airborne flow. Second, the turf grasses, like other cover crops such as wheat and rye, are generally shallow-rooted. They can reduce flow of nutrients, called "surface flow," only to the shallow depth of the roots, usually about four to six inches. Grasses have an important role in a wetland buffer, but only to stop surface flow.

Third, the greatest amount of flow of nutrients, pesticides and heavy metals, is called "subsurface flow." This flow occurs in the area below the bottom of the roots. Introducing turf grass would not prevent unlimited subsurface flow of nutrients into adjacent water. Deeper-rooted trees and shrubs are necessary to reduce subsurface flow. Cutting down trees and shrubs to enhance a view will accelerate undesirable nutrient flow into our surface waters. (You don't have to hug the trees, just don't cut them down!)

Even with an ideal forested, vegetated wetland buffer, though, subsurface flow of chemicals including herbicides, pesticides, bacteriocides, fertilizers and heavy metals, will proceed. True buffers, and not just wetland buffers, share features that include width, species diversity, variable root depths, and a variety of vegetation, including grasses, shrubs, and trees.

Conclusion: If you don't want it in the river, either don't put it on the land—or else limit its use to buffered land.

Having natural wetland vegetation grow on buffer areas of width from 50 to 100 feet provides substantial restriction of airborne flow, surface flow and subsurface flow. Restrictions in one of these three components of wetland buffers weakens the whole buffer. The Pocomoke has trees and vegetation along its edges for a very narrow width. The crops that are grown along the river from Pocomoke City to the Chesapeake Bay are cultivated to the water's edge. Was there any reason that these limited wetland buffers would restrict subsurface flow, especially of copper?

Nope.

There was no reason at all ... or at least, none that I could see.

By now, I felt like I'd earned a graduate degree in Chicken Manure. But the time had been well spent, and the new knowledge would prove enormously helpful in pinpointing the chemical culprit that lay behind the pfiesteria plague.

It was time to begin putting my brand-new "copper theory" to the test!

chapter 6

Copper, Copper Everywhere ...

July 10

As the long, hot summer of '97 inched slowly along and the public debate over pfiesteria grew more rancorous, I found myself increasingly immersed in a subject which has always been dear to my heart: organic chemistry.

I was on the trail of "copper as culprit" in the epidemiology of pfiesteria ... and the first step in the process was to begin analyzing the ways in which Eastern Shore farmers have traditionally used copper in food production.

For the past 50 years, as it turned out, our local farmers had been combining disease-fighting agents (known as "dithiocarbamates") with copper to prevent bacterial attacks on tomato plants. After a rain, bacterial diseases such as "speck" and "spot" can wipe out an entire tomato field overnight, if left unchecked. By spraying with the complex chemical described above, the farmers can be pretty confident that the ubiquitous bacteria will leave their plants alone.

But there's a price to pay for this protection. (When you interfere with the natural order of things, there's *always* a price to pay.) In the case of the dithiocarbamates, the drawback is that they easily "complex" with copper in water—in a chemical process (chelation) that binds the copper tightly to the pesticide molecules.

Curiously, agricultural officials on the Virginia side of the Eastern Shore have recommended using alternatives to the dithiocarbamates (such as chlorothalonils) for many years now. The chlorothalonils usually produce satisfactory results—although they're not quite as good at protecting tomato seedlings as are the dithiocarbamates.

As researchers at Duke University explained it to me, to clear copper from a water column, you simply add dithiocarbamates which bind to copper quickly and firmly. Copper dissolves only in water, but the copper dithiocarbamate complex dissolves in fatty tissue. And that's important ... because it means that copper can be delivered to the inside of the cell of organisms larger than algae or pfiesteria. Once inside the cell, the copper attacks the enzymes necessary for regulating cell functions—including enzymes such as superoxide dismutase. (This is an enzyme needed to prevent oxidative stress damage to the cell.)

The bottom line is this: When excessive amounts of copper pile up inside their cells, larger organisms, including phytoplankton such as rotifers, are killed rapidly. And these microorganisms feed on organisms such as pfiesteria.

Interesting, no? The more I looked at how copper attacks cells, the more fascinated I became. Soon I was reviewing the data from some studies done by Dr. Jonathan Phinney in the San Francisco Bay in 1997. Phinney had shown that combinations of dithiocarbamates with copper and dithiocarbamates with nickel don't kill phytoplankton equivalently. In every case, said Phinney, it was the copper complex that did the killing.

Phinney's conclusions nicely supported some data that had been published in 1987 by Dr. Fritz Riedel, who had demonstrated clearly that the toxicity of copper is enhanced when that metal is complexed with fat-soluble organic molecules.

What did it all mean? The conclusion seemed simple, and inescapable. Maryland's Eastern Shore faced a very real risk, based on its agricultural practices: the danger that excessive amounts of copper could be leached into the water table, particularly after a rain.

If that happened, copper would surely complex with chemicals that are applied to plants after a rain, and then begin to kill organisms that have the capability to eat pfiesteria.

Of course, copper is also an algicide. It's adept at killing algae (including blue green algae), as well as cryptomonads directly. And the cryptomonads were the favorite foods of pfiesteria in its benign "amoeba phase."

In the amoeba phase, remember, pfiesteria will engulf its prey and digest most of the food components. But it will carefully preserve the algae's functioning chloroplasts—which keep right on producing the huge amounts of energy that the pfiesteria use for fuel. And with all of this extra fuel available, it should be no surprise that the amoeba phase of pfiesteria can grow to huge sizes, swelling approximately 50 times bigger than the toxic phase of the marauding bug.

The evidence also seemed clear that amoeba phase-pfiesteria had been hanging around the Pocomoke River for many years before the 1996 outbreak of the toxic version.

Slowly, the pieces of the puzzle were now coming together. They told me that if there was increased killing of the cryptomonads and the blue green algae due to excessive amounts of copper being washed into the river after a heavy rain, then the pfiesteria might be motivated to transform into a smaller phase that wouldn't be dependent on eating these chloroplast-containing organisms.

The sequence of steps seemed perfectly in tune with Darwin's "Theory of Natural Selection." Deprive the pfiesteria of their natural diet, threatening them with starvation, and watch them swiftly mutate into a second, far more aggressive (and toxic) organism!

But we shouldn't forget that pfiesteria, itself, serves as food for other organic creatures—whether in the amoeba stage or toxin phase In the toxin phase, it's eaten by rotifers and other phytoplankton—creatures which were also being poisoned by the copper dithiocarbamate complex, according to my new hypothesis.

Without significant numbers of predators on hand, it seemed quite possible that the pfiesteria toxin-forming phase could grow to huge numbers ... especially if the presence of fish triggered a bloom. Indeed, the numbers might rise extraordinarily high if predators of the amoeba phase, cyst phase and zoospore phase were somehow killed off.

According to Dr. Burkholder's earlier findings, any small amount of enrichment of phosphate or nitrate would be enough to fuel this transformation into a toxin producer. With an adequate supply of food for the amoeba phase, though, you would hardly expect to see blooms of the toxic zoospores—even at much higher levels of nitrates and phosphates.

Of course, the only difficulty with this analysis was that copper exists in several forms in the water column. Like other metals, it can change its positive charge, depending on what other chemicals surround it. In its lower or "cuprous" charge (plus 1), copper is stored in tidal wetlands and in sediment. But in its plus 2 form ("cupric"), the copper is dissolved in the water column, but is quickly taken up by organic complexes such as dithiocarbamates, and more slowly by other organic compounds like humic acid.

Measurement of the water column will give no clear picture of total copper content in the river ecosystem. Similarly, copper in the plus 1 charge is not bound to the dirt in the sediment of the river or the sediment of the tidal mudflats; it is dissolved in the water *between* the particles in the soil in the mudflats and the sediments. And measuring the dried-out sediment is not the way to accurately determine the amount of copper in those areas, since any sudden mobilizing of the water between sediment particles by tide or current could produce a local surge in copper concentration that could not be measured.

The Maryland DNR had steadfastly maintained that copper levels were normal in the Pocomoke River, while citing measurements of copper in the water column and then copper in the dried sediment. Yet these DNR measurements done yearly, all were about 15 parts per million (ppm), some more than 15 ppm of copper, seem appallingly high to aquaculturists and aquatic researchers. With dithiocarbamates easily pulling copper away from humic acid, for example, any copper in the water column could be transported across cell membranes and into organisms within ten minutes. (Let's face it: Copper levels in water are difficult to measure!)

The measurement discrepancy has been researched very carefully by scientists from UMES in Princess Anne, specifically Dr. Gian Gupta, who has studied the water lying within the sediment of the rivers of the area, including the Pocomoke and Wicomico Rivers. This water between the sediment particles, called "porewater," is significantly enriched with copper directly adjacent to waste water facilities and adjacent to areas of poultry operations and farms applying manure to soil.

As fate would have it, the highest amount of copper in the porewater of the Pocomoke River is found just north of Shelltown. The amounts of copper in the porewater can approach 70 parts per billion. And levels over fifteen ppb (see appendix) can begin to kill algae directly. It certainly seems logical that following a rain, these sediments can be stirred up, releasing a surge of copper that could have a negative effect on mobility and reproduction rates of phytoplankton, in addition to killing blue green algae and cryptomonads directly.

Was this the driving force that had pushed pfiesteria from its benign amoeba phase into its toxic phase?

The answer was yes. I was sure of it ... especially after seeing the results of some experiments that had been performed by Virginia Institute of Marine Science researchers, including Dr. Andrea Dietrich, a member of the research faculty at Virginia Tech's Department of Environmental Engineering. Dr. Deitrich had measured copper levels immediately adjacent to tomato farms in four separate creeks of the Virginia Eastern Shore. All of them have similar hydrology, soil type and tidal flow to that of the Pocomoke though the watersheds are much smaller.

Dr. Dietrich's study documented levels of copper approaching

200 ppb in the runoff for six to eight hours after a rain event. In spite of these high copper levels, however, there had been no fish kills in Virginia Creeks where farmers used chlorothalonils instead of dithiocarbamates!

The mystery was becoming clearer with each passing day.

And one basic fact now seemed obvious, as the Pocomoke City's long hot summer reached its height.

The data regarding copper had not been used adequately in assessment of the predator-prey relationships leading to the pfiesteria blooms in the Pocomoke River.

Somebody needed to blow the whistle—and fast.

chapter 7

And Now for a Few Words From the State of Maryland ...

July 10

After several days of grappling with the enigma of the fish lesions, I needed to stop and catch my breath. What had I learned so far, and what did it all mean?

As always, the thing that would help me most was a brief visit to the river. I needed to sit for an hour on the dock I'd built in the shade of some overhanging cypress trees. Six feet in diameter, these beauties always soothed me, helped me to think about solutions to problems. I settled in near the rope swing I'd hung out over the water, and soon I was watching the timeless Pocomoke ripple past my feet. One by one, I addressed the perplexing questions that troubled me. What information did I have in hand? What should I make of it?

Well, for one thing, I knew I had some initial data strongly suggesting that the basic principles of evolution and natural selection were at work here. Of course, my researches had also helped to remind me of some of the basic principles of wetland ecology ... principles that applied to kingfishers and otters and pfiesteria, just as they did to all biological systems.

One by one, I ticked off some findings that now seemed unmistakably clear. First: Our local version of pfiesteria was active in low concentrations in the Pocomoke. In high concentrations, such as those documented in the Neuse River, the fish had been killed directly by toxins, and without enough time for lesion development to occur. Obviously, lesioned fish like the ones that had gone belly-up in the Pocomoke were fish that had lived long enough for the skin eruptions to show. The implication seemed to be that we were now in the early phases of a pfiesteria invasion that would either remain at a low level or explode as the water temperature increased.

So much for the physiology of the lesions. But what else could I deduce from the chain of pfiesteria-related events that had led up to the present moment? Okay, for one thing, I remembered that back in January of 1997, TV reporter Scott Groom (Channel 2, Baltimore) had interviewed DNR Secretary John Griffin and Maryland Health Commissioner Marty Wasserman on the subject of the Pocomoke fish kill. Each had confirmed that he was aware of the situation, and each had suggested that the problem was due to factors other than pfiesteria. They'd also been careful to note that no reports of pfiesteria-linked human illness had emerged from the region.

Dr. Wasserman had then pointed out, quite correctly, that if a cohort of sick patients with exposure to the river could be isolated, he would certainly consider that evidence enough to warrant an investigation into "health aspects" as related to humans. But there *was* no such cohort, said Dr. Wasserman; therefore, the river must be deemed safe.

But those findings were about to be challenged by the regional news media, which would begin asking the government officials about "sick watermen" in the month of June (well before my own investigation began).

As the media began to intensify up its coverage in late spring of 1997, anywhere from 40 to 50 percent of the fish that were being caught along the banks in the back water and slack water near Shelltown were marked by lesions. But the big news story wasn't dying fish—it was sick people. By now there was plenty of pressure on the State Health Department to start looking more carefully at the watermen's health problems. Their complaints included memory loss, nausea, diarrhea, abdominal cramping, recurrent episodes of pneumonia, upper respiratory illness and skin lesions. After a larger than normal fish kill, many of these afflicted watermen had also experienced an abrupt onset of muscle cramps and aching.

The unusual neurologic problems reminded me of a patient from 1996 who had been suffering from abdominal pain, a wheezing cough and severe nerve pain. I had looked for every disease I could think of—but had come up with nothing more definitive than a weakly positive test for porphyria (the wolfman disease). As it turned out, however, this patient had been doing research on submerged aquatic plants in the bays near Ocean City. Suddenly, I'd found myself wondering: Had he been stricken with the same illness that had overcome the watermen of Shelltown?

Questions! By the middle of June, the Maryland news media was beginning to flood local health officials with queries of this kind. And the State Health Department's response? It was quick, and it sounded good at first, but it was essentially devoid of useful information. First the Department issued a communique to all physicians in the area of the outbreak, suggesting that the doctors should carefully evaluate any illnesses reported by individuals who believed they'd been poisoned by pfiesteria. The docs should also be "quite careful" in weighing these cases—especially if there was evidence that more than 20 percent of the fish were sick or dead in an area.

Finally, the Health Department bulletin called for everyone (including the physicians) to use common sense when it came to the hazards presented by lesioned fish. What did "common sense" entail? Apparently, it meant that we should not cook or eat these tainted specimens ... and that if we possessed any, they should be discarded immediately. It was also important to wash carefully with soap after being exposed to areas that contained lesioned fish.

After eyeballing this curious document, my friend Bruce Nichols and I looked at each other and asked the same question: "How do they know what a '20-percent fish kill' is?" Really, you didn't have to be an editor at Field and Stream to understand that expired fish don't usually float up to the surface wearing a tag marked "Dead Fish"! Many sink to the bottom, as do humans in this tragic circumstance. Others will be eaten by gulls, crabs or other fish. How many would get hung up in weeds or lily pads?

Common sense, indeed! Even though it was patently impossible to make such a judgment, we were being asked to determine which areas had experienced a 20-percent fish kill. (Meanwhile, of course, the local fishermen went right on finding 40 to 50 percent of their catch covered with lesions, or dead outright.)

Relaxing beside my cypress tree, I watched the river slide past— and reflected once again on the marvelous obfuscation that flowed night and day from our state bureaucracy. I recalled, for example, how the DNR had trolled the Pocomoke River on two separate occasions in the third week of June, in an apparent attempt to count lesioned fish. They had used nets to harvest the fish from the main stream of the Pocomoke channel, in water that was cool and rapidly moving.

As you might expect, their nets showed only a few fish (less than two percent) with lesions. But lesioned fish would *never* be found in the mainstream of fast-moving water! Anyone familiar with the pattern of fish kills could have told them that the lesioned fish had turned up in areas of low current, regions that contained nearly stagnant water. (River biologists refer to these as "boundary layers," in which little tidal or current flow washes across the river edges.)

Had the DNR sample been rigged to hide the problem, or had these experienced researchers simply made a mistake?

At any rate, the mainstream fish-hunt continued, and the predictably low results were then duly trumpeted in the Baltimore and Washington papers. This river was safe, no doubt about it. There could be no threat to humans, and no illness was associated with pfiesteria.

Of course, Dr. JoAnn Burkholder—the North Carolina expert— would later explain that rapid flushing of the pfiesteria toxin is the best defense our ecosystem possesses against fish kill from pfiesteria. And her theory made good sense: If the toxin attacked fish that swam into it, the best response would be to simply wash it away.

As I eased away from my river-perch and started the brief hike back to my home, the epidemiological evidence seemed quite clear and compelling. No matter how you sliced it, these pfiesteria toxins were making people sick. Why weren't the state officials as alarmed as I was?

I didn't know it at the time, of course, but later events showed that they were very concerned, indeed. By the summer of '97, in fact, Gov. Parris N. Glendening had quietly ordered four different state departments—Environment, Health, DNR and Agriculture— to bear down on the problem with all the resources at their command.

Pfiesteria and fish kills were about to assume a "high-priority" status in Maryland, and DNR Secretary John Griffin was about to become the point-man who would coordinate the overall state effort.

I wished them well. But the record spoke for itself, and it wasn't encouraging. Were the state bureaucrats going to attack this problem directly and openly? Or were they going to opt for a public relations whitewash aimed at protecting both the seafood industry and the tourist traffic over at nearby Ocean City?

All along the Pocomoke, folks like Lori Maddox and Jack Howard were waiting anxiously to find out.

chapter 8

Introducing ... The Mouth Of the Pocomoke!

July 15

In the beginning, they called me "The Mouth."

As a kid playing Little League baseball outside Chicago, I loved to "talk it up" in the infield, while yelling furious encouragement to my teammates. They responded by inventing a nickname for me, and the moniker stuck. The truth is that I felt complimented every time somebody called me "The Mouth"! As far as I was concerned, yelling your head off was a great way to get into the spirit of the game.

That nickname didn't last long, as my family moved from place to place. But my willingness to speak up—especially with opinions that I thought were correct—didn't diminish with the passing years. By college and medical school, in fact, I'd become quite vocal, first as a medical student who launched his own publication dedicated to the budding "Primary Care Movement" in the U.S ... and then later during my hospital residency, when I developed an organized plan for a rural health care delivery system.

While beating the drums for that second project, I'd been able to help establish a "satellite" health clinic in smalltown Emporium,

Pennsylvania. What a victory for "The Mouth"! As a young, idealistic doctor, I soon came to regard the opening of the clinic as a defining moment—the kind of galvanizing experience that sets the tone for the rest of your career. After that, I knew that I belonged in a medically under-served area, and that I liked doing medicine apart from the starched white coats of hospital-based specialists.

But where was I to go? My choices for place of practice after graduation from residency were limited somewhat by my participation in the National Health Service Corps. This organization, popular in the early 1970's, financed the medical school educations of people like me: docs who wanted to practice in rural areas. In return, the scholarship recipients would provide one year of rural service for each year of scholarship rendered. This was very acceptable to me, because I'd been seeking a rural experience to begin with. (I also wanted to find a neighborhood where you could get lots of fresh crabmeat!)

Neah Bay, located at the top of Washington's Olympic Peninsula adjacent to the Olympic mountain range, looked like the perfect choice. I loved the area, and the Dungeness crab was a culinary show-stopper. But the wide, clear-cut logger swaths on the mountainsides persuaded me to look elsewhere ... and to seek a region where the landscape hadn't been gouged out for the sake of a buck.

Pocomoke was a natural second choice, with its easy access to the Chesapeake Bay. The beauty of the area attracted me. So did the possibility of developing a comprehensive health care facility in a medically under-served area.

As I began my practice, the emotional and professional rewards that came from doing what I was doing seemed impressive. I was happy to be married, happy to be a father and happy to be able to work with my hands on historic restoration and wetland construction in my spare time.

It was obvious, though, that the Eastern Shore had very little political voice. The political forces that ran Maryland were headquartered in the populous Baltimore area, and in the two thriving counties that flank Washington D.C., Montgomery and Prince Georges. There simply wasn't much political clout to be found in sparsely populated Western Maryland or on the rural Eastern Shore —in spite of the huge annual revenues generated each year at the wildly popular Ocean City beach resort.

No clout! As you might imagine, it didn't take me long to realize that the residents needed a hand in dealing with the fishkills and the ugly fish lesions. They needed The Mouth. It was time to go public with some of my findings about the actual cause of the illness that was loose in our watershed.

Reporter John Bentz from the Salisbury Daily Times came by to do an interview about my copper theory. I'd been told that copper was used in chicken feed as a catalyst for enzymes which improved growth rates. I'd also been told that copper had been used in chicken feed to prevent water loss in the early stages of chicken development. But I hadn't been told the truth, not yet: the fact that copper is simply a fungicide. Talking fast, I gave John Bentz all he needed to know to convey my theory regarding copper levels in the river to the public.

I understood that things were going to get a bit hairy, and fast, as a result of my speaking out. I knew that taking the position that copper was harmful to the Pocomoke River might alienate the powerful poultry industry—along with the tomato growers and the politicians who were supported by these industries. I also knew that I'd probably alienate the Department of Natural Resources, which did not agree that copper was a poison in the river.

And I was right. The DNR quickly dismissed my suggestions. Oh, they were polite enough, all right. But the putdown was quickly delivered, and it was crystal-clear.

My copper theory was published on July 17. By July 18, the DNR had nixed it, while contending that there was "no evidence" of extra copper in fish. But I had never contended that copper hurt fish. My theory involved predator and prey—basic principles of biology.

I had merely suggested that the excessive copper was disrupting predator-prey relationships at the phytoplankton level. I wondered if they'd read anything I'd said, before making their snap judgment.

But the DNR's position was actually quite reasonable, when compared with the reaction of some of the poultry professionals. A major part of the pfiesteria illness-problem, said some chicken-growers, was that people who didn't know anything were being listened to by reporters!

Hoping for some support, I quickly called Dr. Fritz Riedel, who had studied organic molecules, including pesticides, and metal concentration in phytoplankton. His colleague at the Academy of Natural Sciences, Dr. Richard Lacouture, helped me understand more about predator-prey relationships in phytoplankton. Neither gentleman said I was right—but neither said I was wrong, either. Dr. Riedel seemed intrigued with the theory I outlined to him; he also seemed delighted by the fact that he possessed the equipment required for proper testing. For his part, Dr. Lacouture simply pointed out that there was nothing to discredit my theory. And the tomato growers? They said nothing at all. They were busy with their crops, and preparing for the next rain, which began on July 21.

That heavy rain, a five-inch drought-breaker, continued through July 23. If the copper theory were correct—the theory that said pfiesteria blooms were made worse by runoff due to rain or by the stirring up of sediment brought on by rising water levels—then we might expect to see some evidence for it emerging very soon.

Meanwhile, the fallout from my copper theory hadn't stopped with superficial denials from DNR. Brad Bell, the Washington TV reporter, seemed to take great delight in telling me about the derision my theory was evoking from scientists working at the Maryland State Estuarine Lab at Horn Point and elsewhere. "They can't believe you're for real, doc!"

I fretted and fumed for a day or two, but then my spirits rose after I got a call from Dr. Gian Gupta at UMES. (I was destined to find out later just how much Dr. Gupta knew about copper toxicity in the Pocomoke River.) This busy researcher had taken the time to call me with an important message: He thought I was "right on track"! Indeed, his own data had shown that sediment from the Pocomoke River contained huge amounts of copper, especially concentrated near areas of poultry farms.

I could hardly believe my ears. For a moment at least, "The Mouth" felt vindicated! At long last, a scientific researcher was supporting my theory ... instead of simply issuing the usual disclaimer about how "copper and toxic pesticides are an 'improbable cause' of the pfiesteria blooms."

Greatly encouraged, I resumed my detective work. I wanted to find out just how these noxious blooms were attacking the people who lived and worked along the river. Another few weeks, surely, and I'd crack the case!

chapter 9

The Petri Dish
By the Compost Pile

July 18

As the struggle to understand the dynamics of the pfiesteria attack continued to unfold, I called Tony Mazzacarro,
who was happy to share with me some of the very exciting work
that he had done recently on the control of algae blooms in his own
fish ponds. I soon found myself wondering why nobody in the
state DNR had asked Tony for some help in interpreting the fish lesions.

This respected scientist had retired a few years before from his
position as the Ph.D. in charge of the Aquaculture Extension Service in College Park. He'd also decided to employ his own expertise
in order to make his second career enjoyable and profitable. Known
as "Mr. Aquaculture," this accomplished fish scientist began to use
the Manokin River as part of an "open river system" in which he
was feeding two ponds containing hybrid striped bass.

Tony was convinced that the era of harvesting fish in the wild
was over. He was determined to find a way to ensure quality control of his product, a strategy that he figured would bring an excellent market price. But I don't think Tony would have predicted that

his knowledge of copper, potassium permanganate and dinoflagellates would open the way to solving the problems of pfiesteria in the Chesapeake Bay!

Tony was using standard aquaculture practices, including the deployment of copper sulfate as an algicide in the ponds. But he'd changed his modus operandi in 1995, when his ponds suffered a massive fish kill caused by a dinoflagellate named gymnodinium. That bug causes what is called the "mahogany tide" (no, not the "red tide" most of us have heard about), named for the color of the water during a bloom.

As you may recall, all dinoflagellates are food sources for other creatures, including rotifers, copepods and other dinoflagellates. Copper in low levels, around 250 parts per billion (ppb), usually controls harmful growth of nuisance algae and dinoflagellates, but not always. Gymnodinium can survive copper levels as high as 1 part per hundred thousand!

Why, then, don't we always have gymnodinium blooms in aquacultures using copper? (Of course, you could ask the same question about pfiesteria.) The reason is that there are seasonal changes in river chemistry that affect algae—both simple (prokaryote) and complex (eukaryote), along with diatoms, dinoflagellates, cryptomonads and other protozoans of many kinds.

Some of these seasonal changes involve rainfall; others are tied to the levels of chemicals such as potassium, manganese and calcium. Of course, acidity, water temperature, oxygen content and chemicals washed into the river also play a part in the size and shape of these blooms. The more I read, the more complicated the picture got. The phytoplankton world was subject to great changes in reproduction, based on small changes in water chemistry.

Interestingly enough, Tony had never been hit with gymnodinium blooms or algae blooms—despite the amount of chicken manure used as a recycled fertilizer for agricultural lands near his fish farm. How I wish that I'd been able to get a sample of his pond water, on the night when the first-ever gymnodinium bloom arrived! I'd have quickly tested it for dithiocarbamates ... which I was convinced were killers of the major predators of both gymnodinium and pfiesteria.

The bloom in Tony's ponds was catastrophic; his entire acreage of hybrid striped bass, worth nearly half a million dollars, was being zapped by the gymnodinium. At first, the oxygen level in the ponds went up sky-high, almost to 20, an unheard of level, as the gymnodinium bloomed. During the fish kill itself, however, oxygen levels plummeted. The high oxygen level might have killed the gymnodinium, which then released a toxin that killed the fish.

To set the assault in context, it's important to remember that there are blooms of dinoflagellates all over the globe; mahogany tides, red tides, black tides and pfiesteria infestations represent just a few of these one-celled invasions.

The carnage was ghastly, but Tony Mazzacarro was a fighter. Hoping to stop it, he and his aides dumped buckets of potassium permanganate into the water. Permanganate is a powerful oxidizing agent. And the chemistry worked as follows: The combination of manganese and oxygen normally is one part of oxygen and one part of manganese. Permanganate is a supersaturated compound with four parts oxygen and one part of manganese. This compound is unstable; it can donate oxygen to another molecule, particularly an organic compound, functionally oxidizing (destroying) it.

Tony was enormously relieved to discover that when the toxin produced by the gymnodinium was oxidized, it was destroyed.

He told me that as he attacked the dinoflagellate toxin with permanganate, the air around the water had a "peppery" feel. His skin felt hot and prickly. And the water seemed warm, even though the water temperature was only 66 degrees. (His hand actually "burned" when he put it in the water.) Next to the oxygen aerating machine, it was difficult to breathe and his eyes felt irritated. The water also had a "chocolate-brown" color in the moonlight. I would see this phenomenon myself later on. Rick Dove had also seen it before many times, down there on the pfiesteria-laden Neuse River in North Carolina.

I was eager to show the DNR experts when they arrived in August that pfiesteria and its toxin could be stopped by using Tony's permanganate strategy. How to proceed? Luckily, Ray and Lori Maddox had two tanks they used for holding fish. They were willing to loan them out for my experiment, although one tank wasn't working quite right and wouldn't be employed until our second round of experiments.

At any rate, we quickly went to work. Ray put 1,000 gallons of river water from areas with fish kill into the tank. Lori added 2½ teaspoons of permanganate, making a two-part-per-million concentration, as Tony had suggested. The water started churning and foaming. And yes ... it looked nearly chocolate-brown. The air took on a peppery feel so pronounced that Lori's eyes were irritated. The water felt hot. And so did we—because we were finding toxin!

Now Ray added 20 fish, ten perch and ten trout, two species that had been readily attacked by the toxin. And the fish lived. Two weeks later, when the experts came to view our experiment, Ray had changed the protocols somewhat. He added fish and additional river water, but not very much, to the protected fish. The levels of permanganate had, of course, fallen as the permanganate molecules had broken down over the past two weeks.

The fish all died within six hours, some with lesions, some without. Obviously, the toxic elements in the river were still there—but the protection of permanganate had been only short-lived.

Thrilled and excited, we asked ourselves the next logical question: Was the pfiesteria on the normal looking fish, or in the water? Also: Did the presence of the fish turn a nontoxic pfiesteria phase into a toxic zoospore, just as Dr. Burkholder had predicted in her ground-breaking study of the problem?

Enormously encouraged, I resisted the urge to crush Roy Maddox in a massive bear-hug. We had pfiesteria's number now; there was no doubt about it. But could we make the state officials listen to us?

Salisbury Daily Times
Letter to the Editor 7/26/97

Our Best Rivers Are Dying

I am writing this letter as a concerned waterman. I live in Mt. Vernon and depend on two bodies of water to make my living in the summer.

The Wicomico River and Monie Bay have been good to me over the years.

I have seen things on these waters that people on land could only dream about.

It's what I don't see now that worries me.

Hundreds of porpoises used to make their yearly visit to these waters, and it was the most beautiful sight you could imagine.

When skates came to visit, there was so many of them that you were almost afraid to sail through them.

Thousands of loons (diving birds) were everywhere and so were turtles. Crabs were so plentiful that it made these two bodies of water some of the best crabbing areas in Maryland. Oysters were so bountiful a private planter could harvest all summer.

In the last few years, the porpoises and skates have quit coming. The loons and turtles are all but nonexistent. Crabs don't run up these waters anymore, and now these two bodies of water have the worst crabbing bottom in the state.

Oysters quit reproducing, and the water quality is so bad sea nettles haven't even appeared this year.

Something is seriously wrong with these areas. I've tried telling the state, but it's as if I'm talking to deaf ears.

There is some chemical run-off in these two rivers that is keeping these sea animals away and killing what stay.

Our sea creatures are speaking, but the state isn't listening.

The Pocomoke River is lucky to have someone like Dr. Ritchie Shoemaker working to solve its problems. Dr. Shoemaker will get no help from the state, only roadblocks.

I hope all citizens of the state who love the Chesapeake Bay and its rivers band together and get behind Dr. Shoemaker's efforts.

If enough people get together, then the state would have to listen. If we don't, then all our rivers as we know them will be just a memory.

Walt Benton
Mt. Vernon, MD

chapter 10

Finally Diagnosing The Sick

July 30

The water skier was my first pfiesteria patient.

He called on July 30, introduced himself, and then described how he'd gone water skiing near Williams Point, only three days before. (The first big Pocomoke fish kill would occur just 500 yards upstream the following week.)

Heart racing, I did my best to calm both of us down. Then I probed his story for all the detail I could get. Yes ... he'd fallen frequently. But hey, he'd had a great time, even though he was a novice—because the Pocomoke River in its lower reaches is wide and shallow, so that it doesn't kick up a lot of wake to ruin a water skier's first attempts.

This patient was young and healthy, and running his own drywall business. Within three hours after exposure to the river, however, he got hit with what he described as the worst headache of his life. But things soon got worse. Within the next hour, he couldn't walk very well. He was clumsy, and he couldn't speak very well, either. His muscles ached. He thought he had the flu and went to bed, figuring he'd be better in the morning. Not true. He woke up still hurting—and covered with at least 30 dime-sized skin lesions that were unlike anything he'd ever seen.

They were also unlike anything *I'd* ever seen, prior to his visit of July 30.

As the patient related his story, I knew I needed help. I called Dr. Delaney, and while the water skier was still in my office, Dr. Delaney described to me what he'd seen on the skin of people with pfiesteria exposure. As he described the lesions in detail, I studied the same skin eruptions on the man before me.

There could be no mistake; my patient had been exposed to pfiesteria.

But there was no time to waste. Moving quickly, I did a skin biopsy to try to learn more about the rash. Then I dispatched the patient to photographer Bob Huey, who interrupted his regular business to take medical photos. Dr. Taylor had agreed to look at the skin biopsies for me.

Imagine my consternation, later that same day, when a second pfiesteria patient walked into my office.

This gentleman described his problem as "funny looking zits." He said he'd been swimming just north of the area of the impending fish kill. He'd only been in the water for 15 minutes, splashing around with ten of his friends and family members at a picnic. Nobody else had skin lesions, and nobody else was sick—he was sure of it.

I examined him carefully. Patient number-two displayed lesions very similar to those of the water skier. Photos were taken of this patient as well. Arrangements were also made for a skin biopsy. Why had this man gotten lesions—while the children and the pregnant woman with him hadn't?

The next day, patient number-three arrived. She was a young mother who'd been cavorting with her children in the shallows of the Pocomoke River near Williams Point. She'd also watched the water skier for a bit, even applauding some of his spectacular falls.

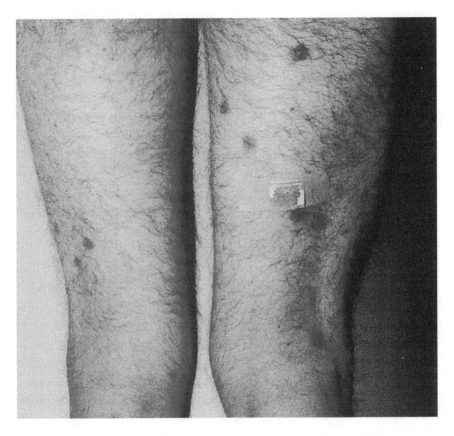

The Waterskier had over 30 lesions unlike any I had ever seen.

But patient number-three didn't have any skin lesions. Instead, she complained of an agonizing headache, while also describing a profound case of "watery diarrhea" without blood or mucus. She had terrible abdominal cramps, too. She said the diarrhea was worst right after eating—but that it continued to occur, whether she ate or not. It was so bad that it was even interrupting her sleep. And nothing seemed to stop it—not Kaopectate, not Pepto Bismol, not Imodium. Even the antibiotics for "traveler's diarrhea" seemed to be powerless against hers. But her tests for infection were all negative.

What did it all mean? For starters, I felt certain that I was dealing with "secretory diarrhea," which is marked by the characteristics she'd described: It lasts for more than a week, doesn't include blood or mucous, and frequently interferes with sleep. That last symptom means that a disease is affecting the lining of the small intestine, and that it sometimes could be caused by a problem with absorption of bile salts.

The body manufactures bile in the liver, stores it in the gall bladder and then releases it into the intestine (along with cholesterol) after a meal in order to digest fatty foods. The cholesterol is dissolved in the bile, as is the case with other fatty substances. After the fat is digested, the bile salts and cholesterol are reabsorbed farther along in the intestine. The recycling of these complex molecules, called "enterohepatic recirculation," saves the body a lot of energy.

If the bile salts aren't absorbed farther downstream in the bowel, however, they can cause a diarrhea like my patient had. A medicine used to lower cholesterol, called cholestyramine, works by binding cholesterol and bile salts, preventing reabsorption. This medicine is frequently constipating, though, which limits its use in medical practice. Still, it's a great tool in the treatment of secretory diarrhea.

Knowing that cholestyramine was also a useful treatment for diarrhea caused by a clostridia toxin (c. dificile), I decided to try it with this patient, who was rapidly becoming dehydrated.

It worked. The diarrhea ended within two days. So did her headache. Was it all a coincidence? Maybe she'd simply been stressed out about her diarrhea, thus triggering the headache? Or maybe pfiesteria toxin in her bile had been causing diarrhea and headache both? I couldn't be sure.

Meanwhile, the local newspapers were reporting on an approaching scientific pfiesteria conference that would include "experts and invited guests," along with some local politicians and watermen. I was rather startled to find myself invited as well. But with my eight-by-ten color glossies of my first two patients in hand, I was ready to convince anyone who'd listen that there truly were health risks associated with the river. Still, I knew that it would be tough sledding, since the State health officials were continuing to insist that the river was safe, with no risks to humans from the fish with lesions.

The possibility of a pfiesteria infestation was now drawing more and more attention. Why, the State was even showcasing Dr. Jo-Ann Burkholder, who would be attending these meetings! The top scientists of Maryland were coming to hear what she had to say.

I couldn't wait to quiz her, myself.

I was eager to ask the "leading expert on pfiesteria" some pointed questions about copper and DNA and predators and prey and cholestyramine and human health. ... *Easy, Ritchie. Better catch your breath.*

chapter 11

"How Can Humans Be Hurt by Fish Suffering from Crab Pot Scrapes And Propeller Blade Cuts?"

August 1

What tension was in the air at the DNR conference! The moment I walked through the door, I could see that the political stakes, already high, were about to get much higher. There were millions of tourism dollars at stake, after all—to say nothing of the financial hazards that pfiesteria might soon present to the Eastern Shore's immense poultry industry. *Tighten your seatbelt, Ritch.*

I'd been a last-minute guest on this "show," and that's the right word for what followed. As always, DNR Secretary Griffin did his best to project an air of relaxed, easygoing calm. Jovial and high-spirited, he reminded me of a football linebacker with personality. But Health Secretary Wasserman was definitely on edge. Hunched over his notes at the front of the hall, he looked like a nervous swimmer on the starting blocks.

There were several other individuals on hand whom I recognized, including some local politicians, a couple of high-powered scientists, Dr. Eric May, six or seven watermen and a few newspaper reporters. (But no TV folks, at least not yet.)

The purpose of the meeting was supposedly to "narrow the universe" of thoughts, ideas and opinions about pfiesteria, and the featured guest was the authoritative Dr. JoAnn Burkholder. Dr. Karen Steidinger from the state of Florida—another dinoflagellate expert—would not be present today, but she'd sent a research associate in her place.

The dinner on Friday night was a buffet featuring ... you guessed it, chicken and fish! I quickly introduced myself to Dr. Burkholder, and as we made our way through the buffet line, I bombarded her with questions about ways in which copper might stimulate DNA synthesis in dinoflagellates. Dr. Burkholder said that she found the "copper concept" logical, although she hadn't yet researched it in any detail. And yes, she was aware of the information that I'd already submitted, stating that copper appeared to be an important factor in determining DNA replication of one-celled organisms.

Even better, from my point of view, was her confirmation of the fact that pfiesteria in its toxic zoospore phase was eaten by a variety of phytoplankton—especially rotifers and copepods. But the N.C. State expert seemed unaware that dithiocarbamates complexed with copper to get into these creatures and kill them quickly.

And what about the diet enjoyed by pfiesteria? Dr. Burkholder listened carefully to my questions, then confirmed that pfiesteria, in its benign amoeba phase, eats blue green algae as well as some types of bacteria and some types of dinoflagellates. But the major food-source was the type of protozoa known as "cryptomonads." And all of these creatures were sensitive to the levels of copper found in the Pocomoke River.

As you might imagine, I wasn't the only person who wanted to talk to Dr. Burkholder. It was impressive to see that so many people wanted to learn from her, and were eager to hear her keynote address, which was scheduled for the next day. After watching her deal with dozens of probing questions—including my own—I wondered how she survived all the pressure. Of course, I'd heard that she'd been forced to battle entrenched public and scientific opinion to reach the level of acclaim she now enjoyed. ...

I had no idea, at that moment, that I was facing a similar uphill battle if I wanted to expose the human health risks from river water exposure, while also going public with my diagnosis of the pfiesteria illness syndrome. In fact I was about to lock horns with some powerful adversaries, as I attempted to outline treatment methods required to turn back the persistent human health syndrome and explain the importance of the high levels of copper and dithiocarbamates found in the Pocomoke River.

During a break in the conference, I showed my case photos to Diane Matuszak, M.D., MPH. A high official in the State Health Department, she told me in very strong language, that I needed to do "additional work" on my patients. I needed to conduct a wide variety of cultures and laboratory tests, in order to confirm that absolutely nothing else could have caused the lesions my patients exhibited. Then, and only then, said the unsmiling Dr. Matuszak, would I have earned the right to say that their illness was due to pfiesteria toxin. Obviously startled by my audacity, she informed me that no one had reported illness from pfiesteria toxin.

Dr. Matuszak was certainly correct; I did have more work to do. But her credibility began to erode, in my mind, as soon as she suggested that a different germ, mycobacteria marinarum, might have caused the skin lesions shown in my photos. I'd witnessed the effects of the mycobacteria marinarum—and it caused an obviously different lesion.

How could Dr. Matuszak justify telling me to do more clinical work, when her own remarks showed that she hadn't seen or treated either mycobacterium marinarum infections *or* pfiesteria lesions?

I was in no mood to be brushed off by a physician who didn't see patients, and who didn't want to acknowledge the "remote possibility" that I might be right ... and who changed her tune completely as soon as her own boss, Secretary Wasserman, joined the discussion.

As I understood it, Wasserman meant "waterman" in German. How ironic! I watched calmly as he was introduced and then presented himself with an air of quiet confidence. He spoke proudly of his daughter, who attended a university in North Carolina—the school with the "better basketball team." I wasn't sure of the relevance ... but my gut told me that his aggressive posture meant only one thing: He wanted us to know that he was taking firm command of all public health issues regarding pfiesteria.

I liked Marty right away. He sported an appealing "jock mentality"—a breezy manner full of locker room-style putdowns and bravado. He was also a quick thinker and a careful speaker. Although he was a lawyer, Wasserman had worked as a pediatrician in a rural setting and in some big hospitals, too. Watching him go about his task, it was easy to see that he was positioning the health department to control the pfiesteria health issue.

But my own feeling was different: I wanted the state's practicing physicians to lead the way. The health department could do the surveillance. Why not leave the questions about human health effects of pfiesteria to the practicing docs?

Next I showed my photographs to some area politicians to whom I had not been introduced, but who seemed to know who I was. None of them was aware of the problem with copper—even though all claimed to have at least a limited knowledge of agricultural techniques and practices in the Pocomoke River watershed.

I found myself shaking my head, as each politico bragged about how agriculture in this area had made enormous progress at reducing nutrient pollution in the Pocomoke River. It was highly unlikely, they all said, that farming practices had anything to do with the growth of pfiesteria itself. Each of them also warned me not to share my photos with anyone else. The public might become unduly alarmed, and wind up thinking that the river was unhealthy!

When I informed them that I was the medical director of the River-Associated Rash and Illness Center, I got a few raised-eyebrow looks from some, while the others quickly averted their gaze.

But the media were not so easily fooled. The story of the lesion-afflicted water skier was featured on the TV news in Washington and Baltimore, and my photos would soon be displayed on the front pages of many newspapers. Foolishly, I'd assumed that such compelling evidence would force the health officials and politicians to acknowledge that there were some people who'd been made sick by exposure to pfiesteria. I'd also assumed that the investigation would be initiated and ongoing by now.

Better think again.

On Saturday morning, the tone of the conference sessions became heavily scientific. Speaker after speaker presented information regarding water quality in the Pocomoke River, agricultural practices in the Pocomoke watershed, and analysis of the waste water treatment facilities in the region. I sat listening in amazement, while the experts concluded that everything looked fine! There was no evidence of any nutrient enrichment, for example, with normal levels of phosphates and nitrates appearing in the water column. Why, current levels of nutrients were no different than in any year since measurements had begun in 1986. Nor were there were any obvious problems with dissolved oxygen, carbon, turbidity of water, chlorophyll (signifying algae blooms) or temperature.

According to Chief Scientist Don Boesch, Ph.D., in fact, all of the nutrient measurements in the Pocomoke River were completely normal. This statement would change later, however. By mid-September, those same "normal" nutrient levels would be described as evidence for a severe pollution problem caused by "nutrient runoff"! What had happened to "science"? Was it being held political hostage to fear of economic loss?

I badly wanted to set the record straight. For one thing, I knew that the Pocomoke is called a "blackwater river" for a reason: It's full of tannin and organic materials that wash out from swamps and wetlands. It was also true that the record-breaking rainfall of 1996 had lowered salinity as expected. It had lowered pH, also as expected. And the rainfall had also raised the water table in this flat land. Surface flow and runoff after a rain was increased—which meant that flushing of swamps and tidal wetlands was increased. Subsurface flow was dramatically increased because of the height of the water table.

What did all of that mean? Quite simply, it meant that the current levels of nitrates and phosphates in the Pocomoke were essentially the same as those of other rivers in the Eastern Shore—with some, such as the Nanticoke and Wicomico, displaying even higher phosphate and nitrate levels. (Western shore rivers, such as the Patapsco, Patuxent and Potomac, had nutrient levels similar to the Pocomoke's.)

In other words, the data presented at the conference appeared to show that agriculture was doing a good job with its management practices, that the Department of the Environment was doing a good job monitoring waste water treatment facilities and that the DNR was doing a good job surveying fish and counting and classifying lesions.

So what else is new? During many years of observation, I've never found a government agency that would admit to doing anything less than a "great job"!

Nonetheless, I felt certain that the heavy rains had distorted the data. And that was only one of the questions I couldn't get an answer for. What about the high levels of copper? The delegate from the Department of the Environment confessed to being unfamiliar with Dr. Gupta's work showing copper enrichment in porewater.

In addition, the fish pathology analyses had not been completed from the month before—and these would have been enormously helpful in understanding what the reddened meninges of the autopsied fish meant. Another problem: The agricultural practices did not include an analysis of the wetland buffers. Yes, the agriculture expert acknowledged that cover crops could not prevent subsurface flow of any nutrient or of heavy metals ... but there was no agreement as to how wetland buffers should be used in and around major ditches and creek banks, not to mention the river banks themselves.

By morning break, I knew that I'd re-earned my "mouth" nickname, although Secretary Griffin had done his best to remain jovial and relaxed, while steadily referring to me as "Doc." He was working hard to make sure the truth got out. How could I help?

Thinking ahead, I'd brought along some leftover "Bird" T-shirts from a Nature Trail fundraiser. On the spot, I created a "Waterman's Fund" designed to help some of the workers who'd been made sick near Shelltown.

But when I asked Secretary Griffin to announce the establishment of the "fund," to be administered by the Pocomoke Trail Committee, he surprised me: "Why not do it yourself?" Well, my father had been a salesman, and maybe something had rubbed off—because in the end, I sold 25 shirts to the captive, interested audience.

It was a rewarding moment, but the most significant part of the morning took place when Dr. Burkholder took the mike. Speaking to a rapt audience, she pointed out that the Florida dinoflagellate research group had announced the finding of a new species of pfiesteria in the Pocomoke River. Would she be able to make the link between the North Carolina-Florida version of the bug, pfiesteria piscicida, and the creature now running loose in the Pocomoke?

Dr. Burkholder's presentation confirmed our worst fears. The Pamlico Sound had been hit hard. Fish kills were in the billion range in 1991, millions had died in 1995, with uncounted kills occurring again in 1997. Many other different animals had also been hit, including crabs, and oysters.

Dr. Burkholder discussed the life cycle of pfiesteria, based on her previous publications (discussed in Chapter 6). She noted that the pfiesteria organism varied in its size, ranging up to 460 microns in its benign amoeba-like phase.

This phase, she said, was characterized by chloroplasts, engulfed from prey species, which continued to live and function well with the amoeba. If adequate supplies of food such as blue green algae and cryptomonads were available, the amoeba phase wouldn't turn into a toxic zoospore without a tremendous enrichment of nutrients in the water, especially phosphates.

The bottom line of her message was stark and dramatic: The organism responded to a substance excreted from fish that invariably turned on toxin production!

By now I had three pages of notes, each jammed with questions for Dr. Burkholder, as well as for the environment people who'd ignored copper and dithiocarbamates. I yearned to ask Dr. Burkholder about human health, especially hypersensitivity, but she was soon gone, swallowed up by crowds of others who also had questions.

Dr. Burkholder had presented slides demonstrating the "insidious" health effects of pfiesteria. She'd isolated substances that were carcinogenic from pfiesteria. She'd discussed chronic health syndromes, including her own, which she felt were due to pfiesteria.

Secretary Wasserman couldn't have been pleased to hear about pfiesteria and cancer. Human illness was bad enough, but insidious diseases, too? Ever resourceful, however, he immediately did some expert political maneuvering. First of all, he steered Dr. Burkholder away from the group of waiting questioners (including me) into a protected anteroom where he could talk to her himself. There I was, waiting impatiently in line, and there *they* were, discussing the dictionary definitions that should best be applied to delayed, serious, occult health problems!

The public relations "spin" was becoming all too obvious. Clearly, Wasserman felt that the word "insidious" was inappropriate. Increasingly frustrated, I was sorry to see the lunch break end and the afternoon meetings begin.

I was confident that I would be able to speak at both of the afternoon sessions. The first would be the technical section, with experts talking about water quality and environment issues. I felt hopeful that my copper theory and fish autopsies would provide some useful insights for everybody on hand. But that hope would be disappointed. I was also certain that my experience with three patients suffering from river-associated illness would be of interest at the health section meeting. Wrong again, Ritch!

At the health meeting, I found Dr. Matuszak sitting at the head of a long table, flanked by the heads of three local health departments. There were several other people attending the health committee meetings whom I did not recognize.

Apparently, I was the only active practicing physician there. Even if the others at the meeting had had a chance to see patients, none had seen the river-associated illness that I'd observed. Still, I did have my photos, my research and my files of data with me—along with the solid information from Dr. Delaney and Dr. Morris. Surely, this contribution would be welcome!

Dr. Matuszak started things off by announcing that the health committee had a long series of items that needed to be reviewed and discussed, with decisions about policy that had to be completed within a six-hour time frame. Only members of the panel would be allowed to participate in the discussion, she said. Others, like me, would be allowed to watch.

"Wait a minute," I argued. "Secretary Griffin said the first half of the afternoon session would be open for all of us to have input."

"Oh no," Dr. Matuszak replied, "there's too much to be done. Besides, I don't think we need to spend a lot of our time on health issues regarding fish that have been scraped in crab pots or cut by propeller blades."

Although Dr. Matuszak later developed a constructive working relationship with me, as additional data became available in the ensuing weeks to confirm the existence of human illness from pfiesteria, her comments during that painful session seemed unbelievable. If I hadn't been there to hear her utter them, I never would have believed it. But when I asked her to repeat her statement, she refused.

I sat there smoldering, while the health committee discussed how to determine whether or not the river should be closed, should there ever be evidence of fish kills. Based on the information from Dr. Burkholder, the pfiesteria toxin was short-lived ... and within a day following cessation of a fish kill, there should be no concern about human health.

Boggled, I shook my head. If there were no "health concerns" to begin with, as the State had said, why was there a concern about the safety-period that should follow a fish kill?

Another conclusion troubled me: According to the State, a fish kill was not significant unless lesioned fish represented more than 20 percent of the harvested fish. But most fish sink when they die; they don't float! Divers working the bridge construction site at the Neuse River had reported that during a fish kill, they would see the entire river bottom covered with stacks of fish corpses.

Fish on the surface, on the other hand, were usually in the throes of death. They floated only until they were washed away with the tide or eaten by seagulls. Well, I'd already heard about flocks of thousands of seagulls devouring fish. How could "twenty percent of harvested fish" be correct, if the total numerator of dead fish were unknown? More importantly, that 20-percent criteria was based on troll nets of the DNR's boats—and not on the counts done by fishermen looking at their nets full of sick and dying fish.

I simply had to speak. "Whose criteria are you going to use?" I asked. "Are you going to use artificial ones created by counting dead fish in places where fish don't die—or are you going to use counts of fish from areas where there have been fish kills?"

Dr. Matuszak looked at me and then said that, unfortunately, the committee had a long list of items to cover and they could not entertain comments from the observers. Comments or questions would be addressed after the committee had reached its policy-making decisions—perhaps by suppertime or, at the latest, by 10:00 p.m. It was now 1:30.

My feet did not fail me. I couldn't believe it. What a whitewash! As I walked quickly out of the meeting—my fascinating bits of evidence tucked carefully under my arm—I spotted Dr. Wasserman still talking to Dr. Burkholder. Any illusions I'd maintained about the technical and health meetings being open and not already scripted were evaporating into the storm clouds that were now forming outside.

If the state was going to act this way—taking credit for conducting "open proceedings" but then slamming the door on them—my one voice wouldn't make any difference at all. I walked back to the car, as mad as I've ever been. Were they going to silence us completely—those of us who merely wanted to discuss the true causes and effects of the pfiesteria plague?

What could I do? Right then, I was one lone voice, no more. I sat behind the wheel for a few moments, mulling the problem. ...

The media! How many times in the past had a single voice managed to multiply itself in the newspapers, or on that flickering television screen? It had happened before: One voice, amplified by the media, had stopped wars and brought down presidents.

Maybe the media could stop the hype from the State and challenge the false idea that the river was safe and that humans don't get sick from pfiesteria.

The conference wrapped up on Sunday morning, but I didn't attend. I'd made up my mind that it was going to be my job to show that there *were* human health risks from pfiesteria, and that the river was not safe. I had proof!

As good fortune would have it, Jack Howard, one of the watermen who attended the conference, called me Sunday afternoon. He'd been at the wrap-up session. He described it as something of a "circus." He pointed out that there had been no report from the Health Committee. The Technical Committee had reported that the fish had been injured by stress linked to low salinity and low pH. Nutrients were not a factor. The stress had contributed to the fish lesions, especially in combination with injuries received from fish nets and crab pots, along with "seagull-inflicted punctures."

Pfiesteria was not to blame. Not at all.

Jack was as angry as I was. He wondered how they could "get away with this."

"All right," Jack said. "You have to prove them wrong, and I have to prove them wrong—and we won't give up!"

chapter 12

"Pfiesteria Hysteria" Becomes A Very Tiresome Rhyme

August 4

It rained hard that Sunday and Monday after the DNR conference. Yet the summer had been dry, with drought-like conditions prevailing until now. Later on, agricultural runoff—in this drought-stricken year—would be blamed for the pfiesteria blooms.

Sorry, but that theory simply wouldn't wash. If the State had said that the drought had been responsible for high levels of nutrients by concentrating them in ditches, guts, washes and creeks, I could have believed it. But not runoff. In fact, the five-inch rainfall of July 21–23 had helped to fill up our ponds and, coincidentally, had triggered the pfiesteria-surge that had struck my first three patients.

The same pattern of rain (followed by an increase in the numbers of lesioned fish) had begun in October of 1996. And if that pattern held true, we were due for a big fish kill by Wednesday.

Later on, when farm runoff was being blamed for algae blooms and an increased food supply for pfiesteria, I would be amazed at how the "nutrient theorists" could possibly justify the state's position in the absence of elevated nitrates, phosphates and chlorophyll.

Dr. Don Boesch would be quoted in August as saying that the nutrient levels in the Pocomoke River weren't too high. Later, however, his opinion would change dramatically—even though his shifting opinion was still reportedly based on the same data that had been evaluated at the DNR conference.

We also knew that nobody was complaining about the "Best Management Practices" procedures for controlling nutrients, as promulgated by the State Department of Agriculture. According to the myth, those practices were working well to control harmful river pollution. But we had eyes, didn't we? We saw the tomatoes being sprayed, and we heard about the Snow Hill sewage plant dumping sewage on weekends when no one was looking (after the State inspector went home for the weekend). And then there always was my cohort of sick patients—if you needed any more evidence of what was really taking place here, that is.

Frustration! Luckily, however, the Chesapeake Bay Foundation was already looking at what copper runoff had done to clam beds and the grass shrimp populations near Painter, Virginia. Even if the technical committee of the DNR conference had failed to note the possibility of pfiesteria, the CBF would be able to search for the true causes of the initiation of pfiesteria blooms.

I was hoping against hope that the Chesapeake investigators would review the facts as we knew them—starting with the fact that once pfiesteria entered a toxic phase, it had several "choices." It could reproduce, make a cyst and become quiescent in river sediments, change to an amoeba phase, make another toxic zoospore —or get eaten by a rotifer or by something else.

I was also hoping that the Bay Foundation would rally around the fungicide flag—but no such luck. Instead, the CBF merely suggested that individuals exposed to bay water in suspected pfiesteria waters should wash themselves with bleach if they were splashed.

Too bad. But things were beginning to move off dead-center. The next day I picked up the Baltimore Sun, and got a powerful jolt:

STATE'S TOP DOC SAYS STOP THE HYPE

Was Dr. Wasserman talking about CBF and bleach, or me? Or was he simply blowing smoke? But I'd seen how carefully Dr. Wasserman had chosen his words in the past. Once again, he appeared to be trying to regain control of the public health issue. And he would be successful—for about an hour.

That's exactly how long it took for Lori Maddox to call me with the startling news: "There's a big kill getting started here now!"

The phone began to ring off the hook. Suddenly a dozen different TV stations and newspapers wanted to interview sick patients. A vet from Ocean City called; he was caring for a dog who'd gone into the water at the Cedar Hall Landing, near Shelltown. Now the dog was struggling with bizarre lesions. A man from Fishing Bay, farther north on the Chesapeake, had developed lesions that no dermatologist could identify.

A commercial diver had seen lesions on menhaden near the Francis Scott Key Bridge—10 years ago. And some Virginia residents remembered that the Rappahannock menhaden kills had been blamed on low oxygen 15 years before.

The media firestorm had begun in earnest. A local TV station was running a series on pfiesteria, cleverly entitled "Pfiesteria Hysteria." They wanted my input. But I was growing weary of that cute rhyme.

It wasn't hysteria, I told them, and the sooner you stop making "the Cell from Hell" look so mysterious, the better off we'll all be. The station didn't run that clip.

As I sat at my desk, watching the rain fall softly, I wondered if the kill by the Maddox dock was "the big one"—or just the first of many big ones to come. Once pfiesteria moved into your neighborhood—according to my copper theory—it would continue to live there, as long as you kept killing off the creatures that held its numbers in check.

I went back to work. I started looking at water samples from the

Pocomoke River under lower lens magnification in my microscope. There were so many life forms in a drop of water! Leeuwenhoek couldn't have been more amazed than I was at the diversity of size, shape, motion, feeding behavior and intracellular inclusions of the water world. Imagine trying to catch such a tiny creature, isolate it, study it, understand its physiology and anatomy, Then imagine trying to figure out its various predator-prey relationships!

Sounds pretty formidable, you say?

Now imagine going through the same incredibly detailed and minute process in a scientific arena where ruthless competition often leaves professionals acting as much out of jealousy and envy as they do out of their much-ballyhooed "scientific disinterestedness."

What was it going to take to make the State officials listen? Was somebody in the State's family going to have to get sick, before the State would face up to the facts?

While I was musing on the questions, the media blitz was continuing. And it was producing effects. I understood that fact with crystal-clarity a few days later, when Dr. Wasserman called me at home.

The gentleman now identified himself as "Marty," Suddenly, I had become "Ritchie"! I listened carefully. Obviously, Dr. Wasserman had been watching the TV news. And now he had a request.

"Of course I'll help!" I answered him. And then I promised to let him know—immediately—about any new cases of pfiesteria-related human illness that I was treating in my daily practice beside the Pocomoke.

chapter 13

Sick Fish, Sick People
The Link Is Clear

August 6

"**Dr. Shoemaker? It's for you**. It's Lori Maddox."

It was Tuesday morning, ten o'clock. Lori was calling from Shelltown with some very disturbing news: Dead fish were once again floating belly-up along her stretch of the river.

"It looks like a big one, Doc. Some of the fish have lesions, and some don't. But we've got several hundred of 'em floating in the water. Same pattern, too—a period of heavy rain, and then the fish start dying the next day.

"Are they going to blame this kill on the 'pfiesteria hysteria,' too, Doc?"

Like many of her neighbors, Lori had grown weary of hearing her concerns described as "hysteria." Were her fears really so unreasonable, when the toxin-threat lurked in her own backyard? Lori certainly didn't seem hysterical to me. She seemed quite calm and collected, in fact, as she explained that most of the fish in the current kill seemed to be menhaden—a species that travels the estuarine waters of the Eastern Shore in huge schools. Known as "filter feeders," the menhaden are fished commercially. They're sold as bait in many areas, but they also turn up quite frequently as ingredients in dog and cat food.

Lori's careful report about the scores of dead menhaden in the river seemed quite pertinent—especially when I recalled how Dr. Burkholder had described the species as being extremely susceptible to attack by pfiesteria. The North Carolina expert had postulated that there's something in the fish excreta that causes pfiesteria to become incredibly toxic, while also "turning on" its reproduction process and thus triggering blooms.

As I mulled Lori's description of the latest carnage, I was remembering the rather unusual geography of the river near Shelltown. In this area, nearly fresh water from the upper reaches of the Pocomoke meets the brackish tidal flow from the Chesapeake Bay. Nutrients in the upper portion of the stream are then washed by the downstream current, which mixes with the incoming tide in this region.

At this point the river flattens out—so that the long, narrow and fast-moving current slows, producing an increased proportion of surface area to volume of water. Here in the "junction zone," the slightly acid water from the upper river mixes with the more alkaline water of the Bay.

During the summer, I recalled, large schools of menhaden are frequently found migrating into waters such as the Pocomoke to feed on abundant plankton. As the waters cool, the schools of menhaden move elsewhere. This year, however, the menhaden had obviously ventured into Shelltown at the wrong time. And now they were dying everywhere along that stretch of the tainted river.

How would the DNR respond? To their credit, the agency rapidly mobilized containment, enforcement and communications personnel, along with the required water-quality samplers. The Department had insisted that it would be prepared to analyze exactly what was happening in the event of a fish kill—and now they were doing it.

Their water-quality tests had been heavily criticized only a few days before, with at least one expert describing them as "inadequate." But not this time. Major Mike Howard (a neighbor) was in charge of the current operation, and that meant the job would be done well, since Howard is widely respected for his quiet, no-nonsense efficiency.

The DNR went straight to work, but they faced numerous difficulties. For one thing, the number of dead fish could only be estimated. For every thousand dead fish on the surface, there seemed to be as many sea gulls eating them. And who could say how many fish had sunk to the bottom of the river? Who knew how many had been consumed by birds or crabs?

These were open questions, no doubt about it. But one fact *had* been established, beyond a reasonable doubt: The Pocomoke was experiencing a fish kill.

How many fish had actually died? (Maybe it was time to start asking ourselves how many had lived!) Although the number remained highly suspect, the DNR finally decided that the death toll in this early August kill had been about 15,000, give or take a few thousand. But nobody at the Department seemed prepared to answer some other disturbing questions about the plague.

Question: If the fish were being killed, why weren't the gulls who ate them dying as well?

Question: Where had all the otters gone? Nobody along our stretch of the river had seen one for the past four months. Had they taken a hit, along with the fish?

And finally: What about the human population? Were we more like the otters, or more like the gulls? Were some of us about to start taking the kind of punishment that had been inflicted on the menhaden?

Lori Maddox wanted answers, and she wasn't afraid to take a few chances in order to obtain them. Soon after calling me, she found herself on a boat in the Pocomoke, watching Yvonne Lawson—a 20-year employee of the Maryland Department of the Environment

—go about her job in an adjoining craft. Yvonne was scooping fish into her boat, then separating those with lesions from those without. Leaning over the rail, Yvonne was working as fast as she could ... while occasionally splashing water on her forearms. She was wearing gloves—but her forearms kept getting wet.

"Yvonne, you're gonna get sick!" warned Lori. "Get your nose away from all that!" But Yvonne kept insisting that she felt fine, and she kept on working. Besides, she told her frowning companion, nobody had ever gotten sick by touching the fish!

But Yvonne Lawson did. That night, the skin on her forearm started to blister and peel off. She coughed, she wheezed, and her eyes turned red. That was alarming enough ... but her husband became truly frightened when he saw how her mental processes had begun to deteriorate.

Dazed and forgetful, the disoriented Yvonne didn't return to work the next day. (By then the fish kill had begun to slacken.) Yvonne improved slowly ... and assumed that she'd been walloped with a sinus infection, a frequent problem in the past. Yet none of her previous infections had been quite like this one. Her skin felt like it was "burning," even as it peeled away in long flaking strips, as if from second-degree burns. Her memory also seemed to be faulty, and it was getting worse. What was happening here?

While Yvonne struggled with her illness, the fish kill had brought a swarm of reporters to town. They quickly found out that the downed water skier was growing sicker. He couldn't remember even the simplest things. He couldn't move his neck without making his headache worse. He wobbled badly if he tried to stand up with his eyes closed, and his halting speech sounded thick and wandering.

Had all of these symptoms been caused by a single hour of water skiing on the Pocomoke? It was time to find out, and so I asked the on-call physician at McCready Hospital to admit my patient for observation.

To the credit of the hospital's medical staff, the patient received every service—and every test—that might help us to understand the pathology. A spinal tap revealed nothing abnormal in the spinal fluid; there were no cells of the type that might signal the presence of meningitis. Nor were there any changes in sugar or protein values of the kind that might show encephalitis. Baffled, we asked ourselves: What could be causing this man's horrible headache, his pronounced change in mental status?

Soon it was evident that his blood tests, CT scans and MRI exam had all checked out "normal," as well. His headache was getting somewhat better with anti-inflammatory medications. Antibiotics had been started, based on the possibility that he might be suffering from a serious infection; those medicines were now stopped.

The patient improved slowly over the next two days. Looking back on it now, his recovery might have been quicker had it not been for the many reporters who came to see him, with one each asking the same questions. But each had a story to report, and each wanted answers, details, photos.

The state continued to react to the media attention by bringing top officials into the forefront for open communication, and soon it was announced that Secretary Wasserman and Secretary Griffin would come to Pocomoke for a public meeting on Monday night, August 11.

I was quite surprised to get another phone call at home from Secretary Wasserman. Once again he introduced himself as "Marty," and once again he was polite and friendly. He assured me that he was evaluating the "human illness factor" as carefully and quickly as he could. And he wanted me to understand his situation, as the public health official for the entire State.

In order for him to report that there was an illness associated with pfiesteria, he needed absolute proof. And he couldn't use a clinical diagnosis as such proof. He needed hard information upon which to base public policy. It wasn't enough, he said, simply to qualify his health alert by using a phrase such as, "To a reasonable degree of medical certainty." No, Marty required 100 percent convincing proof.

I listened carefully and then told him that, without being able to identify a toxin and without a blood test or a culture that would pinpoint the pfiesteria organism or the pfiesteria toxin as an agent of human illness, there was simply no way I could be "100 percent sure." In fact, true medical certainty would depend on human autopsy—or on the kind of controlled experimentation that the famed Dr. Koch had designed.

Marty thanked me and asked me to be "patient." He also requested that I stop referring to my sick patients as "cases," and start calling them "suspected cases." I told him that I didn't have a patient bone in my body, but that I understood his point of view and would do my best to cooperate with him and the State. I didn't want to be an obstacle—but I also didn't want to be dismissed without a hearing by the Department of Health, as had happened during my attempt to communicate my concerns to the DNR.

The "town meeting" was held at the log cabin in Pocomoke. Located on the Pocomoke River near the public golf course, this rustic meeting place lacks ventilation. With a standing-room only crowd on hand, it was stifling inside. Instead of engaging in heated words, though, both Secretary Griffin and Secretary Wasserman were doing their best to provide open, honest answers.

After recognizing me as "Ritchie," Marty went to great pains to point out that the State was doing everything necessary to investigate and then combat the plague.

Once again, the place was swarming with reporters. By now, I was getting to know some of them rather well—including Angus Phillips, an accomplished writer for the Washington Post, who promptly asked: "Why can't you call these sick people 'cases'? Why are you beating around the bush?" Good questions, Angus!

After listening to Marty Wasserman's plea for "100 percent proof," I knew that I needed to nail down the kind of definitive diagnostic criteria that would convince not only a reporter, but also Maryland's embattled medical establishment. Why not start by sending our stricken water skier down to Duke University, where the highly knowledgeable Dr. Schmechel could examine him at length?

After a few minutes on the phone, I had set the wheels in motion. With Dr. Schmechel having promised to perform any tests that we couldn't handle at McCready Hospital (including the neurocognitive exam), the skier headed off to Durham.

Dr. Schmechel had evaluated other people with significant pfiesteria exposure from Dr. Burkholder's lab in the past, and I felt absolutely confident that if anyone could confirm a case of pfiesteria-related illness, it would be Don Schmechel.

I received the results of the water skier's evaluation a few days later. And they were compelling, to say the least: The abnormalities on neurocognitives of the water skier matched those of the NC State lab worker! The exam had turned up major, widespread defects in executive and cognitive functions—such as recent memory, sequencing, abstract thinking, simple math and calculation, along with reasoning. All this, from a single hour spent in the water!

The other N.C. State lab worker, remember, had been a brilliant Ph.D. who'd been reduced to grade school-level thinking. But the skier had dropped out of school in ninth grade. His defects hadn't been blamed on schooling or intelligence; they were obvious throughout his entire mental functioning.

The case was made. I was convinced that I'd heard the last of that tired old refrain: "No one gets sick from the river."

Soon after we got the results on the skier, Yvonne Lawson's husband called to schedule an exam for her. She would be my next "neurocognitive positive" case.

But we'd already crossed the Rubicon. The scientific evidence was now clear and compelling and impossible to refute. It was time to sound the alarm about pfiesteria!

chapter 14

Tell It to the Governor!

August 11

Although I didn't know it at the time, the public meeting at the Log Cabin would lead to a major political opportunity —the chance to warn both Maryland Governor Parris N. Glendening and U.S. Senator Barbara Mikulski that pfiesteria posed serious health risks to the citizens of the Eastern Shore.

The sequence of events that led to these high-level exchanges began when environmentalist Jan Graham stood up to address the Log Cabin gathering. A fervent campaigner for causes she believes in, Ms. Graham can speak at length at times. But her focus that night seemed clear and sharp, as she talked about the environmental damage that was being done by pfiesteria.

I was also thrilled to hear her describing the dangers of waterborne copper. At last, my "copper theory" was beginning to be heard at public gatherings around the state!

After the meeting, I caught up with Ms. Graham and told her about my two pfiesteria-related cases and my copper theories. I pointed out that several of the pieces were still missing, but that I was making good progress in understanding both the mechanism that regulated pfiesteria life cycles and the process in which the dinoflagellate sometimes bloomed out of biological control.

"Forget the reasons why," urged Jan Graham. "No one will listen to your speculation. You must tell others about the human health problems. This is a political issue. You should tell it to the governor!"

She asked me if I planned to attend the meeting that Governor Glendening had set up for the state's Democratic county executives. That gathering was set for Thursday, August 14, in Ocean City. No, I told her, I wasn't going. I certainly hadn't been invited. Jan nodded. Then her eyes lit up. "You can come with me. You need to meet these people—and I can get you in the door!"

That August 14 meeting might have been assembled from the "Who's Who of Maryland Democratic Party Politics." Although I didn't spot Secretary Griffin or Secretary Wasserman among the party faithful, I later learned that both had been present. As promised, the hard-charging Jan Graham trotted me out to meet one politico after another. Talking fast, I described for them how permanganate prevents fish kills and how copper serves as a major trigger for the plague.

Of course, I also outlined my cases for all who would listen— while pointing out that Dr. Schmechel had called me from North Carolina only that morning in order to convey his strongly held medical opinion on the subject of the water skier.

According to the expert Schmechel, the water skier definitely had neurocognitive deficits matching those he'd seen in the North Carolina laboratory worker who'd been felled after significant exposure to pfiesteria toxin.

In other words, the water skier was now a "case," as opposed to a "suspected case." And that fact was going to be very helpful, as I struggled to win credibility for my contention that the bug was making people sick along the river. (Of course, I also had those powerful photos to display, along with the news from Dr. Schmechel.)

Onward, Dr. Ritch! For a few hours, anyway, I would have access to some of the top elected officials in Maryland—and I intended to take maximum advantage of them. First I spoke with Comptroller Louis Goldstein for 15 minutes, and did my best to outline the problems on the Pocomoke. Next I moved on to the Baltimore County executives. I talked to the head of the Young Democrats, Gene Ransom, who also worked at "Med Chi," the state's American Medical Association-sanctioned physicians' organization.

I had an exchange with Governor Glendening as well. I stood in line to shake his hand—and quickly presented him with one of our famous bird T-shirts from the Nature Trail. Then I handed him my report, which contained both a description of my cases and a brief survey of the "copper theory."

It was a short but interesting discussion. When I saw that the Governor didn't recognize my name, I simply told him: "I'm the fish doctor from the Pocomoke!" He nodded and said that he'd seen me quoted on the subject of pfiesteria in several newspapers. We chatted amiably for a few moments while the photographers cranked off picture after picture. The Governor promised to read the report I'd given him, along with all the others he'd been given, and we said our farewells.

Access! Imagine my delight, a few minutes later, when Maryland Democratic Senator Mikulski began to quiz me on the subject of copper and pfiesteria. She listened carefully and asked lots of questions. She also pointed out that the federal Centers for Disease Control (CDC) should be alerted, because that national agency is charged with investigating public health threats from disease.

Senator Mikulski went on to insist that the investigation into pfiesteria's health effects was properly a federal task. The State of Maryland should not be directing the probe, but the CDC, which has immense public health resources.

Besides, noted the senator, the bug wasn't just a Maryland problem: It had also shown up in North Carolina and Florida in recent years. This was a national health issue, and deserved a national response.

The Governor liked the bird shirt the fish doctor gave him.

All of this was music to my ears, and I left the meeting feeling quite hopeful about things. But I also left early—because the sight of all those politicians grinning at each other became nauseating after a while. (The perfume was also overwhelming; those cloying fragrances could have killed every buzzard roosting on a manure wagon in Worcester County!)

Still, I was greatly heartened. Finally, somebody was listening! In little more than two weeks, Maryland had gone from hiding its collective head in the sand to exploring substantive methods for actually coping with the disease threat.

The pace was definitely picking up—a fact which became obvious the next day, when I received another call from Secretary Wasserman. He wanted me to contact him "directly," if I discovered any more cases. He said he was in the final stages of assembling a team of experts from Johns Hopkins University and the University of Maryland that would explore the problem. He said there had been some in-fighting among the medical experts, and fretted that it might be slowing the process down. Still, he felt that he'd achieved a good "balance" by tapping experts from both Hopkins and Maryland. Hopefully, both institutions would emerge from the process with their egos intact.

Later that day, Yvonne Lawson dropped by my office. She looked terrible. Her husband, Hon Lawson, who had been featured in a recent book (*The Last Waterman*), was certain that his wife had been seriously stricken with this new illness. Although Yvonne was a smoker, her lung disease had flared as never before. Her sinus problems had also gotten worse—they were now producing headaches exactly like the ones that had tormented the water skier and the woman swimmer. Yvonne's forearm was healing, but I biopsied it anyway. How about her memory? "Gone," she said.

Yvonne was already involved in negotiations with Workmen's Compensation. Had the river make her sick while she was doing her job? Was this obvious damage permanent? Hoping to help her, I'd called Dr. Orest Hurko at Hopkins. He's a highly regarded professor of neurology and genetics, and he runs a sophisticated clinic where some of my patients with unusual diseases have been helped. But Dr. Hurko was out of town, so Yvonne Lawson went to see Dr. Schmechel at Duke. The bottom line was that no physician in Maryland was ready to receive or evaluate cases like hers.

Within a few days, the verdict arrived: Bingo! Another confirmed case. Dr. Schmechel now had three cases—two of which happened to be mine.

But the next case involving an employee of the Maryland Department of the Environment (MDE) would introduce complications outside the field of medicine. This patient, like Yvonne Lawson (as well as two others whom I had not yet seen), had been sickened by pfiesteria on the job, while working at the Pocomoke site.

But the issues raised by her illness weren't strictly medical; now the lawyers were becoming involved. As if the newspaper and TV reporters weren't enough to deal with, dozens of attorneys, State officials and public health experts were all beginning to muddy the waters with their own pronouncements on the plague!

Events were moving fast. "MDE Case Number Two" also became a treatment case, abut six weeks later, while still suffering from hand injuries inflicted by the bug. Number Two was a shellfish coliform tester—a job he had performed without incident for more than 20 years. His work assignment required that he take a water sampling tube with his bare left hand from a rod that he immersed with his right hand.

And the results? Skin from his left hand desquamated, burned, and then developed lesions at the finger tips and palm. The diarrhea started, too. For six weeks, nothing had helped the man's rash; his diarrhea had also persisted, as in the case of the woman swimmer. But the injury to his hand was especially painful, and the only time he'd obtained relief from the palm lesion was when I injected the area with lidocaine prior to a skin biopsy.

In the end, the emergence of these sick MDE workers would prove to be decisive. My own attempts at sounding the alert had drawn lots of media coverage and public notice—but I still wasn't able to reach the state officials in charge of managing the plague. This upcoming convocation of medical experts armed with "tertiary care opinions" and "neurocognitive tests" and "PET scans" would surely galvanize the state's emergency health apparatus. After all, the PET scans had finally convinced the governor, hadn't they? Here was the 100-percent certainty they'd been looking for!

For several weeks, nothing happened. But when the state's own workers began to come down with obvious—and horrifying—illnesses linked to pfiesteria, the government decided that it was finally time to move.

Maryland was about to execute a classic military maneuver ("Detail halt ... about face!"), while reversing several of its earlier pronouncements about pfiesteria and human health.

What's Cooking: Permanganate

"What's Cooking" is a weekly food column.

Instead of my normal food article this week I am writing a recipe to show you how to prevent the next Pocomoke River fish kill which is likely to happen again after the next rain. I hope the DNR will listen to the "little guys": This is your political concern but it is our life and our river.

On 8/11/97 Ray and Lori Maddox will show all the visiting reporters, politicians, secretaries and celebrities how to beat pfiesteria. I have learned from Tony Mazzacarro how to bind and eliminate the pfiesteria toxins from river water.

Our preliminary experiment lasted three weeks. Ray and Lori put 10 perch and 10 catfish into a 1000 gallon aerated tank of river water after adding two teaspoons of potassium permanganate. The fish lived during the time the river was turning toxic.

The permanganate is a powerful oxidant. It binds organic molecules like the pfiesteria skin toxin and then breaks down into naturally occurring non toxic chemicals.

Now that Ray has two tanks working, here is the experiment. Fill two tanks with toxic river water, without dead fish. Look at the surface. It has a foam and a peppery feel to it. It isn't an oil slick but it isn't normal water either. There are 900 toxic zoospores of pfiesteria in a gel per milliliter of water. They are reproducing every twenty minutes. This is bloom water.

Add the permanganate to one tank but not to the control tank. Look at the bubbles but don't breathe them. The water turns brownish, foams a little, then turns pink. This is just what Tony saw in his ponds after his big fish kill. He only uses permanganate now; his striped bass live well in pink river water.

We used two tablespoons of permanganate in the first 1000 gallon batch. Too much? Maybe, but there were so many zoospores of pfiesteria in each drop and who knows how much toxin in that water. Don't use too little permanganate. Stop adding it when the river water turns to pink.

I am confident that the fish will live despite the awesome power that the pfiesteria toxins (s) have, if permanganate is there to bind toxin and save fish. Can permanganate save humans who might be sickened by breathing toxin from the river?

This is an experiment. I'll tell you next week how the permanganate fish are doing. The fish in the untreated tank died within 12 hours. Some had lesions but some didn't.

The permanganate, added a teaspoon daily, kept Lori's fish alive in the bloom water for three weeks. She finally let them go. None of the State officials who either walked past the test tanks, saw them or heard about them said anything about the benefit of permanganate or about the total cost of 75 cents to protect fish and us from 1000 gallons of bloom water.

–by Ritchie Shoemaker, MD

chapter 15

Shutting Down the River

August 17

The first unmistakeable sign that Maryland's "about face" was underway appeared when the state brass suddenly stopped repeating that famous old quote: "The river is safe."

It happened in early August, when the news broke that the Somerset County Health Department had posted a "river advisory" warning people against the health hazards caused by pfiesteria. Those of us who lived and worked along the Pocomoke could hardly believe our ears.

After months of listening to the state's endless refrain—"The river is safe for humans!"—we were shocked to discover that county health officials had reversed themselves by issuing an alert on the dangers of exposure to toxic blooms.

Imagine our surprise a few days later, when the same officials complained that local residents weren't taking their warning seriously enough—and promptly closed the Pocomoke to the public!

Although their decision affected relatively few people living in a single Maryland county, it would have major ramifications state-wide. For one thing, this startling announcement was the first public admission by the State Department of Health that there were significant risks of illness associated with pfiesteria.

My friend Lori Maddox felt thoroughly vindicated by the county's unexpected pronouncement, since she'd been demanding such a closure for the past three months.

How long would the pfiesteria menace threaten our neighborhood? N.C. State's Dr. Burkholder had said the toxin was short lived—it broke down in less than 36 hours. After a fish kill, she predicted, the danger to fish and humans alike would be eliminated in two to three days.

Sure enough, when the Pocomoke River was reopened a few days later, all seemed well. The fishermen jumped back in their boats, and the kids climbed back on their inner tubes. Things went swimmingly, for about two weeks ... until another pfiesteria bloom suddenly erupted. Once again, the Pocomoke had been blind-sided by the vicious toxin. And once again, there had been no increase in nitrates, phosphates, chlorophyll, salinity, turbidity or any of the other "causes" of the invasion that the state had been frantically measuring for the past few months.

The zoospores were back. They also appeared to be increasing their range: This second kill stretched from Shelltown downriver to the Virginia side, and upriver, too. Pfiesteria was now dominating the Pocomoke. Were we supposed to take comfort in the fact that "just a few thousand fish" had been killed?

Even more alarmingly, the zoospores appeared in both Kings Creek and the Chicamacomico River, where fish kills that met the "20-percent" criteria were now taking place. Soon we learned that similar kills were occurring in *many* local creeks. The "20-percent fish kill criteria" simply wouldn't work here.

Once again, the local officials shut down the Pocomoke, along with Kings Creek and the Chicamacomico. And the losses were piling up: According to one economic analysis, each closed creek would cost the seafood industry another $100 million.

How many creeks should the Governor shut down? My answer was a simple one: As many as necessary to protect public health. And that was precisely the stance taken by Maryland Gov. Parris N. Glendening. I'm convinced that if he hadn't acted quickly and courageously, many more individuals would have gotten sick. I was also amused to notice that when reporters asked me about the river closure and I said something complimentary about the Governor, those comments never showed up on the six o'clock news.

In the end, the Baltimore Sun was the only newspaper to run my "courageous" quote about Gov. Glendening. But I was quite sincere. Under his leadership, I felt, the State had taken the proper steps to safeguard people and also acknowledge the truth about pfiesteria.

This was no small accomplishment, either. Even as I praised the Governor's actions on TV, I was remembering how those who had spoken out about the threat of pfiesteria toxin had been treated in North Carolina. I wondered how Virginia would deal with this issue. There were reports of fish kills in the Rappahannock ... and the mantra of "No one is sick, and the river is safe" had already taken on an Old Dominion accent.

Because this was an election year in Virginia, pfiesteria instantly became a political issue in a hotly contested Governor's race. My prediction was that Virginia would act more like North Carolina than Maryland, when it came to deciding how to handle the health threat presented by those nasty toxins. But the Virginia seafood industry was very concerned, as the big crab and fish merchants asked themselves if they were going to take the same hit that had leveled their Maryland counterparts.

Time would tell. But one thing seemed clear, as we raced toward the middle of August.

Nobody was pretending anymore that the Pocomoke was "safe"!

chapter 16

Hung Up on Modus Ponens

August 18

By the middle of August, most health officials in the State of Maryland were willing to admit that there was a link between human illness and pfiesteria blooms in the estuaries of the Chesapeake Bay. But what factors had set off the zoospore invasion, and how exactly did it make people sick?

When it came to answering those kinds of questions, the satraps who ran Maryland's medical and natural resources establishment were far less forthcoming. To be blunt, they were determined not to upset the state's seafood industry by coming up with "findings" that might threaten the sale of crabs or rockfish, or leave charter boat captains sitting idle on their docks, with no customers in sight.

While the State officials were playing ostrich, however, the pfiesteria assault was getting worse. Soon I would be diagnosing two dozen victims of the bug's nasty toxin ... in between frequent calls from Washington, Baltimore, and Annapolis. All too soon, in fact, I would be locking horns in Washington with University of Maryland Agriculture Professor Dr. Tom Simpson, as the two of us debated intensely over water quality measurements and other arcane eco-logical matters.

For the moment, however, I was content to treat my patients and hike around the Pocomoke, while doing my best to under-stand the DNR's new emphasis on "nutrient overload" as the cause of the plague ... when every water-measurement I'd heard about continued to be perfectly normal. According to every aquatic scientist, the levels of phosphates, nutrients and "chlorophyll a" were right on target. Nor was the river displaying a low pH or a low oxygen-count.

I didn't get it. These readings were right in the middle of the scale. DNR Commander Mike Howard told me "everything is still normal"—a shocking statement, really, when you considered the kind of information that was being disseminated by the state's health establishment. Startled by his assertion, I asked Mike how these modest nutrient-levels could possibly account for the bug invasion. He didn't answer.

I'm sure you can imagine the consternation we felt, when we learned later that the State scientists were quoting these same harm-less numbers in testimony before the Pfiesteria Commission ... as evidence that nutrient-runoff had caused the plague!

Had I been misled, when I asked about those measurements? I didn't think so. If the "nutrient theory" were correct, the scientists would have to be able to show high levels of nutrients, chlorophyll a, dissolved organic carbon and other substances. Where was the proof?

More than anything else, the brouhaha over the water-quality data reminded me of the famous "modus ponens" problem in logic —a principle that illustrates how easy it is to confuse cause and ef-fect in everyday affairs.

Simply put, *modus ponens* tells us that if the model doesn't fit the data, and the data are right, then the model must be wrong. The *modus* approach says that, "If *a*, therefore *b*; given *a*, one may con-clude *b*." (Given *b*, however, one may NOT conclude *a*!) In other words: If we know for certain that excessive nutrients and algae-growth will cause pfiesteria to turn toxic, killing fish ... and then we observe a huge increase in nutrients and algae and the presence of pfiesteria, we can safely assume that we'll end up with a fish kill.

But what if all we have before us is a major fish kill ("given b") ... and then in order to explain it, we rush to assume that nutrients and algae must have been responsible. What have we done? It's simple: We've just concluded "a," when we had no logical right to.

Modus ponens! Wrong, wrong, wrong ...

Anyway, you can be sure that Marty Wasserman wasn't eager to listen to my environmental theories. Just as I was getting warmed up on the subject of how copper affects DNA transferases, and how dithiocarbamates change cell wall permeability for copper, and the dynamics of enhanced pulse killing by copper in runoff of primitive but nutrient-rich cryptomonads, and the death of rotifers from copper complexed with dithiocarbamates—why, Marty politely suggested that I should go easy on the heavy science!

And he was right: Old-fashioned science was definitely out of place in these proceedings. When I looked at the Pfiesteria Commission's report later, what I read was one-sided science ... or, as in the case of the "Cambridge Consensus" report on predator and prey relationships, toxic pesticides and heavy metals, no science at all!

According to Marty, most people simply wouldn't be able to grasp the complicated chemistry and molecular biology I was describing. But I simply couldn't accept that idea.

While fending off my "science attacks" with one hand, of course, the harried Wasserman was also working on the selection of his blue-ribbon panel of physicians, in the hope of assembling a balanced representation from Maryland medical schools. Watching him struggle, I yearned to send my cases to Duke, where there wouldn't be a problem of rivalries. But this was a Maryland problem, and so I waited ... and waited.

Marty called me again on Monday, August 18th. Now he wanted reports sent in by mail, not by fax. The media seemed to jump on every bit of information quickly. He explained that his team would be in Somerset County on August 22. Would I be able to supply them with case reports and clinical material on each of my pfiesteria-related illnesses? Of course I would.

Next I got a call from Rosanna Kroll, a prominent member of the Department of the Environment. She wanted my recommendation: What was the most effective way to prevent illness, after a possible exposure to pfiesteria? She'd already been told that distilled water, soap and water, and bleach were ineffective weapons against the bug-toxin. I strongly suggested potassium permanganate. The best plan was probably to protect yourself with plastic or vinyl or leather, if your schedule called for a water exposure in a potentially tainted stream.

On this issue, by the way, the State of Maryland seemed to agree with me. Within a few days of Rosanna's call, DNR workers in biological decontamination suits began to show up on newspaper front pages all across the state.

Next, Dr. Richard Lacouture of the Academy of Natural Sciences called back. He'd received my messages, but had been out of the office. He agreed that copper-poisoning was a very interesting theory and found the concept "exciting." He told me that two of his co-workers, Drs. Jim Sanders and Fritz Riedel, had both scrutinized heavy metals—especially regarding toxicity—and that both would be available for testing aimed at determining the toxicity produced by the complex of copper and dithiocarbamates.

Dr. Lacouture also provided me with some useful information on the "food chain" of pfiesteria. According to the Academy scientist, the staples on the bug's menu included blue green algae, (cyanobacteria), cryptomonads and other dinoflagellates such as prorocentrum. We talked for a few minutes, and he told me that the theory about copper's destructive effect on the prey of the vegetative amoeba-cell phase of pfiesteria made "a lot of sense" to him. He suggested that more testing should be done to find out if my ideas were just an interesting hypothesis, or actually described the reality at work here. I hoped—but didn't ask—that since he was in charge of the phytoplankton assays for the Chesapeake Bay Program, he might recommend that they designate the Pocomoke as an additional monitoring station.

After this inspiring call, I went back to writing up my cases in preparation for the "Blue Ribbon Committee" physician-meeting scheduled for August 19 prior to their site visit of August 22. This would be their first-ever session, and nobody in the State of Maryland knew exactly what to expect.

TV reporter Scott Groom had somehow obtained a copy of my cases. There they were on Channel 2 in Baltimore! I had written them up—there was my letterhead on the TV screen. Had the cases been sent to Channel 2 by Dr. Wasserman's office? I remembered Marty's suggestion that I let him know "first" about any new cases.

Wherever the cases had come from, I now looked like the "bad guy" who had leaked the information. And that hurt. Patient confidentiality is important to me, even when names aren't used, and faxed information simply isn't confidential.

But things looked a little better on August 20, when Dr. Schmechel telephoned me to say that he'd completed his evaluation of Yvonne Lawson. He agreed that her exposure was a "highly probable" scenario for a pfiesteria syndrome. He said her health problems were typical of those whom he'd evaluated in other pfiesteria cases, and he told me that the neurocognitive tests were pending.

It looked as if the fingerprint of pfiesteria-linked human illness was about to show up again—this time inside the brain.

Next Senator Mikulski's office called. One of her aides explained that any request for CDC assistance would have to come from the State, or from local health officials. Even though Senator Mikulski had made it clear at Governor Glendening's meeting that she wanted the CDC involved, the State officials had decided not to make the call.

Frustration! As the next few days passed, I continued receiving calls from people who thought that they or their loved ones had been stricken by pfiesteria-related illness. But these were folks from outside the Eastern Shore. I wasn't quite sure how they'd gotten my name. Apparently, the DNR and the Chesapeake Bay Foundation were both referring people to me for telephone consultation. My pfiesteria case-list was growing fast.

One especially interesting gentleman had been sailing in the Pocomoke Sound near Crisfield in June, well before any of my cases had dunked themselves in the suspect waters. This victim noted that sores had developed on his right arm. He'd also been afflicted with a burning feeling and itching that lasted three or four months. A skin biopsy had been done by a dermatologist, without any diagnostic findings.

I suggested strongly that he be examined again or, if possible, that he might come to the Pocomoke area to let me see his lesions. Then another patient, this one from the Chester River, called to say that his lesions were "slow to heal." This caller had shooting pains in his arms and legs coming from the lesions, themselves. I recommended a biopsy, and also a visit to my office.

By now, I couldn't help wondering: Just how widespread was the pfiesteria infestation? And then I reflected back on the "20-percent" fish-kill criteria. It didn't make a whole lot of sense, did it?

Soon the results were in on the neurocognitive testing that had been done on Yvonne Lawson. They showed a pattern similar to the water skier's, and also similar to the North Carolina laboratory worker's. But the good news was that we now had a way to diagnose cases!

The State experts were coming to the Pocomoke River area the following day. I wondered if they'd see what I had been looking at over and over again. What would they make of all these cases?

It was raining again, and even harder this time. Not good. I stood beside my office window, watching the deluge slash at the sidewalks along Market Street. Three and one half inches of rain had fallen in a single day!

Would the experts who were traveling to the Pocomoke get here just in time for another massive fish kill?

chapter 17

Do You See What I See?

August 22

The experts arrived at the Somerset County Health Department on Aug. 22. Marty's team had been assembled after some highly complex negotiations with the provosts of The Johns Hopkins Medical School and the University of Maryland Medical School. Pfiesteria was a hot topic, and his task had obviously required a lot of diplomacy. As you might imagine, both institutions were eager to land significant roles as "expert consultants" in the unfolding investigation.

As I watched the furious jockeying for position that accompanied the selection of the "panel of experts," I couldn't help remembering Jerry Clower's well-known aphorism: "It's amazing how much can get done, if it doesn't matter who gets the credit!"

Glen Morris, M.D., was the team leader. He'd had considerable experience with dinoflagellate research earlier in his career, while working as an epidemiologist with the CDC. These days, however, Dr. Morris was serving as a full professor at the University of Maryland. Also on the team of experts from Maryland were Mark Lowitt, M.D., Dermatology; Richard Hebel, Ph.D., Epidemiology;

Lynn Grattan, Ph.D., Neuropsychology; and David Oldach, M.D., Medicine and Virology. From Hopkins came Trish Perl, M.D., and Professor Patricia Charache, M.D.

Among these esteemed experts, Dr. Oldach stood out a bit because of his special interest in marine biology. His manner was relaxed, calm, easygoing … as I quickly discovered, after arriving at the offices of the Somerset County Health Department late in the afternoon. At that point, the team was finishing up its detailed evaluation of 13 patients, most of whom I had diagnosed.

I found Dr. Oldach engaged in an animated conversation with Marion East. Marion looked at me for a moment, then told Dr. Oldach: "A lot of us have been sick and having these problems, and if it hadn't been for him [pointing in my direction], none of this would have come to light. I don't mind telling him to his face that he has done us a favor!"

Dr. Oldach nodded. Then he pointed out that each of the "expert physicians" had noticed a rather distinctive pattern of illness. Most of the cases involved some common features, such as contact with water, burning of eyes, and a burning sensation in the areas exposed to water.

There were several other types of symptoms as well, and most of the patients had a consistent pattern of a memory impairment.

As the daylong examinations concluded, it became clear that the consistency of the abnormality in the patients' signs and symptoms was becoming the major theme. I'd been worried, until then, that the medical team might have been set up as "window dressing"—a whitewash tribunal that would allow the State to insist that there were no health problems along the river. Instead, these skilled physicians were confirming my clinical observations! And they soon went on to document the criteria that the CDC would later adopt for case definition of pfiesteria-related human illness.

Georges Benjamin was attending the session as Secretary Wasserman's representative. While we were waiting for Dr. Morris and talking about a book I'd recently published on the subject of weight loss and nutrition, Dr. Mark Lowitt entered the room. I'd spoken to him just the day before about a mutual patient who had a rare skin condition called "mycosis fungoides." Dr. Lowitt had asked for a special test—known as a "sezary prep"—which turned out to be positive.

"Did you see that flow cytometry report?" I asked.

Dr. Benjamin looked at me a little differently, from that moment on. There I was, a country doctor, talking to one of his experts as if we were old buddies ... and discussing a disease that appears only once in a million patients.

Soon the medical team had finished its evaluation. Dr. Morris took a moment to inform me that I would receive copies of the reports soon. He also told me he'd keep in touch. Despite his quiet manner, I could sense his enthusiasm.

All that remained now were the neurocognitive tests, and these would be performed by Dr. Grattan. The pattern of abnormalities among the patients was similar, concluded the researcher, and matched what Dr. Schmechel had seen in the NC State laboratory worker. In only one day, Maryland had documented more cases of pfiesteria-associated cognitive defects than North Carolina had managed to nail down since 1991!

The most striking defects, said Dr. Grattan, were in cognitive functions called "executive." These functions involve higher orders of intellectual processing, such as sequencing, problem-solving and math. Deficits were seen in attention, concentration and memory as well. And the defects in attention, concentration and executive functions created a recognizable syndrome—while the memory loss was reported to be more subjective. (Safeguards against malingering are craftily built into the neurocognitive tests themselves.)

Special brain chemistry tests, called "PET scans," were performed at no charge to the subjects at Hopkins on five patients, and a global reduction in sugar use by brain tissue was noted. PET scans cost over $2000 each; this test is usually reserved for cases with a strong indication.

Things were moving along quite nicely now. Dr. Oldach called me on August 29th, and pointed out that the team had reported its findings to Dr. Wasserman. He in turn would report them to Gov. Glendening. But the issue was no longer in doubt: We'd clearly gathered enough evidence to convince the Health Department that contact with pfiesteria caused human illness.

Within a few days, Governor Glendening announced the medical findings to the press. Maryland had now become the first state to recognize the pfiesteria human illness syndrome. But it had also became the first to suffer the economic and political consequences of a river that made both fish and people sick.

In the days immediately ahead, those consequences were going to exact an increasing toll on all of us.

chapter 18

A Tiny Organism with A Big Economic Stick

September 1

Governor Glendening's official announcement that the State now recognized the "Pfiesteria Syndrome" created no small amount of hysteria in the public.

Almost overnight, the anxiety triggered by this mysterious microbe spread from the placid confines of the Pocomoke to the seafood produced within the region. Suddenly, there was a wide perception that eating seafood from the Chesapeake Bay area—*any* kind of seafood—was actually dangerous.

As you might expect, seafood sales plummeted immediately. And the panic went far beyond the seafood produced along the Pocomoke. All too soon, consumers throughout the mid-Atlantic region were refusing to buy crabs, shrimp, scallops and clams.

This overreaction by the public was truly unfortunate. And it certainly was unwarranted. So far, after all, the region had produced a relatively small number of sick and dead fish—and fewer than 20 sick humans. There had been no human deaths at all. But the scientific facts counted for little; within a few days of the panic-attack, there was a 50 percent decline in consumption of Chesapeake Bay region seafood.

Interestingly enough, a similar pfiesteria-panic had not occurred in North Carolina. Was that because the North Carolina health officials had been able to keep the lid on the issue? As a doctor, it was good to know that Maryland was leading the way in announcing health complications, and was also working to ensure public safety by closing waterways that had experienced fish kills.

But the economic hardship now facing the seafood industry was regrettable. And that hardship soon spread to its spinoff industries. Crab houses started cutting back on staff, as sales dwindled. Restaurants saw fewer tourists. Motels and inns in the area witnessed increasing vacancy rates.

Everywhere you looked in the region, the story was the same. A canoe rental facility on the Pocomoke lost almost all its business. Gas sales fell off at marinas, and charter fishing boats in Crisfield sat moored day after day. Tourist excursions to once-popular Smith and Tangier Islands also took a wallop.

The roll call of the economically afflicted went on and on ... even though the weather had turned cooler, with a falling water temperature (53 degrees), little rain and no further reports of fish kills or sick people on the Six O'Clock News.

Already devastated by a drastic falloff in its oyster population, the Chesapeake region was now struggling with a pfiesteria-induced decline in summer tourist revenue. And the economic results would soon make themselves felt ... as a steep slump began in sales of previously owned homes, and in new business "startups."

Meanwhile, the number of business closings was growing daily in the small towns that surround the Chesapeake. Nonetheless, both the tourist and homebuilding industries were booming in the areas surrounding Ocean City and Salisbury, due to the immense popularity of the ocean resort. For residents of the Eastern Shore, it was truly "the best of times and the worst of times."

In the end, this would be the quietest summer that JoAnn and I could ever remember along the Pocomoke. Motor boats only occasionally roared past our wooded wetlands. Strangely, our otter visitors had also abandoned us—and we missed the summertime ritual of watching them feast on bluegills in our ponds, or frolic on their usual bank slide at Stevenson's Pond near the Nature Trail. We saw an occasional osprey and, rarely, a kingfisher ... even though they'd been daily visitors in previous years.

We couldn't help wondering if the pfiesteria plague had somehow discouraged our woodland and swamp friends from making their summertime visits. Still, we found no lesioned fish in our fresh water ponds ... although there were reports of largemouth bass with lesions struggling upriver, near Snow Hill. Hoping to check that story out, a reporter from USA Today accompanied a fishing guide in search of these alleged fish victims.

In one of the spookier incidents of the summer, she found some bass with lesions, all right—but they hadn't been caused by pfiesteria. No one had ever remembered such a bizarre, unpredictable summer season, and we couldn't help wondering: Was there also a "psychic effect" effect from pfiesteria, and were we all feeling it, as we walked the streets of Pocomoke City under the broiling August sun?

At some point in August, a local revivalist preacher decided that the lesioned fish were evidence of man's unworthiness. We had forgotten God, he said, and despoiled our beautiful blue-green planet! And with reports flooding in on "black tides" in South Africa from dinoflagellates, on red tides everywhere, and on horrifying blooms running amok in Australia, I found it difficult to disagree with the fulminating preacher.

At least *his* business was booming, as dozens of pfiesteria-frightened folks lined up for absolution!

Somewhere toward the end of the month, I got another call from Dr. Wasserman. Marty was getting to be like an old friend! As usual, he inquired politely about my wife and daughter, then shifted gears and got down to business. How would it be, he wanted to know, if he and his wife Barbara came to our house for a nice seafood dinner—with several members of the media as invited guests?

"I'm not gonna feed the media, Marty!" I snapped. I was remembering several media events that had included food—and also remembering how some apparently starving reporters had wolfed down immense quantities of every available item.

Marty's idea was pure public relations. He figured that pictures of both of us enjoying some local seafood, if displayed on TV and in the newspaper, would reassure people that the local fish were safe to eat.

I thought it was a fine idea, but JoAnn was hesitant. For one thing, she was caught up right then in the major effort of preparing for her school year, and any teacher knows what that means. Still, she eventually agreed, and we put together a guest list that included the Pocomoke Mayor, Curt Lippoldt; McCready Hospital's Chief Executive, Dr. Allan Bickling, and two of our neighbors, Bonnie and Bob Rose, along with pals Don Malloy and Bruce Nichols.

The fare was outstanding. I drew loud applause for my crab cakes—whipped up on the spot—and the fish entrees were also widely praised. The media seemed to enjoy the proceedings, as well, and my crabcake platter made the 11 o'clock news on Channel 2 in Baltimore that very night. What a delight it was, though, to watch some of the out-of-town reporters dig into the clams and crabmeat (as if pfiesteria could not harm these creatures)—while carefully avoiding the widely advertised fish entrees from the Pocomoke River!

But these sneaky scribes hadn't counted on Bruce Nichols, who was especially brilliant during this "media op." He went around the room, serving utensils in hand, and very politely made it impossible for the malingerers to say no to eating the trout from Pocomoke Sound!

As scientists who had been studying the outbreak of pfiesteria for several months, we knew that eating the seafood was safe. And yet a few doubts lingered: What if we *did* happen to get sick, after this crab and rockfish feast?

How could we treat ourselves for such an illness ... when nobody really understood how the toxin worked on humans, or how to combat it?

chapter 19

An Exciting Helicopter Ride ...
And a Disappointing Photo Op

September 2

⬜ **The dinner with Barbara** and Marty played well in the metropolitan media—and especially in the Washington Post, which ran an interesting photo of our little gathering. The picture showed a can of Stroh's beer sitting on the table in front of me, while Pocomoke Mayor Curt Lippoldt regaled us with a funny story.

Marty Wasserman perched cheerfully between us in the photo, next to a tall glass of dark liquid. And although Marty had suggested to a reporter that this liquid was merely "iced tea," I knew better. My own special brand of "home brew" had made it into the news columns of the Post! Marty seemed to enjoy the beverage, too.

So much for the hypocrisy of public figures who won't admit that they enjoy having a beer now and then. Actually, I was quite pleased that Dr. Wasserman had been able to enjoy a glass of the brewer's art—one draft of which certainly hadn't affected his judgment.

Things were picking up, all right. At ten o'clock on the morning after Labor Day, Major Mike Howard called me from Annapolis. Could I possibly make it to the State Capitol that afternoon for a discussion of the pfiesteria problem with Dr. Burkholder and Governor Glendening? Sorry, I could not. I had patients booked right through to one p.m.—my usual Tuesday schedule—and it was a two-hour drive to Annapolis. Too bad, I thought, as I thanked Major Howard and hung up.

Fifteen minutes later, though, the phone rang again. It was the DNR commander, with one more question: If he dispatched a helicopter for me, could I board it at noon in Pocomoke in order to attend the meeting with the Governor at one in Annapolis?

You bet I could. The novelty, if nothing else, would make the afternoon spent traveling worthwhile. (Mike would drive me back from Annapolis to Pocomoke, himself.)

The small bubble helicopter arrived on the minute, and landed in Mike's backyard. I walked over to his house wearing my regular work clothes for the office: a short-sleeved sports shirt with slacks that probably needed a press. I clambered into the chopper and off we went.

Airborne, I searched for something to hold onto. No such luck. I've never been terribly fond of heights, and when I looked down at my feet, I discovered that the ground was now far, far below them. Ah, novelty! The pilot smiled cheerfully, then told me that if I had to throw up, that was fine. "Just use the bag, Ritch!"

But the view from above the marshes and the Chesapeake Bay was spectacular. As we clattered westward, I noticed how the natural marshland was being replaced by a different vegetation. We call it "exotic"—since it didn't grow here ten years ago. The incursion was especially visible as we approached the Cambridge area, and then zoomed over the Black Water Wildlife Refuge.

What was happening here? Studying the changes in the landscape, I remembered that nutria, a large water rodent like a muskrat, had been introduced to this area as a potential source of fur some years ago. Since then, the furry mammals had wiped out most of the natural marsh, while eating everything they could get their teeth into. The nutria had caused a disturbance of the natural ecology of the wetlands, since the vegetation that remained was there only because the nutria wouldn't eat it.

Importing nutria hadn't been a very good idea, and these days, the DNR had a bounty on nutria. But trapping had become a disappearing art, and it looked as if the nutria were here to stay. Trying to manage wildlife is an exercise in futility. Yet we obviously hadn't learned this lesson—since we were now trying to manage pfiesteria the same way, by manipulating nutrients!

As the Blackwater habitat changed, the red cockaded woodpeckers had disappeared; the unique caryx sedges had vanished, and pfiesteria was in our midst. Did that mean that the "dinoflagellate problem" was simply part of an accelerated evolutionary process? After all, whenever a species dies out or a nuisance species (like those phragmites grasses far below our helicopter blades) begins to flourish, isn't that just part of life's ceaseless activity?

Maybe. But that wasn't the entire story, because pfiesteria was also causing fish death and human illness, even as it expanded its own habitat along the Pocomoke.

As we roared toward Annapolis, I resisted the temptation to pump up my ego with the knowledge that the Governor had sent a DNR helicopter to ferry me to a meeting with him. Come on, Ritch! Down deep, I felt pretty certain that this canny politician was far less interested in my expertise than in a strategic "photo op." I knew I was just being used for someone else's political gain.

The helicopter pilot pointed out creeks, herds of deer, wetlands and oyster reefs. Observing how the rivers and creeks that traverse the Delmarva Bay coast had cut switchbacks and zigzags into the land, I marveled at the sheer beauty of this kingdom by the sea. No wonder I loved living here so much! As for the politics and the controversy and the "photo ops" ... well, they were like the chiggers and the ticks, that's all. They weren't much fun, but they also came with the territory.

Touchdown. The helicopter delivered me to a parking lot adjacent to the DNR building in Annapolis. Mike was waiting for me, and promptly escorted me to the hall where I was supposedly to meet Secretary Wasserman, Secretary Griffin and Governor Glendening. But the governor was in the middle of a six-hour meeting with the auditors who were developing Maryland's credit rating. I didn't see much chance of his being able to slip out for a few minutes—and he probably didn't, either.

Once again, the modus operandi had been lifted straight out of the U.S. Army Manual: Hurry up and wait!

The meeting hall was packed with reporters and officials. I recognized numerous people, some of whom acknowledged me as well. When I arrived, the State DNR representative, Dr. Robert Magnien, was wrapping up a presentation of his theory on pfiesteria. I watched raptly while he explained how the low-oxygen-content, black water river system that is the Pocomoke swept nutrients downstream into the brackish estuary area around Shelltown. As the downstream flow mixes with the tides, the nutrients were mixed, oxygen levels went up and algae blooms took off.

It was an interesting theory, but it wasn't supported by any of the data that DNR had reported for the month of August. Specifically, the levels of nitrates and phosphates had not risen during the month. The level of oxygen in the water had remained within the "normal" range, and the amount of "chlorophyll a" (an indirect indicator of algae blooms) showed only minor change, nothing like the levels of chlorophyll that are seen in a true algae bloom.

Another troubling consideration: The Magnien theory didn't account for the lack of fish kills in the black water creeks of Virginia, which had similar hydrologic features to the Pocomoke (though on a smaller scale). The blackwater creeks of Virginia had seen plenty of pfiesteria but no fish kills. My copper theory still looked good, especially when compared to the "Blackwater River Explanation." If the data don't fit the model, the model must be rejected!

I was rather surprised to discover that no one at the State House knew about our planned meeting with Governor Glendening. Did anyone understand why had I been flown there at State expense?

I fretted for an hour, and then the word finally came down that Governor Glendening would meet with Secretaries Wasserman, Griffin and Nishida (Department of the Environment). Don Boesch, Ph.D., Dr. Burkholder and I would also join the confab, which was set for 3:30 p.m.

I had been anticipating a round-table discussion, but the reality turned out to be far different. In fact, all we had before us was a brief photo opportunity. And of course, everyone else would be wearing proper government attire. I didn't mind standing out, however. My shirt was clean, wasn't it? They had summoned me to Annapolis for my thoughts, right? Who would care if I wasn't stuffed into a suit?

Mike Howard drove me home, after leading me on a brief tour of the Tawes building, headquarters for the DNR in Annapolis. I had never seen so many tiny cubicles, each with a telephone and stacks of paper ... but everyone had departed for the day by four o'clock, when we arrived. Mike cleared up some work, and we were finally ready to head home.

I thought back to my most recent chat with my good friend Marty about how "different" he became when he was around Governor Glendening. Marty was an independent-minded, creative thinker, and he was doing a good job with a difficult problem. And yet, whenever the Governor called, Marty would snap to instant attention.

I felt quite pleased that I didn't have to worry about my "role in government," as I shook Governor Glendening's hand that afternoon. Nor did I feel compelled to talk about "what a great job" he was doing, as Dr. Burkholder had. I simply asked him if he'd heard about the use of potassium permanganate to stop fish kills. Had he read my preliminary work on treatment of pfiesteria? The chief executive looked at me quizzically, and I quickly promised to send the material to him. And I still wonder from time to time: Are the papers I sent him part of an unread bundle of similar documents that his staffers filed away over the years?

What really struck me about the day's events was the way that the Governor had interrupted his crucially important meetings on the credit-rating for the sake of a pfiesteria photo op. He'd been grappling with nine billion dollars' worth of loans, bonds, interest rates and the like ... and yet he'd broken off those grave deliberations for a quick meeting with the pfiesteria players. It was fascinating, the way that media attention could heighten the urgency of a relatively minor, regional problem, and then put it at center stage, even briefly.

On the way home, Mike outlined another aspect of the fish kill for me. Did I know that the owners of loblolly pine plantations sprayed chemicals that were toxic, too?

After the pines were harvested, an arsenic spray was routinely employed to reduce the rate of growth of neighboring hardwood trees, but without hurting the pine trees. Pumping arsenic into the Pocomoke River was not such a hot idea, said Mike; why couldn't the tree growers use something else?

I called Bruce Nichols for clarification, and he straightened me out in a hurry. It turned out, explained Bruce, that the chemical Mike had described didn't actually contain any significant heavy metals. Fair enough. But I found it striking—the fact that the DNR commander had raised the possibility of an "arsenic theory" of pfiesteria bloom. Obviously, it wasn't just me who was scrambling hard to find answers.

I was more than a little surprised when David Oldach called me that night. He and Dr. Lynn Grattan were coming to the Eastern Shore on their own time and at their own expense to survey groups of watermen with occupations similar to those in Shelltown. But their subjects would not have had exposure to the Pocomoke River or any other pfiesteria-laden river. The subjects would be used as "controls" for the article that these two were preparing for publication. And their plan made sense. Controls were certainly necessary for any scientist who hoped to confirm a unique syndrome in people who had been exposed to the pfiesteria toxin.

Make no mistake: Up to this point, the public health research on pfiesteria had been quite limited. A North Carolina study had compared the health of watermen from pfiesteria-tainted waters to the health of watermen from elsewhere, while also comparing both groups to a control group of non-watermen. The study found that more illnesses had cropped up in the watermen who were compared to the controls group. The watermen who had been exposed to pfiesteria, though, weren't any sicker than watermen from elsewhere. Sounds like pfiesteria is no big deal, right?

However: The watermen were all crabbers! And *no* crabbers had gotten sick, here on the Pocomoke. The fishermen became ill, but the crabbers remained healthy. (As a matter of fact, Jack Howard started crabbing to make some money, after he stopped fishing because of his health. And Howard remained healthy while catching crabs.)

Later, Rick Dove came up with some additional insights that raised doubts about the validity of the North Carolina crabber study. Because of factors that included a different type of water exposure and different handling of baits, the crabbers seemed to be facing a significantly lower risk of illness. Nonetheless, exposure to toxin from fishing and crabbing was still an exposure. Some people got sick, but not everyone. What were the risk factors that determined susceptibility?

Over the next two months, all of my contacts with the University team would be through Dr. Oldach or Dr. Grattan. (I assumed that the other team members were busy, or that the team had been deactivated.)

During this period I heard lots of dramatic stories about research grants "pouring in" from all directions to the pfiesteria team. Yet David and Lynn were the only ones I knew who were actually seeing patients. One of David's primary roles was to act as a communicator. He seemed particularly skilled at helping bring together the diverse contributions of a diverse group of talented researchers, scientists and dedicated workers.

We needed those communications skills badly, right then. Out of touch with each other and uncertain of the medical facts, the

State of Maryland's health professionals were in danger of losing their grip on the pfiesteria plague.

By then, I understood only too well that I had traded my idyllic life of family and nature for a chance to remain in the middle of the pfiesteria battlefield.

chapter 20

Five Cases That Changed My Medical Career

September 4

By Labor Day, I'd become accustomed to reporters calling at odd hours, both day and night, in search of information for "a story on pfiesteria." I didn't mind the relentless pursuit by the Fourth Estate, but JoAnn and Sally had grown weary of it. The blunt fact was that I'd traded away a fair measure of my privacy in order to get the word out on a public health threat.

Well, enough was enough. I'd expended huge amounts of energy in my battle with Maryland's entrenched health bureaucracy. Having been treated as a "kook"—or was it "quack"?—from Day One of the outbreak, I'd been seeking personal vindication. But it was also true that I'd enjoyed many of the interviews. I liked the idea of being the first kid on my block to pinpoint the hidden links between pfiesteria and human illness. Still, the struggle had been all-consuming, and for now it was time to return to normal life.

All that remained for me now was to present my five cases of "pfiesteria human illness syndrome" to the annual Med Chi convention. After that, I would let the researchers take over. Terrific! I could hardly wait to get back to my enjoyable Tuesday and Thursday afternoons of outdoor activities ... building, bird watching, digging in the soil. I belonged out there on the river, paddling alongside the cypress knobs—not standing in front of those blazing TV lights, or sitting for hours at a time on the phone with scientists, researchers, politicians and the print media.

Besides, I was still seeing 700 patients a month in the office, in addition to all of this media hustle. And I was paying a high price for all of this work—it seemed like years since I'd spent a Saturday afternoon just having fun with my family. Had I changed, and maybe for the worse?

Sally put her arm around me one night. "Dad," she said gently, "you used to be puttering around the yard or building something when we got home. Now you're always writing an article or talking to someone on the phone about pfiesteria."

That was a tough moment. My family means everything to me.

No sooner had I made these vows to "rest from pfiesteria" for a few weeks, however, than the phone rang again. And this call was different. The reporter wanted to know: How had I become involved with the cases? What had I learned? What was my reaction to the State's breezy dismissal of my theories?

The caller was Del Wilber of the Baltimore Sun. I'd expected the usual drill, in which the reporter quickly zeroed in on my patients, asking if I knew of any who would agree to an interview. Instead, Wilber wanted to talk in Ocean City, then write a story about me.

"Why, Del? The story is the watermen and the microbe and the illness, not me."

"The story is the watermen and the microbe *and* you."

"Look, it's ten p.m. I'll talk to you in Ocean City."

▼　　　▼　　　▼

I was pleasantly surprised to discover that Med Chi, led by Gene Ransom, had seized the publicity initiative.

There I was, an active Med Chi member, doing clinical research of national interest. Why not prepare a Med Chi report on my involvement with pfiesteria? I quickly agreed to help, and got ready to make a presentation to the semi-annual Med Chi convention in Ocean City on September 5.

At this point, it had only been five weeks since the water skier's office visit. And Rick Dove was certainly right: The State of Maryland was doing the right thing in acknowledging the health hazard that was pfiesteria. "Maryland found the truth in 30 days," said Rick Dove, "and North Carolina is still looking for the truth after six years."

The State would no longer argue with me about "suspected" versus "actual" cases of pfiesteria-related illness in humans. The pfiesteria problem was real. It was in the news constantly. And Med Chi was right to insist that organized medicine should lead the way in diagnosis and referral.

I didn't know what role the Health Department would play in funding clinical research on the bug. But if funding for pfiesteria came from a state agency, it would come with a political spin, as well. Suddenly I was glad to be an "outsider"—and especially glad of the fact that no politician could threaten me with a job-loss if I spoke up with the truth about pfiesteria.

I now understood that I was going to be the first physician in the United States to present cases of "pfiesteria human illness syndrome" (PHIS).

I guess I was just the right doctor in the right place at the right time. Deep down, everyone wants his 15 minutes in the spotlight. This was mine, if you discounted the brief attention I'd gotten for my environmental and medical work in the past. But the spotlight was getting crowded and I wouldn't mind leaving it.

A lot of people don't believe this, but most doctors are dedicated idealists. But the public had trusted us much more in the past than they did now. Their faith, understandably enough, had been eroded by uncaring practitioners, by technocracy, by "third-party payers."

But the fact remains: Your doctor should be your friend and confidant. Once upon a time, the preacher had taken care of the afterlife, while the docs looked after you in *this* life. No longer.

Like me, most modern, science-based physicians yearn to accomplish something dramatic. As a young medical student, I had been determined to cure cancer. In the end, however, I found my drama in preventing heart attack, in treating pneumonia, in helping grandmothers with their grandchildren's ear infections. I worked hard to help patients with depression, and I tried to teach people with joint and muscular problems how to minimize their pain and enjoy life more by stretching properly, adequately and often.

Drama! Somehow, I'd gone from being a busy country doctor to an "expert" who would be the first to prove pfiesteria caused illness in humans. And that was fine with me. It brought back the boyhood dream of doing something special, maybe even heroic, in order to serve people.

And now it was showtime. I was scheduled to present my cases just before Dr. Matuszak spoke. And I was eager to perform; after all, Margaret Burri, Med Chi Executive Director, had said that this convention would be one to remember. Well, my public speaking style rarely allows listeners to snooze. To put it in Jerry Clower's words, I wanted my audience "inflamed and enthused."

I knew that Dr. Matuszak would insist loud and long that DHMH had accomplished great things during the bug invasion, while also piling up tons of knowledge about it. She would quote the North Carolina crabber-study showing that watermen didn't get pfiesteria.

Well, crabbers don't, unless they fish as well—and I would be sure to include that point in my talk. Let Dr. Matuszak quote that study after I had destroyed its credibility!

During my presentation, I did my best to be emotive but professional. My homemade slides, full of important information, weren't as graphically impressive as Dr. Matuszak's—but the content was better. Homemade slides fit my style.

I walked back and forth and talked to the audience as individuals. When I finished speaking, they gave me an enthusiastic ovation. One older physician later congratulated me, saying mine had been the best talk he'd heard in all his years of going to continuing medical education conferences.

Dr. Matuszak had to follow my act. Her presentation seemed reasonable enough, but the podium separated her from the audience. The quiet, evenly pitched tones and dull, professional-looking slides overwhelmed the morning coffee ... and left several attendees lost in Snoozeland! Later, the question-and-answer session woke everyone up. Unfortunately, however, it was cut short, although the topic was obviously important to the audience.

Dr. Matuszak looked at me differently as we departed. Shaking her hand, I felt some concern: I didn't want her to think that my call for physicians to lead the battle against pfiesteria (as opposed to the Health Department) was a comment aimed at her. I was glad when she agreed that physicians with clinical experience at treating pfiesteria should be partners with the state. That sounded fine ... although I couldn't help wondering if being a "partner" with the state meant that, subsequently, you would be prevented from doing any meaningful work!

I left the Med Chi Convention and met Del Wilber for the interview. His slant on the pfiesteria issue was that I had pushed the State of Maryland to acknowledge the pfiesteria-related human illness. Wilber asked questions designed to fill in details about me—details that would show how I'd been working on projects related to the environment for some time.

When the article emerged, I got a pleasant surprise. Secretary Wasserman had called me a "dedicated physician" who had pushed from the outside, while helping to keep the system on track as it responded to a perceived public health need.

Del Wilber provided a perspective regarding my message that I had always hoped to make clear. Practicing, real-live, thinking physicians bear the responsibility for diagnosing pfiesteria-related illness. We cannot abdicate our role of patient advocate in favor of others. No organization and no public health group can do what we do, since we spend our days consulting with patients. We diagnose. We treat. We heal.

No group—especially a surveillance organization such as the CDC or the Department of Health—should ever displace the physician from the role of care-giver and leader of the health team.

Organized medicine must provide teaching, coordination of resources, support in diagnosis and treatment of any illness—not just the one caused by pfiesteria.

The pfiesteria issue was a medical and environmental "call to attention." The attempted takeover of the role of the physician by the Health Department represented a disturbing threat. If doctors sit back and let insurance companies, HMOs, health departments and corporations treat them as nothing more than lackeys with a license that no one else has—but a license they all need for their own agendas—then we'll be replaced by treatment protocols, computerized diagnostic modules, formulary mandated drug choices, quality assessment checklists ... you name it.

Many of the Med Chi delegates were not politically inclined physicians. They were convinced that most rhetoric is overheated and overstated. But my rhetoric was real; watching their reaction, I could tell that it had hit home.

The ride back to Pocomoke was a breeze. I had achieved one of my goals: presentation of pfiesteria human illness syndrome to a group of my peers. And I'd departed with the acceptance of most.

It was one thing to have bucked the State bureaucracy as a loner, and another thing entirely to have been validated in my opinion. As you might expect, I had enjoyed the second experience much more than the first!

chapter 21

A Diagnosis of Pfiesteria-Human Illness Syndrome

September 6

What had happened to my family's summer vacation?
Between trips to Shelltown, countless phone calls, media interviews, library time and time spent writing, I hadn't enjoyed the Eastern Shore summer with JoAnn and Sally as I usually did.

Instead, I'd pored through more than 200 articles in many fields of science that lay outside the realm of medical practice. By now I felt quite comfortable with the theory that copper and dithiocarbamates were the keys to pfiesteria blooms. They obviously affected both the predators of the toxic zoospores and the prey of the bug's benign amoeba phase. The State of Maryland might not have been convinced by my explanation—but they didn't seem to have any better theories ... or at least, none that were convincingly supported by data.

In addition to these certainties, I felt quite confident that permanganate was the "magic bullet" that would stop toxin production by zoospores. And I was heartened by the fact that my diagnosis of a human illness linked to pfiesteria was now a matter of public record.

Not bad for a single summer's work ... although I deeply regretted the time lost with my family.

By now the Med Chi case reports had been through their final draft. I submitted the text that follows to the Maryland Medical Journal in October.

Margaret Burri promptly referred my article to Vivian Smith, the managing editor, who read my cases and sent the manuscript on to Marion Friedman, M.D., editor of the Journal. Dr. Friedman wanted the cases to be published. His editorial board agreed. After months of unremitting struggle, I was gratified that my cases would be the first regarding pfiesteria human illness syndrome to be published in the world's medical literature.

But what about treatment? I was especially interested in the fact that the woman who had been stricken after watching the water skier (Case No. 3 in the following article) had enjoyed a coincidental improvement in her headache, after being prescribed the cholestyramine that successfully fixed her diarrhea.

What if her recovery *hadn't* been a coincidence? What if the toxin was in bile?

The article that follows was submitted to the Maryland Medical Journal. It was published, with editorial changes, in the November/December 1997 issue.

▼   ▼   ▼

Author Information

Dr. Shoemaker is a family physician in Pocomoke, Maryland. He has now evaluated over 50 patients with the pfiesteria human illness syndrome.

Abstract

These are the first case reports of human illness caused by exposure to pfiesteria piscicida toxin (s) acquired outside of a laboratory. Though pfiesteria, a toxin forming dinoflagellate, is responsible for killing billions of fish in estuaries in North Carolina, its role in human illness has remained controversial, in part due to lack of identification of the toxin. A recent fish kill in the rivers of the lower Eastern Shore has permitted careful investigation and identification of a distinct clinical syndrome resulting from exposure to the pfiesteria toxin. Called the pfiesteria-human illness syndrome (PHIS), afflicted patients have memory losses, cognitive impairments, headache, skin rashes, abdominal pain, secretory diarrhea, conjunctival irritation and bronchospasm. Not all patients have all elements of the syndrome. A treatment protocol for these patients will be reported in the next issue of MMJ.

A cluster of patient have exhibited signs and symptoms after contact with water, aerosol, or water droplets containing toxins from pfiesteria piscicida. Pfiesteria is a dinoflagellate with small, toxic forms called zoospores and large nontoxic amoeba forms. Despite the documented presence of pfiesteria in Maryland's Chesapeake Bay, and the Neuse River and Pamlico Sound in North Carolina, there were no prior reports of an association of pfiesteria in the wild and subsequent human illness.

This report is the first to associate pfiesteria toxin exposure with acute human illness. Discharge summaries of five patients I saw fit this presumption. As more is learned additional information will be presented, hopefully with details as to etiology, prevention, and therapy.

CASE 1

The patient is a 23-year-old white male who had water skied 500 yards downstream from the site of a fish kill (Shelltown) which occurred the following week. He had been in the water for approximately one hour, having fallen rather frequently. He had been healthy before exposure. Within three hours he began experiencing a severe pounding headache with reduced recent memory, as well as abrupt onset of nausea and dizziness. Because of these symptoms, he retired early. The following morning he awoke with an increasing headache and approximately 30 unusual skin lesions arrayed in an asymmetric distribution on his lower extremities and groin. The lesions, measuring 1.5 cm to 2 cm in diameter, had circumscribed borders which were slightly pruritic, displaying evidence of follicular eruption without evidence of cellulitis. Routine cultures were negative. No fungi, hyphae, or spores were noted. The lesions were similar to those seen by physicians in a laboratory in New Bern, North Carolina.

Skin biopsy showed significant eosinophilic infiltration with a nonspecific inflammatory response. No induration, central punctum, raised edges, or skin atrophy were noted. Skin lines were maintained and a few petechiae were seen. The patient was treated with a potent steroid topically; no other medications were administered. The tentative diagnosis of human pfiesteriosis was made.

The patient continued to have severe headaches three days later, at which time the patient also complained of mild shortness of breath. The patient's brother, who had less water exposure on the same day, also noted similar skin lesions. Over the next several days the patient deteriorated, developing a severe stiff neck as well as changes in his mental status including difficulty in recent memory, mild dysarthria, mild ataxia, and mild difficulty in rapid alternating movements.

The patient was admitted to the local hospital. CAT scan of the brain was normal. Magnetic resonance imaging (MRI) revealed some mild inflammation of the mastoid and a possible polyp in the maxillary sinus. The spinal fluid was clear with a total protein of 27 and a glucose of 59 with a simultaneous blood sugar of 90 (all normal values). Two cells were found. A comprehensive battery of studies done on the spinal fluid did not show any additional abnormalities. He was treated with non-steroidal anti-inflammatories for his headache; however, his mental status did not clear. Because of this persistent abnormality, the patient was referred to Dr. Donald Schmechel at Duke University, who has evaluated patients with possible pfiesteria-related illnesses in the past. Dr. Schmechel's evaluation showed persistent defect in memory with specific abnormalities in psychometric testing. He thought the neurocognitive defect was to a reasonable degree of medical certainty, related to the pfiesteria exposure.

CASE 2

The patient is a 26-year-old white male who was swimming at the Pocomoke River on the same day as the water skier (Case 1). He was somewhat upstream from the Shelltown area. He had an abrupt onset of two lesions, one on his forehead and one on the nose, each approximately 1.5 cm x 2.5 cm. There was a difference in the forehead lesion in this case when compared to the index case. At first glance, this lesion looked like a tinea type infection but there was no scale, KOH preparation was negative, and the edges were not indurated. The lesion on the nose was more typical of those seen on fish affected by pfiesteria. Biopsy of this lesion showed an eosinophilic infiltrate on a nonspecific inflammatory background. He was treated with topical steroids and made an excellent recovery. There were no additional symptoms including neurologic, respiratory, or gastrointestinal problems. The patient was seen for follow up on August 13, 1997, with full recovery.

CASE 3

This patient is a 30-year-old white female who was swimming with her children in the Pocomoke River in the vicinity of the water skier (Case 1). She related that she experienced an abrupt onset of nausea, a profuse watery diarrhea, and headaches after the river exposure. She had a mild loss of appetite. At first, the diarrhea was osmotic (i.e., it was worse after she ate something), but later it became secretory with nocturnal bowel movements. The diarrhea was watery with associated urgency and without blood or mucus. Stool cultures were attempted, but specimens were not satisfactory. Examination for ova and parasites were negative.

The patient had a sharp periumbilical crampy abdominal pain in association with her headaches, which she described as daily and bitemporal. The pain was not associated with the temporomandibular joint nor with any trapezius muscle spasm. She had previously been well with neither abnormal social stresses nor abnormal bowel history. She reported that she had been using full bottles of Kaopectate and Pepto Bismol without relief. The patient was treated with Cipro as is used to treat traveler's diarrhea. After four days her symptoms did not improve. She was given cholestyramine as a bile salt binder. The patient improved quickly over three days. She was well two weeks later. Her headache cleared as the diarrhea abated.

CASE 4

The patient is a Department of the Environment worker who was sorting fish at Shelltown during the active fish kill the first week of August. She was wearing protective gloves extending to her wrists. Her shirt left her forearms exposed, resulting in significant river water splash on this area. Her forearm felt burned; the sensation persisted despite washing with distilled water. Within six hours she began noticing memory problems as well as a productive cough and wheezing. The memory problems were such that she reported she went to the grocery store three times with a list and on each occasion returned home without completing her list because she could not figure out what she was supposed to purchase.

The next day, a rash appeared on her exposed forearm with small blisters that became confluent. Two days later desquamation of the skin of the right forearm was noted. Her skin healed in about one week. A biopsy was obtained but was nondiagnostic. Because her mental status abnormalities persisted, she was referred to Dr. Schmechel at Duke University for confirmation of possible pfiesteria related toxic exposure and toxic dermatitis. Her psychometric tests at Duke were similar to those of the lab worker exposed to the pfiesteria toxin and the water skier (Case 1). Dr. Schmechel concurred with the diagnosis.

CASE 5

The patient is a 41-year-old state worker whose job of 20 years included sampling shellfish beds for fecal coliforms. He had no history of health problems related to the river. The sampling required that he use a device attached to a rod which was immersed to obtain water samples. He held the rod in his right hand and pulled the wet sample tube off the rod with his ungloved left hand. Soon after exposure on June 3, 1997, he noted development of three lesions but only on the fingers of his left hand. These went on to desquamate as in the patient described in Case 4. The desquamation was pronounced at the distal tufts and at the posterior nail folds. He had what he called a hot spot in his mid palm which had persisted for the previous weeks. This lesion was similar to the index case; it was a discrete macule with maintenance of skin lines but with no evidence of scale or any evidence to suggest an insect bite. He felt that the burning in his hand stemmed from the mid palm macular lesion. When this area was biopsied, he stated that the lidocaine completely ablated the burning for the first time in two weeks. He also had diarrhea beginning June 6th. His symptoms persisted despite treatment from his local doctor.

The patient stated that his memory was reduced from his previous status, pointing out that he had forgotten to call a co-worker, something he normally would not do. He also described a continued watery diarrhea without blood or mucus which was associated with a crampy periumbilical pain. His skin biopsy was not diagnostic.

These cases were among others later evaluated by the DHMH expert physician panel. To date I have referred 35 patients for psychometric testing. The psychometrics give a consistent fingerprint of abnormalities seen with pfiesteria exposure but not with controls. The clinical syndrome is variable but memory loss, secretary diarrhea, conjunctivitis, skin rash, headache, and bronchospasm all may occur.

Use of cholestyramine has not only ameliorated diarrhea, but also has helped improve memory loss and asthma like symptoms.

The lack of illness following eating seafood harvested from the afflicted waters suggests instability of the toxins in food or destruction of toxins by digestive mechanism.

chapter 22

Treatment Begins

September 9

As the summer slowly dwindled away and the story of the "Maryland Fish Kills" continued to make headlines across the nation, I began to receive calls from troubled people who were worried about both fish lesions and human illness.

One day I took a call from a thoroughly alarmed conservation advocate in Oklahoma. I could hear the anxiety in her voice as she described conditions downstream from a poultry processing plant, where she had seen fish and turtles with burns around the anal vent and red fleshy tumors elsewhere. Could she describe the level of pollution in the water? She could ... and quickly painted a picture of a watercourse so fouled with pollutants that the frothing water gave off a sickening mist.

After reviewing the evidence, I told her that I didn't think her community was experiencing a pfiesteria invasion. But so what? Her grim story still echoed the underlying theme of the Maryland infestation: When our streams become sewers, bad things will happen to our wildlife!

Then I got a call from a woman in Atlantic, North Carolina, who wanted to tell me about a relative who had died in 1983. He had been stricken with a mysterious malady, and the lesions on his body had never been explained. It was interesting—and disturbing—to hear that this man had worked in North Carolina's Core Sound, near the Pamlico Sound.

Because pfiesteria has been found in the Sound since 1991, I found myself wondering aloud: Was it a lethal illness? I certainly didn't know. (My caller promised to send along some medical records she thought might be useful, but they never arrived.)

In between the long-distance phone calls, I was continuing to see new patients in my office, many of whom believed they'd been exposed to pfiesteria. Some of them had traveled a great distance for evaluation and treatment. But as I listened to their stories and ran their tests, it became obvious that some of these cases probably had more to do with malingering or attention-seeking than with toxic dinoflagellates.

One of the most unsettling cases involved a 21-year-old woman who lived in Shelltown. She seemed perfectly healthy, and when I quizzed her she admitted that she hadn't undergone any close exposure to the infected river.

This young woman's interaction with the Pocomoke had consisted mostly of watching the sunset from her front porch, which was located about one hundred feet from the river's edge. Nonetheless, she'd been hit with several episodes of wheezing and coughing, starting back in July. She said she'd had no respiratory problems previously; nor had the other members of her family. She'd already consulted several physicians and received a variety of antibiotics and other medications, but these had not helped.

The most alarming symptom that emerged during her physical exam was the continual wheezing. It was so pronounced, in fact, that her pulmonary functions had been reduced by about 50 percent. I prescribed my standard treatment of inhaled steroids and bronchodilators, but they had virtually no impact on her struggle to breathe.

She took her three medications for two weeks without much improvement. Then I asked her to begin the same cholestyramine treatment that I'd used for the patient with headaches and diarrhea—the unfortunate woman who'd been taken ill after watching the water skier.

When the sunset-wheezer returned for follow-up two weeks later, she was off her asthma medicine, her lungs were clear and her pulmonary functions were normal. A coincidence? Had she inhaled pfiesteria toxin? If so, it had to have been in an aerosol form. Up until then, exposure to river water had been a criterion for pfiesteria illness. Was our list of "disease factors" incomplete? A puzzler!

I would later decide to include this patient on my treatment list. But I realized that if she were truly suffering from pfiesteria-linked illness, some of the things I believed about the toxin were wrong. An aerosol dinoflagellate toxin? That would mean the poison could be inhaled. If only I had an assay to rely on! Trying to make a clinical diagnosis and then successfully treat an undefined illness was like swimming in quicksand.

Each day there were new questions to consider. What was the physiology? Did the toxin bind to the cholestyramine that had been added to the bowel—and therefore, had it been removed from fat tissue in the body? If so, removing toxin from brain tissue would explain the dramatic clearing of headaches. At the same time, removing toxin from a different fatty tissue reservoir, surfactant in lungs, might be the reason that cholestyramine relieved wheezing and asthma-like symptoms. If there truly were a circulation of toxin from the biliary tree into the intestine and back (the enterohepatic circulation), then I would be stopping the illness by making the body excrete the toxin.

It was a fascinating theory, but how was I going to get anybody to believe it?

If only I had a few more patients like Jack Howard, I told myself, the theory could be confirmed with ease. Jack had begun the cholestyramine for his episodic abdominal pain and diarrhea, and these episodes had coincided with exposure to pfiesteria blooms. Stepping into my office after another attack, he'd always tell me: "I've been *in* it." Jack had typical pfiesteria skin lesions, he had conjunctival injection, he had the full syndrome. And don't even *ask* him about his memory: It was simply gone.

Yet when Jack took the cholestyramine, he got better quickly. It bothered his stomach, however, and he stopped taking the powder. All too soon, he'd return to the "hot" areas of the river as part of his job—investigating kill sites for the DNR—and get sick once again.

I listened, appalled, while Jack described the more than 30 creeks and tributaries that had lesioned fish. Some kill sites were clearly not pfiesteria-related, he said. In one case, more than 300,000 menhaden had clogged a rivulet, used up all the oxygen, and died. Yes, there were plenty of fish killers out there, in addition to pfiesteria. But with so many rivers involved, and only four having been closed because of the "20-percent lesion" criteria, I continued to be concerned that more people would get sick.

Within a few weeks, I had started two other ill waterman on treatment, and Lori Maddox as well. Lori's main problem wasn't abdominal cramping, but memory lapses and a respiratory illness, similar to the one that had struck the Shelltown native. Lori's family, though, has a history of asthma. Because her family had worked on the water for years, it was hard for them to believe that Lori had gotten sick from the river.

I gave her cholestyramine, anyway. If her memory improved, I knew it would be more compelling evidence of the presence of PHIS—since Lori had the confounding variable of the family history of asthma.

These cases were certainly challenging and dramatic. When all was said and done, however, Tommy East was clearly the "poster boy" for my pfiesteria treatment. Tommy was the hardest hit of the watermen. He didn't quit work, but was coughing all winter long. His doctor told him that he'd had pneumonia seven times in six months. He lost 40 pounds, had funny rashes, chronic abdominal pain, cramping and secretory diarrhea. He explained that he'd lost control of the liquid in his bowel. His memory was gone, too.

By now I had changed my cholestyramine regimen slightly to include sorbitol, a non-absorbed sugar that helped avoid bloating and constipation during treatment. I was eager to start Tommy on treatment, but only after I became more confident of it.

Several days after consulting with Tommy, I saw Jack Howard at a gas station. He was feeling just fine. His abdominal pain and cramping had stopped. He'd also stopped taking his cholestyramine, since it gave him heartburn. I was glad to hear that he felt better —but I knew he wouldn't stop taking his chances out in "it." And that alarmed me, because "it" had just arrived in full force ... in the form of a nine-day-long pfiesteria bloom that was just now beginning in the Chicamacomico River.

I pleaded with Jack to take a lower dose of the cholestyramine if he intended to work in the pfiesteria blooms. Even at a lower dosage of medication, his system would probably benefit.

I was taking a chance by pushing my theory of treatment without any long-term data to show that the medication was helping. Armed with nothing more than anecdotal evidence to support my theory, I knew I was on thin ice. Without scientifically convincing data, I might just as well have been proposing that zinc is good for a prostate problem, that St. John's wort helps people lose weight, or that vitamin C can stop a common cold. *I* might believe it—but I'd never be able to convince a skeptical physician that my results were anything more than shamanism, placebo effect and coincidence.

At any rate, we had an interesting conversation. "Take it, anyway, Jack," I told him. He nodded. "This works for me, Ritchie. I just wish you'd give it to my friend who works for Virginia. He's worse off than I am!"

"Send him in, Jack."

"I'll try," Jack said, "But Virginia is acting a little funny about pfiesteria. ..."

He had a point. But I wasn't working on Virginia patients yet. The Chicamacomico is a tributary of Transquaking Creek, which runs into Fishing Bay just north of the Nanticoke River. If Jack were right, we could expect to find some waterways with pfiesteria between the Pocomoke and the Nanticoke—including the Wicomico Creek—but without any obvious fish kill.

A land-use map of the Nanticoke River watershed showed no significant poultry farms or sources of nitrogen-enrichment of lands in the Chicamacomico drainage area. Rich agricultural lands dominated the area, before the blackwater creek flattened out into the kill site, just like at Shelltown. The chicken manure theory and the nutrient theory obviously didn't apply here.

No matter how you sliced it, there was no one unifying feature that would explain pfiesteria blooms in all these waterways, except agricultural use of fixed copper and dithiocarbamates. It was true that other creeks had no chicken farms nearby, and that a few flanked agricultural fields where manure wasn't employed.

Conclusion: If nutrients were the cause of the infestation, they were only part of the answer.

On the other hand, if copper were the culprit in the Pocomoke, it might be working in combination with phosphates from chicken manure ... even if chicken manure couldn't be blamed in some of the other nearby watersheds.

The "predator-prey" concept still looked good. But now my attention was fully focused on treatment.

The Chicamacomico kill had been described as "low level" by the press. Maybe 10,000 fish had been killed. But Jack didn't agree with that estimate. Over the course of the nine-day bloom, he and a game warden estimated that more than two million fish died. He observed an area of the creek 200 yards wide and five miles long filled with dying fish. And he felt the same warm, "peppery breeze" that was the plague's calling card. It was moving along at about five miles an hour on a windless day—and it was coming directly from the thrashing tangle of dying fish on the river surface.

Jack's story was a grim one. But had he exaggerated the toxic horrors, as some of his critics charged?

Fall evenings on the Shore are often quite pleasurable. The cooler night air sinks over a pond or river, which has been warmed by the sun, and forms a gauzy mist close to the water's surface. What an incredible sight the Chicamacomico was, with a nearly full moon rising over the wooded wetland, casting shadows on the thickening mist as it wafted above thousands of dead and dying fish.

Later, I would hear that the DNR workers who breathed that mist had come down with a touch of the plague, too.

Later still, I would listen to the disturbing story of what had happened to the TV reporters who watched the scene from the bridge. And once again, I would find myself wondering if the toxic invader knew how to go airborne.

chapter 23

A Close Encounter Of the Worst Kind

September 10

Physician, heal thyself!

The days were cooling off now, as the long summer waned and we approached the middle of September. Although I never imagined it at the time, I was about to get an up-close introduction to the miseries that can be inflicted on humans by the pfiesteria toxin.

My encounter with the river-alien began harmlessly enough, when I agreed to provide Dr. David Oldach with a representative supply of lesioned fish. I was quite pleased to take on this chore, because I had a great deal of respect and admiration for Dr. Oldach, who along with Dr. Grattan had been working hard on the human health issues of pfiesteria for one month.

Dr. Oldach was an outstanding communicator and facilitator, and one of his major contributions to the physician-team of bug-investigators was his ability to weave together the diverse talents of a diverse group of researchers, scientists and dedicated workers, including several investigators from DNR.

Dr. Oldach was also doing research with dinoflagellate DNA, which meant that he felt right at home talking about harvesting water specimens, isolating DNA, copying DNA, sequencing it and then developing a tracer or marker for it. Of course, the nation had heard a great deal about "the polymerase chain reaction," or DNA primer, during the genetic-evidence testimony at O.J. Simpson's murder trial.

I found the topic endlessly fascinating, and was soon recalling my own college research days of trying to isolate sites of initiation of DNA replication. It was awesome to talk to a scientist who was actually doing this work—even if his familiarity with DNA research had given him a casual, easygoing attitude about his own mind-boggling endeavor.

David was a researcher; my role was diagnosing and treating pfiesteria patients. But I was determined to help him as much as I could ... by providing him some pfiesteria-tainted fish specimens from our Pocomoke-area waters.

Mike Howard was planning to visit a kill-site along the Chicamacomico that Friday night. Would he bring me some fish? Of course he would. I knew I could safely freeze them, without altering the biochemistry of the DNA. David could then drop by and pick up the samples a few days later for his research.

Mike used a hand net to harvest several hundred fish, most of them lesioned and close to death. He put them into a plastic bag, then double-bagged the catch. He came directly to my house late that evening. Without using a whole lot of common sense, I opened the bag to find several menhaden still flopping in their death throes. I studied them carefully ... and picked up a whiff of "peppery" air above the bag. A telltale sign! My eyes burned a little, but there didn't seem to be any harm done.

About two hours later, I was awakened from a sound sleep by a brutally painful headache. It hurt to move my neck, and my temples throbbed. I couldn't remember ever having had a headache this bad—and I'd been through a few true migraines in the past.

Maybe I was just overworked? After all, I'd been putting in some very long hours without a vacation or even a break. Surely I'd feel better if I just took a little time off? But the prospect of sitting around disheartened me. I also remembered how saddened I'd felt when another pfiesteria-researcher on the front lines had backed away from the work, after declaring that a sudden attack of pfiesteria illness was due to fatigue, which warranted a lengthy vacation.

Anyway, I muddled on. The next evening, the illness settled in my bowel. It was pretty clear what had happened: I'd breathed in droplets of vapor. I had the pfiesteria toxin syndrome, and I was glad I wasn't seeing patients that Saturday. (I didn't know if my memory had been affected or not.)

Without hesitating, I started myself on the same cholestyramine therapy that I'd used with great success in my third patient. By Sunday afternoon, I was back to normal. No headache, no diarrhea, no memory loss. Once again I found myself asking: Was it merely a coincidence ... or was there something about cholestyramine that helped speed recovery from the toxin-mediated syndrome? I chuckled at the irony, as I realized that my "anecdotal data" had developed a personal spin.

Was the pfiesteria syndrome self-limited? I didn't want to wait two months to find out—especially since I was certain that my call for treatment would be criticized for advocating intervention in a disease that "frequently" went away on its own.

No one knew how long the untreated illness would last. What about the North Carolina fishermen who said they were still sick six years after exposure?

Reflecting on my situation, I was reminded of those university physicians who lecture on management of respiratory problems in young children. "Oh, yes, Johnny has a typical self-limited viral syndrome with mucorrhea and fever. Just give him some fluids and he will be fine as nature takes its course."

That advice may be sound, but try telling it to Johnny's mom, who probably has two more children like him at home. She's been waiting two hours to see you, and Johnny is squalling. You can be sure that she's not going to "wait for nature"—she wants action, and she wants it now. And you can also be sure that most academic physicians would back down in a hurry, if they ever confronted the impatient Mrs. Jones: "Well, Mrs. Jones, Johnny has a virus, but I don't like the looks of his illness. Take this antibiotic prescription to your drug store. Give him lots of fluids and you try to get some rest. ..."

It's the kind of scenario that unfolds in a thousand doctor's offices every day of the week.

I didn't like that scenario much, of course. But I also didn't want to underestimate the power of the bug. Obviously, the pfiesteria toxin was far more threatening than the flu symptoms faced by Mrs. Jones. What if little Johnny couldn't remember where he'd put down his schoolbooks, only five minutes before?

"Well, Mrs. Jones, this is a self-limited syndrome. He'll be better in two months." Imagine spending two months without your short-term memory. Is there any doubt that most folks would prefer to try some treatment?

I suspect that even the academic physician would reach for my can of cholestyramine, after coming down with a nasty case of pfiesteria diarrhea like mine!

chapter 24

Enter the Washington Post

September 11

Who can ever hope to grasp the mysterious dynamics of the American news media?

How is it that some stories seem to achieve journalistic "critical mass," and then take off suddenly—bringing swarms of TV and print reporters to town, at least during the two or three days that the story continues to command national attention?

Looking back at the flurry of national TV coverage the "Pocomoke pfiesteria story" began to attract in September of 1997, I suspect that the Washington Post played the largest role in triggering the network TV-blitz that took our story coast to coast.

I'd never imagined that Del Wilber's Baltimore Sun article about my case presentation at Med Chi would have so many spinoffs ... starting with a telephone call from Washington Post editor Steven Luxenberg, who ran the "Outlook" opinion/editorial section of paper. The Sun piece had intrigued him, he said. It sounded like a good story. Would I write an essay for "Outlook"? He might as well have asked Br'er Rabbit if he wanted to be thrown in the briar patch!

As you might imagine, I went right to work. I knew I wasn't going to win the Pulitzer ... but for an amateur writer like me, the opportunity to reach the Post's huge audience was a great motivator. I spent the weekend summarizing my experiences with pfiesteria. I talked about the brutal political pressure and the endless political gossip, and then outlined the fears and concerns that I'd felt as the plague unfolded.

I also did my best to explain that nutrient enrichment was not as important a factor in the Chesapeake Bay as it had been in other estuarine areas of the country. The assignment occupied me all weekend long—an all-too-familiar scenario, these days. But I finally got it done. JoAnn edited the essay and then typed it up for submission to the Post.

Luxenberg had promised me some editorial help from the Post. It came from Frances Sellers, who took my nine pages of essay and edited them into Washington Post-style prose. And when the piece finally ran, its impact was enormous.

The power of the media is awesome, to say the least. Countless individuals phoned me or told me in person that they'd seen the article, and most had favorable comments. Frances Sellers obviously knew her stuff.

Had the word somehow gotten out that "Outlook" was doing a pfiesteria piece as its lead essay—and had that galvanized the national TV networks? The Post article didn't run until September 21, but by then, a couple of the network news teams were already pounding away on the story. Where had the national media gotten all their information?

I've always found it interesting that if NBC or CBS covers a particular story on a particular night, that same story will almost invariably show up on the other networks (and sometimes on the same evening). Did these network news operations run a "pool" of shared stories?

Television is such a competitive business that it's hard to imagine these electronic newshounds cooperating much with each other.

And yet they all seemed to show up at once. First to arrive was the Public Broadcasting System, with Anne Rosenbaum calling for "Health Week." She wanted to dispatch an independent reporter, Bettina Gregory, to cover the story and to interview me. The media blitz had begun.

NBC News assigned Les Krepman to conduct a Friday interview that would be broadcast the following Tuesday. It was an amazing experience, to watch the famous NBC news team setting up its equipment in my treatment room. We were about to do the same interview that I'd been through at least 15 times—but this time it would be for a national audience. Here was the ideal forum in which to get the word out on how degradation of our environment by heavy metals and pesticides had created an ecological niche for a noxious organism that would disrupt the balance of nature.

JoAnn suggested that I simply tell the story of the human health hazards—without climbing onto my soap box to declaim on the subjects of copper as a fungicide, falsely accused nutrients, threatened wetland buffers and ravaged habitat throughout the United States. Besides, I wasn't Rachel Carson, and this wasn't a "Silent Spring"—it was a Screaming Summer.

Next on the list was Good Morning America, which called me over the weekend of September 13. But they simply wanted me to refer them to a patient who'd be willing to speak on camera. At that time, however, none of the watermen that I knew who had gotten sick from the water were willing to speak to the media—especially after what had happened to the water skier. He'd reportedly been traumatized by having to answer the same questions over and over again! I did my best to help ... then got another surprise when Good Morning America called back Sunday evening to ask if I'd be willing to appear on national television to tell my story. I said I would make time.

On Monday morning, as I waited for the 7:30 time-slot that would include my three-minute interview, I had a chance to talk to Mike Howard. And that was a blessing, because I wanted to hear more of the details about the water quality-testing the State had been doing since the first fish kill.

Mike confirmed that there was no evidence of any increase in the levels of either nitrates or phosphates. Except for a rise in fecal coliforms ten miles upriver, the water quality had remained unchanged, regardless of whether the invading pfiesteria had been moving through its toxic zoospore-stage or not.

The only factor that seemed to correlate with pfiesteria activity was the timing of the fish kills, which always seemed to follow a heavy rain. Whatever was being washed into the river after a downpour (or stirred up within it) couldn't be nitrates or phosphates, as the state insisted. Those levels remained normal.

No, something else was associated with pfiesteria activity. And the most telling "normal statistics" were the chlorophyll tests. Chlorophyll levels rose to 60 on one day only—not as in a real bloom of algae, which is usually marked by chlorophyll levels of more than 500 and up to 2000. Remember: If an algae bloom was fueling pfiesteria, then you could expect chlorophyll a levels to be dramatically elevated. But the chlorophyll levels were normal. Obviously, there was no algae bloom! One possible conclusion remained: Either there was no evidence for the theory that nutrients trigger pfiesteria blooms in the Pocomoke—or else some new evidence of elevated nutrients was being suppressed.

The live production of Good Morning America went well. The advance person told me that I'd done okay, and that I looked relaxed. After so many rehearsals, telling the pfiesteria story on television was almost becoming routine. Still, it was gratifying to learn that the events taking place in my home town were worthy of national coverage. Some of my parents' friends in Pennsylvania had also seen the program. They called to point out that I'd gained some weight. And my pal Greg Dennis had seen the show in Las Vegas. ("I fly three thousand miles, and I still can't get away from Pocomoke!" he later told me.)

As soon as I walked into my office after the Good Morning America interview, the phone calls started pouring in. One man reported that he'd developed symptoms after being exposed to water in the Cherry Stone Campground area in Virginia. I sent him to see Dr. Grattan. And I'm glad I did ... because the scary thing in this case was the discovery that his memory loss had begun in 1991, and was still a big problem.

The Cherry Stone caller was my first Virginia case, and he lived in a region that was supposedly pfiesteria-free. But I soon received another call, this one from Chattanooga, Tennessee. This caller said he'd gotten tangled up with a man 'o war jellyfish.

He'd been stung many times, or so he thought, which accounted for his persistent rash, diarrhea, headaches and memory loss. He'd been vacationing in South Carolina, near Hilton Head. Did he have the pfiesteria syndrome? His doctors certainly didn't know what was wrong with him, nor did I. But he'd gotten my attention: All at once I began to wonder if pfiesteria might have been making people sick along the Eastern seaboard for many years. Had we mistakenly blamed symptoms like his on something else?

The next phone call was rather bothersome. A woman who lived in Colorado Springs had developed the usual pfiesteria-like symptoms. She'd gotten sick while visiting in Florida, at Jupiter Beach near the Indian River. Could she have undergone pfiesteria exposure as well? Several reporters from Jacksonville had already told me that pfiesteria activity was present in low levels in the nearby St. John's and Indian Rivers, and one conclusion seemed evident: Pfiesteria might be more widespread than we realized.

But the pfiesteria outbreaks didn't cover the whole East Coast. There were areas skipped in Virginia, South Carolina, and Georgia. How could we account for these "skip areas," as they were soon to be named by the researchers?

Next a crew of reporters from Washington and Baltimore dropped by, making their rounds and assembling their predictable news clips. "Just hold on for a 'two-shot' and make like you're talking to me," they all said. Debbie Hudson, the office manager, gently reminded me that patients were now having to wait 20 minutes for their appointments, when previously I'd had been on time.

Then one of the Washington reporters told me that the story had reached the White House. I flippantly answered the next phone call at home that evening by saying, "Hi, Bill!" "No, this is Wayne." It was congressman Wayne Gilchrest. The representative from the First District of the State of Maryland wanted me to join his panel of pfiesteria experts at an open meeting in Pocomoke.

That sounded good. I'd already assembled some new slides, and I was ready for debate. Maybe I could convince a few people that nutrients weren't the problem and that farmers were being blamed unfairly.

It was time to go back into battle. And this time, I'd use the DNR's own data (along with my own copper research) to refute the State's argument about the factors that lay behind the invasion of the poison-bug!

chapter 25

Nutrients

September 13

After several months of non-stop bombardment, the Maryland State officials were now beginning to convince the public that nutrients—and especially phosphates—were the actual cause of pfiesteria blooms. From Cumberland to Rising Sun, the theme was repeated endlessly: "What is on the land will be found in the river!"

For obvious political reasons, the state officials and the politicians were eager to blame the nutrients And so what, if the evidence suggested otherwise? So what, if the presence of fish kills in the pristine waters of the Rappahannock clearly contradicted this theory? And why make a federal case out of the fact that there had been no fish kills in the Virginia Eastern Shore blackwater creeks —even though those same creeks were crawling with nutrients, fish, and pfiesteria?

When it came to determining the causes behind the bug invasion, the facts simply didn't matter. Nor did it matter that nutrient-levels had remained normal in the Pocomoke River throughout the plague. The nutrients were the reason for the problem. Why?

Simple. Dr. Burkholder had said so, and the State scientists all agreed with her.

As for the Shoemaker theory, which pointed to the enormous amounts of growth-enhancing copper in chicken feed as a primary source of the bug assault ... well, how off-the-wall could a supposed "man of science" get? And so what if nobody had bothered to find out just how much copper was being fed into the 600 million chickens grown on the Eastern Shore each year? Maybe the doc from Pocomoke would go away, if everybody just kept ignoring him?

How well I remember the comical moment when a frowningly serious politician—he understood none of the science involved, of course—fixed me with an icy stare and asked: "Don't you have *patients* to take care of?"

A bummer! But not everyone who had investigated pfiesteria in North Carolina agreed with Dr. Burkholder. Dr. Hans Paerl, along with his colleague Dr. James Pinckney from the North Carolina Sea Watch program, had performed numerous experiments with water taken from the Neuse River. These tests had clearly demonstrated that nutrient enrichment caused blooms of cryptomonads and blue-green algae, not pfiesteria.

In addition, the USDA had shown that the types of phytoplankton blooms in the Neuse varied by season—providing significant evidence for the notion that the destruction of a major pfiesteria food source by "copper fluxes" was an important factor in triggering the toxic phase.

Soon after the Baltimore Sun published Del Wilber's article— "LOCAL PHYSICIAN PUSHES HEALTH DEPARTMENT"—the same paper ran a misleading headline: "CHICKEN MANURE IS THE PROBLEM." The article implied that manure might be the cause of pfiesteria blooms, but no proof was provided. The adjoining photos showed heaps of manure, crowded chicken houses, and piles of dead fish.

Maryland Governor's Volunteer Award for the Environment 1997.

Obviously, any casual reader would have to come away with the conclusion that nutrients from manure were the problem. (Of course, the article didn't say a thing about copper and dithiocarbamates.)

So much for the Sun's accuracy, on that particular day.

Another interesting study, published by the EPA, lauded the water quality of rivers on the Eastern Shore. Some of the cleanest watersheds were near the Pocomoke, including most of those with pfiesteria. But wait a minute ... whose statistics should we believe?

The State now insisted that degradation of waters by runoff from poultry farms was the source of the pfiesteria problem. A little more than a decade before, however, raw human sewage and raw animal manure had been dumped into the Pocomoke in huge quantities. But no massive fish kills had ensued. If pfiesteria had been around here for eons, as some experts claimed (on what evidence?), why had the "nutrient theory" emerged only now? It certainly hadn't been the conventional wisdom 15 years before.

While I liked Governor Glendening and Lt. Governor Townsend, I was convinced that they'd been hasty in blaming chicken manure for the pfiesteria problem. These were the same two politicians who had presented me with the Governor's environmental award for volunteers in Maryland in April of 1997. I knew they cared about the environment ... and I couldn't understand why they refused to seriously entertain my environmental ideas, just four months after the award.

Most of the talk about nutrients was focusing on phosphates. Although Dr. Tom Simpson from the Department of Agriculture hadn't returned my calls, I knew I would meet him in several days at Congressman Gilchrest's panel-discussion. He'd been busy, he told me—too much phosphate had crept into the soil. I listened respectfully ... but I couldn't help wondering about soil binding and low leachate and lack of chlorophyll and. ...

Interesting, isn't it? Did you know that when you visit an Eastern Shore chicken house, the strong odor you smell is ammonia?

It's true. About 80 percent of the available nitrogen in the manure gets blown eastward as ammonia.

If you told me that toxic dinoflagellate blooms in the Azores are caused by Eastern Shore manure, I probably wouldn't argue with you. But to say that nitrates *here* are the pfiesteria culprit ... well, that isn't documented; it simply defies logic.

Chicken manure isn't just an inexpensive, phosphate-rich fertilizer. Manure is also fuel and food for soil organisms, including plants. Early western settlers used buffalo chips for fuel, didn't they? Have we forgotten history?

Not entirely, it seems. In an interesting recent development, the local State Penitentiary has spent a huge sum of money to improve its wood bark-burning boiler—so that the prison can be heated by burning chicken manure as fuel! (At last, a voice of engineering-reason!)

I remember the day when a local engineer called me. He wanted to know if a chicken house could be fueled by recycled chicken litter. The savings on fuel costs—when combined with ease of disposal of manure—would pay for the smokestack scrubbers that would be required to fend off air pollution. Would the big chicken companies be willing to pay for these incinerator/heating systems?

Chicken manure is a resource—and we simply cannot afford to waste anything, anymore.

Each spring, our ponds have a bloom of a variety of algal species —runoff from fertilized yards is eventually turned into a green plant cover. I simply rake the muck off, removing nitrates and phosphates. But isn't duck weed 19% protein, almost as much as soy beans? Imagine the great food additives my ponds could make if I just knew how to farm and harvest the algae! Once my commercial operation got big enough, I could begin to truck in chicken manure to recycle the "waste" nutrients into cash.

Even if I just were allowed to make animal feeds from my algae, there is no point in wasting nutrients.

Not all algae species have similar food values, though, just like cryptomonads are a better food source for pfiesteria than Euglena. So spend some research money! If the Chesapeake Bay has too many nutrients, figure out how to harvest algae from it.

The Eastern Shore also has a problem with leftovers from commercial crab meat operations. What if crab waste could be ground up with manure and wood chips ... wouldn't that make for some great plant food? Of course it would. The fungi that grow on chitin from the crab shell would slow down harmful nematodes, and the mulch and nutrients would become a valuable organic soil additive! There might not be enough crab waste to make all the manure into a fabulous gardening product, but just imagine. ...

Call the new product "Gardener's Gold." Sounds like a reasonable way to sell undesirable waste products for an environmentally friendly profit, doesn't it? And this is the kind of product that can be manufactured without creating a terrible smell from the composting materials.

The cost would surely be less than half of what we were already pouring into pfiesteria research!

chapter 26

With Congressman Gilchrest

September 17

After several weeks of careful preparation, I was ready to take on any and all comers at Eastern Shore Congressman Wayne T. Gilchrest's widely advertised "Pfiesteria Conference." And right here, I need to make a confession: As unlikely as it might sound, I actually *liked* this politician!

It's true. After Watergate, Iran-Contra and all the rest, I'm sure I've grown as cynical as most Americans about the politicos who run our country day in and day out. But Gilchrest seemed different. He seemed straightforward, even blunt at times, and I liked that. Nor was he given to manipulating issues in order to draw headlines and thus win votes. I was sold. As a matter of fact, I'd become such an ardent supporter of the laconic Gilchrest, that my own father had warned me more that once: "You're gonna become a Republican when you finally grow up!"

Congressman Gilchrest had assembled an expert team for the conference, including Dr. Tom Simpson from the Department of Agriculture, and Dave Goshorn, a DNR water quality expert. Those two notables would be accompanied by Richard Eskin from the

Department of the Environment. The DNR Fisheries and the Department of Health were also dispatching experts.

Arriving at the auditorium with my slide show in hand, I received a mild setback: Somehow, my name had been omitted from the list of approved speakers. I kept my cool, however, and simply waited for Gilchrest to make his appearance. When he heard about the slip-up, he simply waved it away … then informed me that he wanted me to make my presentation, regardless. As a matter of fact, he'd already lined me up as the "anchor speaker."

Fair enough. I settled into my seat at the table on the stage and gazed around the auditorium. Two seats down from me—surprise! —was Dr. Matuszak. She was the health department official who had so brusquely discounted my diagnosis of rash from pfiesteria toxin at the DNR meeting, while also dismissing my conclusion that the estimates of fish kills were not reliable. Despite all the discussions I'd had later with Marty Wasserman and Georges Benjamin from the Department of Health, I had not spoken to Dr. Matuszak until the meeting at the Med Chi Convention, some weeks later.

But things had gone a little better, at the confab in OC; we'd left that meeting with a greater sense of mutual respect. During her presentation on this night, however, Dr. Matuszak continually looked down my way after she'd made a statement—almost as if she were looking for approval. This was a step forward! Did it mean that there had been a shift in her opinion of my credibility?

Once again, my slide presentation went well. As usual, I talked too fast … but a time limit had been set for speakers, and I needed to move swiftly if I wanted to make my case. I opened the talk by outlining the "copper theory" again. But this time I drew on the recent information from DNR showing that the September levels of nitrates and phosphates in the Pocomoke River weren't any different than in past years. Nor had there been a rise in the levels of nitrates and phosphates, either before or after a fish kill, in association with runoff after a rain.

I told the audience that I simply hadn't been able to find the minimum level of phosphates and nitrates required for promoting algae growth in estuaries. Now, it was true that levels lower than the Pocomoke's (.03 to .10 milligrams per liter of phosphates) would, indeed, trigger algae growth (eutrophication) in some cool fresh water habitats, such as a mountain stream.

Those parameters didn't apply to estuaries, however. As a matter of fact, some experts contended that "brackish water" could tolerate phosphate levels of .30 quite nicely! Try as I might, I found it impossible to believe that levels of .10 and .15 of phosphates in the Pocomoke River were the source of the problem. Nor did I believe that lowering them would end the infestation. Why, the North Carolina phosphate levels had been ten times higher in the fish kill areas! The state cutoff there for levels of phosphate that were too high was 1.0 milligrams—three times higher than the 0.3 that I had found.

The truth is that no one knows the threshold of phosphates for eutrophy. There were a number of farmers attending the meeting. Canny as ever, these hard-working folks were well aware of the fact that the State's opinion on nitrates-and-phosphates-as-culprits simply wasn't supported by the data. "Where is the proven science?" they demanded. "Stop the pseudo-science!" they insisted.

They listened hard to my comments about copper—especially in chicken feed. Several seemed to agree, as well, when I laid out my main recommendation regarding wetland buffers: Why not provide financial incentives for those who owned the land where the true buffers would be constructed along major ditches and along river banks, in order to help turn back the tide of pfiesteria toxins?

After all, the State had just announced a $2 million program to provide funds for farmers to plant cover crops adjacent to watershed areas. And that $2 million had been claimed within one week ... with many of the dollars going to farmers from the Western Shore—even though the program had been created to help farmers from the *Eastern* Shore reduce nutrients! Money had flowed the wrong way ... and yet another million had promptly been tacked onto the first two, and just as promptly snapped up.

It seemed clear to me that if the land adjacent to watersheds were owned by a trust such as the Nature Conservancy or the Wetland Reserve—or maybe even managed and monitored by the State Department of Agriculture—then we might be able to stop arguing about who was planting what, and how close to the river. Why not look at wetlands national land in the same way that we viewed national parks or national forests? Just imagine the "habitat corridors" we could create, if our watershed frontages were returned to nature!

Ah, well. Although I hit them with everything I had, my call for a "voluntary switch from dithiocarbamates to chlorothalonils" didn't get very far. The old ways died hard ... and the questions and answers had barely gotten underway, when a farmer triumphantly informed me of the fact that his daddy and grandaddy had used dithiocarbamates—and "there was no problem at all back then!"

I nodded, then asked him when he had switched to a no-till operation. Six years ago, he said. Patiently, he explained that no-till saves money, time, labor, and wear on his machinery. Why, it even prevents erosion! He also pointed out that if he sprayed a whole lot of the new no-till chemicals on his land, he could grow crops right up to the edges of ditches and rivers. Wasn't the point to boost your yield-per-acre to the absolute max?

When I suggested otherwise, he accused me of trying to make him "sell his land to the government for the benefit of wetlands and environment!" What kind of a country was this, anyway?

To his credit, however, Congressman Gilchrest refused to wither in the heat of the opposition. He spoke firmly about the need for voluntary—not forced—cooperation of farmers with any kind of state or federal guidelines involving crop planting and nutrient management policies. Gilchrest didn't believe that any mandatory program was called for, and neither did I.

The activity that follows a formal program of this kind is often the most valuable part of the entire enterprise, as intrigued (or offended!) audience members seek out the speakers for private discussion. And that's exactly what happened on this night, as a TV reporter who had been displaying a rash to his colleagues drifted my way. We talked briefly, and he explained that the rash had showed up a few days before, soon after he'd walked the bridge at the Chicamacomico.

This reporter had a small, but definitive pfiesteria skin lesion. He'd had no water contact at all—so the toxins had clearly been air-borne. His memory was a little fuzzy ... although he also admitted that he'd been working long hours with lots of time- and travel-pressure. He wanted to do an interview with me in my office the next day, and I agreed to examine his lesion more carefully then. (This reporter had never been a patient of mine.)

After that exchange, a commercial diver approached, then stood by waiting patiently, waiting for me to answer the questions of a few others. When his turn came, he asked if someone could get pfiesteria from fish without lesions. Probably, I told him ... then explained that I'd treated a 12-year-old boy from an area on the Nanticoke that had been spared lesioned fish. Yet the boy had end-ed up with symptoms disturbingly like those of some of my other patients.

"Two weeks ago," I explained, "I would have answered that question with a no. I'd have said that you must have direct contact with water in which pfiesteria toxins are being actively produced —which means that lesioned fish would also be on hand.

"But I'm not so certain any more. The differences in individual susceptibility to the toxin appear to be great. Do you have pfiesteria symptoms?"

The diver, Tim Murray, would later describe the Gilchrest town meeting as a "bunch of speakers saying nothing" and a doctor who didn't hesitate to make a pfiesteria-diagnosis on the spot. And yet Tim's case would soon become one of the most important of my pfiesteria treatment cases. That was because of his unique circum-stances: If anyone were at risk from pfiesteria, it would be a diver without adequate precautions. (And adequate precautions could cost thousands of dollars.)

How could Tim make a living diving to repair bulkheads in waters that might have pfiesteria—if he had to use expensive Hazard Level 4 equipment and precautions? How much would his insurance cost? How could the State intervene, when no lesioned fish had been found?

And who honestly believed that 20-percent fish kill criteria meant anything, anyway?

I understood Tim's need to keep on making a living on the water, even if it meant risking his body. But it was less easy to understand the State's refusal to confront the problem—even though the plight of Tim Murray and hundreds of others like him was plainly obvious.

chapter 27

Science, Science Everywhere

September 18

With each passing week, I was growing more and more determined to bring the "copper theory" to the attention of the DNR officials and State health experts who were shaping public policy on pfiesteria. The state had been monitoring copper levels in the Pocomoke, but decided that the results—15 parts per million—were not incredibly high. It was a tough, uphill struggle ... but I got a break near the end of the summer, when I came across some little-noticed research by an expert at Virginia Tech.

As it turned out, Dr. Andrea Dietrich of the Virginia Tech Environmental Engineering Department (part of the Virginia Institute of Marine Sciences) had been monitoring four creeks on the Virginia Eastern Shore, just south of the Pocomoke. Her work had shown that low levels of copper were present in the waters of the Golf, Gargatha, Raccoon, and Nassawaddox Creeks.

Normal levels of 10 to 20 parts per billion (not million!) were not unusual in those waters. But the levels had soared during the wet season of 1996 to more than 100 parts per billion ... and especially after runoff following "rain events." The runoff carried copper levels to more than 200 parts per billion—with the highest readings found in areas adjacent to extensive tomato farming, where the agricultural strategy called for spraying chlorothlalonils and copper every seven to ten days, and also after a rainfall.

The bottom line on all of this seemed compellingly clear: During the crop season, it was logical to expect that there would be "surges" in copper levels after rains that followed the spraying. It was an interesting piece of research, but difficult to apply to our region of the Pocomoke. Here in the Shelltown area, the link between tomato farming and fish kills might have been merely coincidental—since the kills had also occurred in creeks and rivers that weren't near tomato farms (although those waters had seen some exposure to the ubiquitous dithiocarbamates).

While I furrowed by brows and tried to make sense of the data, the news media was continuing to cover the pfiesteria story in great detail. Example: On September 16, I did interviews with five different reporters from Washington and Baltimore, then talked to the Associated Press, two local reporters and four TV stations!

The media crush was exhausting, but I was absolutely convinced that the underlying health issues had to be addressed.

It was a complicated assignment, too, because this story was changing rapidly, as one media crew after another took a whack at it. In the beginning, the news story had focused on the question: Is the pfiesteria active? But within a few weeks, the emphasis had shifted; now everybody wanted to know if pfiesteria made people sick. By September, the newshounds were all asking: Whose fault is the bug-invasion, anyway?

I gave interviews until I was blue in the face, as I struggled to shift the discussion to the one question that I thought mattered most: Can we fix the problem, now that we know we've got it?

As far as I was concerned, the key weapon against the toxins would have to be cholestyramine. The drug had already worked miracles with my third pfiesteria patient, while also helping several watermen with their recurrent exposures. And my own headaches and diarrhea had been cured by this medication.

What if I performed a quick clinical trial that would demonstrate improvement in symptoms? Would that trigger a major news story to change the media emphasis away from fault and back to cure? It was worth the trouble. Within a few days, I had started my patients on a regimen of cholestyramine four times a day, preceded by an initial daily dose of one teaspoon of Milk of Magnesia, first thing in the morning. (This low dose of Milk of Magnesia was something I'd used for a long time to help people with sluggishly contracting gallbladders, and also those who had gallbladder symptoms but no stones.)

The medical terminology that describes this kind of gall bladder misery includes such jaw-breakers as "cholecystopathy" and "post-cholecystectomy syndrome." But my strategy for easing the misery was disarmingly simple. With the help of the Milk of Magnesia, I could give people with mild bile problems a good squeeze of the gallbladder—along with a cleansing flush of bile from the liver. And I soon discovered that if the treatment were administered first thing in the morning, the symptoms would pretty much disappear.

I also learned that if I gave Milk of Magnesia (MOM) in a low dose and followed it with cholestyramine (combined with a substance such as sorbitol to prevent constipation), most pfiesteria patients would recover more quickly.

The MOM idea for bile problems wasn't new, of course. It had been eloquently described in one of my favorite medical texts, *The New American Family Physician*. The title sounds contemporary, but the book actually dates from 1868. And it was there—between the herbal remedies and other antiquated nostrums—that I found the MOM prescription for easing "black bile." The remedy works as well today as it did in 1868, even if it doesn't sound like "high-tech medicine."

I love to browse through this volume, which also talks at length about willow bark (salix species) as an effective remedy for painful menstrual cramps, and about taking a daily dose of willow (we call it "aspirin" now) as a defense against heart attack. Why ignore these classic prescriptions, merely because they're old?

At the risk of being labeled an "unconventional" or "alternative" medical practitioner, I'll confess that my approach to the "gas-bloat syndrome" is quite pragmatic: Do what works! Since modern medications and dietary changes don't seem to help my bile patients, why not try something old-fashioned? Quite often, the end result is patient satisfaction, without side effects and cost. Yes, I do admit that MOM is a little old-fashioned.

In my initial treatment article the MOM idea was harshly criticized. There are no relevant data to show that this treatment is preferred. Other magnesium salts, such as sulfate and chloride, have little effect on release of cholecystokinin—the hormone that makes gallbladders contract.

Although I'd seen my MOM approach work again and again with patients, it was still true that I lacked scientific evidence for it. All I had was a 130-year-old text and some anecdotal data. Example: At one point, I had asked my first two patients to swallow MOM while an abdominal sonogram recorded gallbladder contraction. Within five minutes, their gallbladders were contracting—not much, mind you, but there it was in the sonogram! And that was good enough for me. After all, my primary focus wasn't on assembling "scientific proof" that MOM helps sluggishly contracting gallbladders—but on helping my patients to feel better. I didn't have to prove how it worked, but simply *that* it worked.

By now I had seen more than 30 patients with pfiesteria-related illness (50 by the time the diagnosis article went to press), and most of them were still sick. I'd employed most of the appropriate medications, as had other physicians, including the referral specialists from Baltimore. But I had to face the facts: Treatment with a standard approach simply didn't work. But I badly needed to know more about why cholestyramine worked, before I could justify a clinical trial. I also wanted to understand how the toxin worked, in order to better explain why my treatment worked ... as well as to defend myself against the criticism I'd receive if I claimed to be able to treat the illness. I knew I was right. I just needed the data that would support my observations.

What a puzzle pfiesteria was! For one thing, I still didn't have an answer as to why seagulls had not been hurt by the pfiesteria toxin. During each of the fish kills along the Pocomoke, thousands of the birds had feasted on the lesioned fish. If some had been made ill, wouldn't we have spotted some seagulls flying erratically, or venting horrible diarrhea, or wheezing and unable to fly at all?

I remembered that there had been some experiments at Duke University showing how rats developed memory problems after exposure to injected pfiesteria toxin. How were seagulls different from people and rats? I still hadn't seen any river otters during this entire year, either. I wondered if the river otters had been eating fish and had lost their way home, or worse.

At that point I didn't know of any research groups working on bile and digestive physiology in birds. So I called Cornell University, my parents' alma mater and also the home of a world-class Department of Ornithology. But the "university relations" folks weren't terribly helpful; the "important someone" who was supposed to call me back didn't. Frustrated, I tried to amuse myself by imagining what the "Phone Message" on his desk looked like.

"Family physician working with fish kill and pfiesteria wants to know what protective mechanisms carrion-eaters—and seagulls in particular—have in their bile to inhibit systemic symptoms from toxins?" It was a tough question, but I was hoping for some answers.

Jim Thompson, our family veterinarian, turned out to be quite helpful on the topic; he explained that seagulls have body temperatures which normally range from 106 to 107 degrees. They also have higher uric acid levels in their intestines and in their excretion products than humans. But their bile is very much like our own.

Interesting! I recalled how Louis Pasteur had defeated that dreaded scourge of chickens, Newcastle Disease, by keeping the birds overheated to 104 degrees. But Dr. Burkholder had shown that pfiesteria toxin was not damaged by temperatures of up to 170 degrees! No, it couldn't be body temperature that prevented toxic symptoms in seagulls.

Eventually, help arrived from Cornell's Dr. Benjamin Lucio. A giant in the community of researchers working with chickens, he had been described as "the most respected researcher in the poultry industry" by Bill Satterfield of the Delmarva Poultry Institute. Dr. Lucio patiently explained that the digestive physiology of carrion-eating birds depends on the presence of a proventricle—an organ that secretes a concentrated form of a digestive enzyme, called pepsin.

Now, carrion-eaters do not have binding sites for toxins in their digestive systems. I guess any bird that could bind toxin was an evolutionary dead end. Without binding, the toxin goes right on through. As a result, carrion-eating birds never come down with botulism or tetanus, both of which are toxin-mediated diseases. Question: If the pfiesteria toxin wasn't destroyed by temperature or by strong acids, as Dr. Burkholder had also shown, was the lack of food-borne illness in the gulls due to the lack of a binding site ... or to the activity of pepsin?

As any medical student will tell you, pepsin works mainly on protein. (If you recall that the pfiesteria toxin was acting like it was fat-soluble and not like a protein, you'll realize why I was intrigued by the "binding site" theory.)

At any rate, Dr. Lucio went on to note that copper was merely a fungicide in chicken feed. And there were cost-effective substitutes. If copper in the manure truly caused environmental problems, why not switch? But I didn't have time to follow up on his idea. (Later, I wished I had.)

As I ruminated on the history of the Pocomoke plague, I was impressed that I had never seen a patient who had been sickened merely by eating pfiesteria lesioned fish or fish from pfiesteria contaminated waters. Of course, I didn't have any proof—or even any theories (yet)—about human digestive binding sites for toxins, but it now seemed likely that the human gastrointestinal tract was not the portal of entry for the toxin.

Instead, the pfiesteria illness was probably mediated through aerosol inhalation, like the toxic whiff I'd picked up before falling ill, along with direct skin contact (as in the case of the water skier and the DNR workers). The symptom complex made sense; initially people developed respiratory problems. Then they came down with muscle aches, headaches, memory changes and the bowel problems.

If the toxin came in the form of a small, irritating, fat-soluble poison, it would surely cause mucus membrane problems first. After that, it would dissolve into muscle and, sequentially, spread equally into fatty tissues like the brain and the lung surfactant, before finally ending up in bile. But if you could leach the toxin out of the bile, you would lower the body's load of toxin—because the latter, while dissolving in fat, distributed itself equally. (I thought of water in three flasks, each connected by a tube at the bottom: Drain one flask and you drain them all.)

Earlier, I'd called one of the poultry researchers—Tom Rippen—who was interested in my cholestyramine treatment. He told me to call Sherwood Hall at the FDA, an expert in paralytic shellfish poisoning. Why not, I thought? It was only a phone call. Hall might just want to hear about treatment. I'd learned long ago, after all, that doctors with Ph.Ds always want to talk about human illness. That's probably because medical doctors get to work on people, and Ph.D doctors usually don't!

My hunch paid off. Dr. Hall wasn't just helpful—he was downright enthusiastic. And he quickly suggested I call Dr. Mark Poli, an expert in brevetoxin.

A few weeks later, while delivering a presentation to the DC branch of the American Society of Microbiology, I learned that Dr. Hall had promptly dispatched lab workers to Shelltown, and was doing exciting things with oysters. Under his direction, lab experiments showed that the bivalves had cleared the benign amoeba phase of pfiesteria out of the water, during a test performed in an aquarium.

It's interesting, isn't it, to remember that the oyster population has been devastated in the Bay, with harvests of 10,000,000 bushels ten years ago down to 100,000 bushels in 1996?

Over-fishing, parasites like dermo and MSX (are they protozoans, or are they truly dinoflagellates?), destruction of oyster reefs and habitat and the degradation of water-quality were all getting the blame for the devastation of the oyster population.

What if the oysters had been keeping pfiesteria in check here and elsewhere? Unfortunately, oysters don't survive filtering the toxic *zoospore* stage of pfiesteria. The toxin turned the oysters into empty open boxes; nothing remained but the shells.

Should we add toxic zoospores to the list of oyster-killers? All the more reason to keep pfiesteria eating cryptomonads, with lots of rotifers around to eat the zoospores. Once pfiesteria zoospores smelled fish, they ate it! And they reproduced fastest of all while gorging on their hapless victims.

Of course, fixing a problem through "filtration" is a common health-solution in our world. Why not use the best estuarine filter, the oyster, to do the job? Fix the pfiesteria problem by restoring Nature's most efficient filtration units.

Max Chambers, a local oyster expert, bemoans the loss of algae from the Bay. The algae fed the oysters, he points out, and the oysters controlled the dinoflagellates; food was available for all the species. As Walt Benton had said, the Bay "used to be healthy. And then we cleaned up the Bay by sterilizing it."

Max also liked to point out that healthy bay water was turbid with chloroplast-containing life forms—not blooms of nuisance algae species, such as anabaena and spirogyra, but "good" species, like chlamydomonas.

Does all of this mean that the nutrient-enriched, sewer-like Pocomoke River of 30 years ago was actually healthier for oysters (and the Bay) than the "cleaned up" water in the River now? I wondered how the news media would handle the idea that improving the health of the Bay meant putting more beneficial algae, and *more* manure it. Perhaps Max would agree. But who would listen?

Dr. Poli's phone number rang an office at Fort Detrick, the Army's biological weapons center. What did the Army want with brevetoxin? And what would they want with pfiesteria toxin? What would Saddam do with pfiesteria toxin if he had it? Good questions! Fort Detrick is a center for research for defensive aspects of biological weapons ... and knowing the offense is the key to a good defense.

Dr. Poli called me back. I could almost feel his excitement. The mechanism I was proposing for pfiesteria toxin was exactly what he had proven and published in 1990 for brevetoxin! The red tide dinoflagellate, Ptychodiscus brevii, manufactures brevetoxin ... which is a small, polycyclic ether molecule that dissolves in fat. It leaves the bloodstream within 24 seconds after a dose given intravenously. Brevetoxin then piles up in muscle, goes to the brain, the liver and finally out via the intestine.

Bingo! I sent Dr. Poli my treatment cases, my copper theory, the works. In return, he sent me his brevetoxin paper. Wouldn't it be neat if the two kinds of dinoflagellates made similar toxins that acted in the same way? I was already imagining UN ground troops packing cholestyramine as a defense from brevetoxin or pfiesteria toxin attack. Constipation would then be the new Gulf War Syndrome! (Don't forget to take your sorbitol!)

What a day. So many mysteries. Debbie Hudson reminded me that I was now 30 minutes behind schedule, and gently suggested that it might be appropriate if I started doing what I'd been hired to do, instead of endlessly seeking input from one expert scientist after another in countless different fields of expertise.

Bruce Nichols called to report that normal levels of phosphates in soils were about 150 parts per million. Yet the soils of the Eastern Shore used for manure disposal have phosphate levels of nearly 1200 parts per million.

Good agricultural practice up until now in Maryland involved measuring the amount of manure to be applied to cropland, based on nitrates, not phosphates. The correct ratio was basically 100 parts carbon, 10 parts nitrogen and 1 part phosphorus. Yet so much phosphorus was bound up in manure that the ratio in these soils had climbed to 100 : 10: 4. Wait! Phosphates bind so tightly to soil particles that no significant leaching or runoff occurs until levels go beyond *1500* parts per million. The state had made a big deal about a new study from the University of Maryland that showed that phosphates *do* leach out of sandy soils. But the amount of phosphates that actually moved were less than one pound per acre!

Nitrates are mobile; they wash into subsurface flow quickly, while essentially all of the phosphates stay put. No wonder the phosphate levels weren't elevated in the water, even though they were sky-high on land!

The bottom line was that phosphates in the water are so quickly taken into algae that measuring phosphates is highly problematic. Measuring chlorophyll a is a much better way of looking at nutrient enrichment. And chlorophyll a levels had remained normal in the Pocomoke. The nutrient theory had failed its biggest test.

Meanwhile, the phone continued to jangle off the hook. Soon I was talking to a bait and tackle shop owner who'd been bothered by recurrent symptoms of cough and respiratory problems, followed by abdominal pain and secretory diarrhea. He had had a few funny skin lesions, but nothing diagnostic. He lived in St. Petersburg, but he'd obtained pinfish and menhaden from the East Coast of Florida. During an impromptu over-the-telephone memory quiz, he did rather well. He could remember the numbers and words I gave him; perhaps his short-term memory had been spared.

Still, he certainly fit the pattern of exposure to fish with lesions followed by the development of symptoms. In his case, however, the fish had been frozen. What would it take to stop this formidable toxin? The bug seemed impervious to freezing, scalding, acid baths and mud. Permanganate obviously blew the toxin away, though. Still, pfiesteria remained resistant to normal physical methods of destruction.

Welcome to the wonderful world of the Cell from Hell! What had happened to the normal biological controls?

Bruce Nichols continued to help me all he could. Soon he was explaining that another factor to be considered in both soil and water analysis was the "trickle irrigation" that takes place beneath the black plastic that supports growing tomato plants.

Under this system of irrigation, a fairly constant flow of water through the subsurface moves nutrients along ... meaning that most pesticides which were applied to the plants on top of the plastic got into the water column, producing a "pulse event" of runoff after a heavy rain. At the same time, the nutrient flow would remain constant. If nutrients were truly the cause of blooms, then we would see fish kill whether or not it had rained.

Once again, I'd punched a gaping hole in the nutrient-theory. But could I find a way to make the State science officials finally sit up and take notice?

chapter 28

Calls for Help

September 19

One of the most interesting developments in our "pfiesteria summer" occurred when three news reporters came down with what appeared to be typical mild syndromes of exposure to the bug. I listened to each one at length, noting other factors that might cause symptoms, and concluded that a definitive diagnosis was impossible: There were simply too many unknowns. Without examining or treating them, I explained that I couldn't be sure pfiesteria had made them sick. I suggested that they follow up with their regular physicians. (This was advice I'd given repeatedly.) I also pointed out that I was required to report any suspected cases to the State Health Department.

I called Secretary Wasserman's office in the hope that Marty might provide some reasonable suggestions as to the appropriate medical response. I wasn't the attending physician, after all. I was also preoccupied with several other cases of acute illness that had been acquired in the wild among people who were residents of Maryland. What did the state suggest that I do with the out of state reporters?

Georges Benjamin took the call at Health Department headquarters. He promised to "take care of the details." And sure enough, our local health department contacted me the following morning to find out who the victims were. I complied, as usual, and quickly provided them with what little information I had. I had also suggested that the three reporters consult with Dr. Grattan or Dr. Oldach at the University of Maryland.

The media pace was picking up again. First CBS News rang up to ask if I'd meet them (with photos) in Shelltown on Thursday. No problem. An hour later, USA Today was on the line. What could I tell them about these cases? And the media calls just kept on coming. Meanwhile, in between trying to keep up with my medical practice, I'd begun to treat a second patient from Virginia with a pfiesteria syndrome.

This individual had been fishing on the Potomac River in an area with no sick fish, no lesioned fish and no fish kills. He said he'd been wading in still waters, after which he'd experienced a dramatic decline in his health. He was suffering from pain in his abdomen and loose stools that didn't seem connected to food-consumption. His memory had also deteriorated. He remembered a sequence of numbers, "5-1-3-2-6," as "1-5-3." He remembered my four-word list ("purple, driveway, shrub and canoe"), but scrambled the order of the words.

His main problem seemed to be shortness of breath whenever he exercised. He sounded as if he had asthma. I sent him to see the team at Maryland ... but without knowing that the huge volume of calls to the University had changed the way in which individuals were processed into the research setting. I was disappointed to learn later that he hadn't even been evaluated. Referrals to specialists create cracks into which patients often fall.

The next call for help came from a retired hospital administrator who frequently fished around the Chesapeake Bay Bridge. He'd been using "alewives" (aka menhaden) for bait, which he'd obtained in frozen form, with some of it in chunks and some ground-up. Six weeks before contacting me, he'd noticed red blotches on his hands.

As the rash worsened, he came down with severe headaches. He also noted some hypersensitivity to sound and light, for which he was being evaluated for glaucoma.

This unlucky fishermen would be required to undergo invasive neurologic procedures ... which would culminate in a "neurologic picture" that suggested a variety of dreaded diseases. I asked him to remember five numbers, and he was wrong on every one—although he did manage to recall one word on my four-word list. Alarmed, I asked him to see the specialists at the University of Maryland.

My next caller was not happy. He was one of the afflicted TV reporters I'd counseled, and he left a blunt message on my answering machine. How dare I release his name! I'd done so without permission, and I'd invaded his privacy.

I called him back, hoping to set the record straight. I had *not* released his name to the media. I'd passed it on to the public health authorities, as required, and I'd informed him of the fact that I planned to do just that. I also noted that I wasn't his physician, and that we didn't have a "doctor-patient relationship." I had not initiated treatment, nor had I charged him for my services. All I'd done was to make a helpful suggestion or two, based on his reported symptoms.

I also reminded him that his name was now a familiar one in media circles—since he'd been displaying his lesions to several reporters only two nights before.

Although I finally managed to mollify the miffed TV reporter, he was a harbinger of the explosive "confidentiality issues" that lay immediately ahead. From the beginning, I had sought to steer media coverage of the story towards treatment. No such luck. Reporters wanted names of patients and where they had been exposed. The ongoing saga had begun to focus on a nasty dispute between Virginia and Maryland ... with the Virginians maintaining that nobody in the Old Dominion State had been made sick by exposure to pfiesteria.

Virginia waters were safe, argued her advocates. Sure, there were a few sick fish in the Rappahannock River (Virginia's cleanest, by the way, in terms of nutrients) ... but their illness certainly wasn't due to pfiesteria! Nor were there any bug-related human health problems to be found among the Virginians.

Interesting! Wasn't that the same line we'd all heard in North Carolina, and then later in Maryland? Why did the scientists and the health officials have such a penchant for sticking their heads in the sand?

What a week! Soon a CNN news team was striding purposefully down Market Street, intent on interviews. This time, however, we would talk *outside* the office. Fine. I was delighted to be able to dispense with the nettlesome trappings of the standard indoor interview: the microphone slipped up your shirt; the chair positioned so that the camera focused on the doctor's treatment room in the background.

As it turned out, the CNN reporter had made the usual stops in the Shelltown area, but had come up with a different slant on the issues. She said her concern wasn't limited to human health issues and sick fish in the Pocomoke area. She wanted to know if people in other regions should fear pfiesteria.

Were other areas of the bay likely to be involved in the days ahead? Was there a convincing body of information that would demonstrate how degradation of the environment allowed pfiesteria to flourish in the Bay?

I didn't hesitate. Yes, these other Chesapeake regions were certainly at risk; the many phone calls I'd received were compelling evidence for that fact. I went on to worry out loud that next year we might be seeing outbreaks of fish kills closer to large metropolitan areas. I also suggested that we needed to be prepared for a health scenario in which 15,000 to 20,000 people might be stricken, instead of 15 to 20.

I told CNN that the environmental problem wasn't just runoff of nutrients, nitrates or phosphates, but that heavy metals also had to be a factor ... not to mention other harmful chemicals, such as the dithiocarbamates. The interview went well, and CNN wound up airing the clip repeatedly during the next two weeks, and even including it on their regular Sunday show, "Earth Watch."

Soon I learned that CBS was sending Eric Engbert to do the story at Shelltown. I rushed to get there in order to meet their frantic schedule, and was unable to bring along photos—since I had not yet obtained media releases from the new patients who appeared in them. I watched as Eric assembled his story. He said he would follow me back to my office for additional taping, but was unable to do so. Too bad.

I was amazed at the brutal time demands placed on these national reporters. Without having the luxury of being able to properly prepare in-depth stories, they were forced to compose on the run.

In one week I had seen NBC, ABC, CNN, PBS and CBS all doing the same exact story about the "hazards and the risks." Didn't anyone want to hear about treatment? Nope. The story was sick fish, sick people, closed waterways and economic disaster in the seafood industry, quote, unquote!

But what about copper? Didn't anyone want to hear about the harmful impact of the dithiocarbamates and the lack of data to support the nutrient theory? No thanks, said the reporters.

Sorry ... but there was no way on earth that you could fit all that complicated stuff into a 30-second sound-bite!

chapter 29

Blue Ribbons, but No Today Show

September 20

As the pfiesteria invasion became the subject of daily stories in the news media, the public responded by swearing off Maryland seafood. It was a predictable reaction, and thoroughly depressing, since both DNR Secretary Griffin and Health Secretary Wasserman had done their level best to point out that Chesapeake Bay seafood was safe to eat. Even the Governor was eating seafood at a photo op in Cambridge.

I watched the "seafood panic" spread across the state with a sinking heart. One could only imagine the immense pressure that Governor Glendening must have been getting from Maryland's huge seafood industry. But the problem wasn't going to go away just because the state officials wanted it to. There were new fish kills appearing almost daily now, and they fanned the flames of anxiety even higher. The press didn't hear about the small fish kill sites. What would that have done to the seafood business?

Governor Glendening did everything he could. He'd been praised by the media, during the earlier stages of the plague, for his quick action in assembling an expert medical panel—and for the decision to close rivers wherever necessary to preserve public health. But the Maryland economy was taking a monster-hit from the food panic. What to do? Why not assemble a blue-ribbon panel of prominent citizens to look more closely at the entire problem?

Glendening moved quickly. His panel would include former Maryland Governor Harry Hughes, the chairman, along with three members of the Maryland General Assembly. Several concerned citizens from Somerset County would also be seated, including Rick Nelson, representing agriculture, and Judge Lloyd Simpkins. Will Baker would represent the Chesapeake Bay Foundation, and several other citizens from the Eastern Shore would also join the deliberations.

The panel-members were authorized to hold public meetings, receive advice and testimony from experts, and develop a position on pfiesteria and its cause. They were asked to report to the Governor by November 1. The medical members of the team would include Secretary Wasserman, Dr. Burkholder and Dr. Ritchie Shoemaker, although I was listed as "tentative."

After learning from a reporter that I was being considered for the committee, I called Joe Bryce in Governor Glendening's legislative office. He seemed a bit surprised to learn that I was a "tentative" member ... which told me that my selection as a panel-member had not been unanimous. What was going on here?

Hoping to find out, I called my good friend Marty Wasserman, who explained that he wanted to use me for "local testimony," rather than including me in the Annapolis sessions.

Suddenly, the handwriting was on the wall: The brass at state headquarters had no intention of "legitimizing" my heretical opinions by allowing me to sit on that panel. As Rick Nelson confirmed to me after the event, the testimony at that blue-ribbon gathering would focus on nutrients, nutrients and more nutrients.

And those same proceedings would be heavily slanted in favor of the DNR and Health Department bias on this issue. Example: When Nelson asked for the exact numbers that described nutrient levels, he was given percentages, instead.

The result was nothing less than scientific subterfuge. In one egregious instance, a test showed a rise in total phosphates from 0.10 to 0.16 mg/liter. But that shouldn't have been a cause for alarm; after all, the phosphate-trigger for algae blooms required levels as high as 0.30 mg/liter. Instead of making that point, however, the blue-ribbon experts simply announced that phosphates had "risen 60 percent" in their test.

Sixty percent sounds pretty scary, doesn't it? But the statistic was essentially meaningless, since the increase would have no impact at all on the blooms.

Dr. Burkholder held center stage as the "scientific consultant," joined by Dr. Donald Boesch. But none of the North Carolina researchers who had disagreed with Dr. Burkholder's findings were asked to testify. Later, one prominent NC researcher would flatly deny that nutrients fueled pfiesteria blooms, and sadly conclude: "It sounds like the Governor is running for reelection. If it's convenient to blame pfiesteria on chicken manure, let him do it."

Try as I might, however, I couldn't see how blaming farmers and manure made a lot of political sense. Why not consider some alternative theories—such as my copper explanation—before settling irrevocably on nutrients-as-culprit? Scientists who disagree usually run tests in order to settle arguments. Tests mean research grants and publications, and then even more grants. Why not test copper, as I had recommended over and over again? No such luck. The governor was on the record: "What's on the ground is in the river!" Clearly, the besieged Glendening was thinking reelection politics, each time he blamed nutrient runoff for the plague.

In order to understand the dynamics at work here, let's take a quick look at a couple of numbers. At present, farmers use 1.7 million acres of land in Maryland, while homeowners occupy 1.2 million acres. Those two figures have been changing in recent years, reflecting both an increase in residential use of land and continued development of farm land.

How many pounds of grass-enhancing chemicals do the green-grass crowds of suburbanites use on their closely mowed lawns?

Now, the Blue Plains sewage plant, near Washington, handles 309 million gallons of sewage a day and pours 15 million pounds of nitrates into the Bay yearly. Obviously, that's a lot of human manure. When you consider the fact that the watersheds draining into the Bay originate in Pennsylvania, Maryland, West Virginia and Virginia, the conclusion seems rather obvious. Although it might be politically expedient, the Blue Ribbon Commission's determination to solve the pfiesteria problem by changing agricultural practices on the sparsely populated Eastern Shore simply bore no relationship to reality.

As the week's activity drew toward a close, I found myself feeling grateful that the CEO of McCready Hospital—my boss, Dr. Allan Bickling—had so graciously allowed me to speak to the news media. My practice had not suffered as a result. Indeed, the River Associated Rash and Illness Center was bringing in new patients almost every day. Another positive spinoff from my efforts was the increasing public recognition of the contributions being made daily by the region's friendly neighborhood health center, McCready Hospital in Crisfield.

The considerate Dr. Bickling had not complained when I'd been 30 minutes late getting to the office after the Good Morning America Show. Nor had he complained when I left 15 minutes early to do the CBS Show ... or took the time required for TV interviews and talking to reporters on the phone.

I greatly appreciated Dr. Bickling's courtesy, because the media crush was continuing. Just after lunch on Friday, September 19, Joe DeCola of the Today Show called. Could I stop by the studio tomorrow morning and do an interview? Right, I thought—I'll just drop by New York City on my way home from Pocomoke! But he was serious, and quickly explained that if I could make the flight, NBC would put me up in the Essex Hotel across from Central Park, then ferry me by limousine to the studio in Rockefeller Center for the show.

The invitation couldn't have come at a worse time. JoAnn had been planning a surprise birthday party for her mother, who lives in Wayne, New Jersey, and it was set for the same weekend on which I was due in New York. My wife and her sister Kate had been lining up a major-league shindig, and they were going to bring most of the party-fixings from Maryland to New Jersey in order to salute Ruth on her 75th.

"JoAnn," I said tentatively, "they want me to go to New York tonight to do the NBC Today Show tomorrow morning."

"Go for it," said JoAnn.

"But I won't be able to help you with the party."

"That's all right. You can do it—this is the chance of a lifetime."

Fortunately, I managed to find some available flights that would get me to New York late that night. Soon I was checking into the Essex House, which had an international reputation, after being restored and refurbished by its new Japanese owners. I found three phone messages and two faxes waiting for me. One of them was from the Washington Post, which had called to discuss the story for next Sunday. I'd drawn my maps wrong, said a fretful editor; my diagram of pfiesteria illness-sites contained several errors. I was glad the editor had spotted them.

My interaction with the Post reminded me of Hollywood's version of journalism. Here is the newspaper that exposed Watergate! Here is the newspaper that was quoted around the world, as a source of political commentary! With hundreds of reporters and a circulation topping one million, the Post was media power incarnate.

The paper had assigned Frances Sellers to edit my nine-page article, and she had shaped it into an essay that flowed, while telling a good story. The piece contained a ton of useful information, captured in only 2,500 words. Each time Frances called me with a rewrite or faxed new information, I could see where a different editor had made an impact. A lot of my words would show up in the final version, but polished beautifully by the skillful Ms. Sellers and her fellow-editors.

Being in New York City that night was tough on me. I already missed my family. I also regretted the fact that I'd left JoAnn with a huge amount of work to do in preparation for the birthday-fest. Sure, she'd have lots of help in New Jersey. But where was I, as she struggled to pull everything together for the approaching blowout?

Deep down, I felt uneasy, out of my element. I was a country doctor, not a TV celeb. But there I was, battling my way through the Yellow Cabs and the surging pedestrians of the Big Apple toward an appearance on the Today Show.

Ah, showbiz. Imagine my disappointment when my appearance was suddenly canceled! What a wonderful lesson in humility. As it turned out, Prince Charles was going to be interviewed on the tragic death of Princess Diana. Pfiesteria—and Dr. Ritchie—had been bumped!

Oh, well. Nothing ventured, nothing gained. Happily, the network sent a limousine that would transport me to Wayne, New Jersey, where I could wait for JoAnn's arrival ... and for the arrival of the Sunday Washington Post, which I hoped would made it to a local newsstand.

The party went well on Sunday. JoAnn and Kate pulled it off splendidly. They'd given their mother the best present of all for her birthday: an outpouring of affection from friends and loved ones alike. But no, there was no Washington Post to be found for sale in the suburbs of New York. (The paper arrived in this area on Monday.) Just great. No Today Show and no Post. Well, Debbie Hudson had promised to round up six copies of the Post for me, back in Pocomoke, so I knew I'd be able to get a glimpse at the Outlook section sometime. But it would have been nice to read it in my father-in-law's living room.

While the mob at the party watched the local New York Jets play football on the tube, I slipped away and caught a brief clip of the CNN "Earth Watch." As I'd hoped, the program warned that pfiesteria might one day become a major problem in urban areas far distant from the Pocomoke.

At last, a breakthrough! In spite of the emotional rollercoaster of that frenetic weekend in New York, I'd managed to do something right. The word was getting out at last: Pfiesteria loomed as a potential public health menace, worldwide. Instead, of trying to duck it, we needed to get to work on solutions.

chapter 30

Fish Kills, Facts
And Pfiesteria

September 21
Printed in Outlook
The Washington Post (9/21/97)

Fish Kills, Facts and Pfiesteria

My Patients and the River
Told Me What I Had to Know

On Wednesday, July 30, I got a call at the office where I practice family medicine in Pocomoke City, Md. I think I've got the pfiesteria thing, the man on the phone told me. I asked him to come in right away.

As I examined the man later that day, I looked for clues as to what might have caused the headache he complained of and the rash he showed me. One thing stood out. The man described to me how he had spent an hour water-skiing on the Pocomoke River at Williams Point, just south of Shelltown, Md., three days be-

fore. He had fallen ill within a few hours of coming home. His head hurt; he couldn't remember simple things; he had trouble walking and talking. When he woke the next morning, he had crop of some 30 flat, red sores over his body. They looked just like the distinctive rash described by physicians in North Carolina: it showed up after contact with Pfiesteria piscida, the microbe that has since caused Maryland authorities to close off two waterways. I sent the water-skier off to have medical photographs taken.

About an hour later, a bartender who'd

been a patient of mine for several years came in complaining of funny zits on his face. He had been on a family outing the same Sunday a little upriver. He had spent about 15 minutes swimming. The sores and the similar experiences had to be more than a coincidence. By the next day, when a woman who had been watching the water-skier came in with similar complaints, I was certain that what I had seen were three cases of pfiesteria-related human illness.

I'd been on the lookout for problems from pfiesteria ever since watermen began finding fish with grotesque lesions near Shelltown almost a year ago. And, after a fish kill in May when water samples demonstrated that the pfiesteria microbe was present, the Maryland Department of Health had sent a letter to physicians in the area, telling us to report fish-related illness, using common sense and noting the symptoms in patients around a 20 percent fish-kill area. I had done just that. But now I realized I was on untraveled ground, pitting my local knowledge, my interest in ecology and my medical expertise against the scientific community and political interests that over the past year had been stressing that humans were not at risk from the mysterious microbe.

The Pocomoke River area, where I live with my wife and 13 year old daughter, has been a source of fascination and fulfillment over the past 17 years. I've been involved in conservation projects —a nature trail, demonstration non-tidal wetlands ponds, a wetland garden and a fishing pier.

Pocomoke means dark water or broken ground in the language of the Algonquin tribes. The river's upper reaches are cypress swamps with red bay trees and crossvine, plants generally found in North Carolina. It is home to a vast range of wildlife—otters, bald eagles and ospreys —as well as myriad fish. Local residents like to say the north and the south meet here.

With the Eastern Shore's low elevation, it can take as long as three weeks for the river's water to flow the 13 miles downstream from Snow Hill to Pocomoke City. Twice a day, the current is met with a strong upstream surge, mixing waters from the bay and the Pocomoke Sound with runoff from Worcester and Somerset counties. Though the area is sparsely populated, development along the river banks and the growth of Ocean City as a family resort has changed the contents of the upriver water. From Pocomoke City to the bay, chicken and tomato farms now extend to the banks.

Despite these changes, I had found it hard to believe that our beautiful river could be unsafe for fish when I first started hearing reports last October from watermen of finding quantities of dead fish—at first the oily menhaden, then fish of all species. Many had sores on their sides; on some, the flesh had been eaten away to the bone. Local fishermen I knew, like the Maddox and Howard families who have worked the waters for generations, told me they'd never seen anything like it. The lesions didn't look like the propeller blade cuts and crab pot scrapes that fish sometimes have, though that's how one health official later tried to explain them away. And the fishermen couldn't explain why they had been suffering bouts of pneumonia, abdominal cramping and diarrhea while they were pulling dead fish out of the waters.

Through fellow conservationists, I set out to learn more about the microbe. In early July, Eric May, a fish pathologist with the state-federal biological laboratory in Oxford, Md., explained to me how low levels of pfiesteria destroy enzymes in the protective slime that covers fishes' scales, gills and tails, leaving them vulnerable to secondary infections. High levels of pfiesteria kill quickly. Before they die, affected fish act strangely, swimming in circles, apparently oblivious to predators. May performed autopsies on some and found they had mild brain inflammation.

Continuing fish kills caused mounting concern. In July, the state Department of Natural Resources (DNR) trawled the main channel of the Pocomoke. It found only a rare fish with lesions, far less than 20 percent, and declared the river safe—a matter of days before the water-skier arrived in my office. But the DNR biologists had been looking for dead fish in cool, fast-moving water where they were unlikely to be found. I expressed my concerns to the local paper, which published an article on July 15.

People called me a kook, a know-nothing doctor and a fear monger, but the illness two weeks later of my three patients convinced me I had a case. Armed now with color photographs of the lesions on their skin, I joined scientists, politicians and watermen at a scientific conference on pfiesteria convened by the DNR in Salisbury on the weekend of Aug. 1. There I met JoAnn Burkholder, the North Carolina State University aquatic botanist who pioneered much of the early scientific research on pfiesteria and who knew the dangers of its toxin only too well. While working with the microbe in 1995, she and others in the lab had developed symptoms, including respiratory problems, diarrhea, memory loss and skin lesions. With her corroborating evidence, I tried to show the photographs of my sick patients' skin. One local politician told me, Don't say the river isn't safe. People will panic.

But ignorance, not knowledge, is what makes people panic. Their fear is heightened by flat denials from political figures. I wasn't interested in frightening people. In fact, pfiesteria is only toxic for a brief period, and there is no evidence it can get into the food chain. But for the brief period that the microbe is in bloom, when the water turns to a chocolate color and feels hot and peppery, it is not a good idea to spend time on the water. The public deserves, and needs, to know that.

To my mind, the DNR's assurances that the river was safe were simply based on false reporting; Who's definition of 20 percent fish kill should we use? I demanded. That of DNR trawling in the wrong places or that of fishermen counting dead fish in their nets? that comment and my photos began to draw widespread attention.

The water-skier appeared on TV news state-wide. Yet, while Maryland Secretary of Health and Mental Hygiene Martin P. Wasserman agreed with me that physicians and health departments should cooperate in surveillance, he insisted that there must be 100 percent certainty of the link between the microbe and human illness before notifying the public. When Wasserman called me at home a few days later, he told me he wanted me to be patient.

I didn't have a patient bone in my body. I understood Wasserman's argument that the pfiesteria toxin has not been identified, and that there is no test available to prove the source of my patients' illness. But for me, neurological tests and the clinical diagnosis were enough. And I was particularly frustrated because I had developed a straightforward theory about pfiesteria, backed up by solid scientific literature, that may allow the fish-kill problem to be corrected—cheaply and quickly.

Fish kills have commonly been blamed on nutrient enrichment of phosphates and nitrates in the water, but I believe there may be another explanation. In the Pocomoke River, the levels of nitrates and phosphates have not been unusually high in the past 12 years. But copper—leached from agricultural fields, particularly where tomatoes are grown, and from hog and chicken manure—exists in high levels in tidal wetlands and river sediment. (It is added to animal feed to prevent spoilage.) Copper salts kill algae and small creatures called cryptomonads—organisms on which the harmless amoeba-like stage of the pfiesteria microbe feeds. The copper can also bind to pesticides to destroy the phytoplankton and rotifers that eat pfiesteria when it transforms into its brief toxin-producing phase. Any major rainfall (and each of the fish kills occurred a few days after heavy rains) stirs up this sediment and increases the presence of copper in the river waters.

A solution to pfiesteria blooms seems simple enough: Stop killing prey of the harmless pfiesteria and stop killing predators of the toxin-producing stages. If it lives out here in our river, feed pfiesteria on cryptomonads, not on menhaden and water-skiers.

A dilute solution of potassium permanganate does the job. When added to affected water, it destroys toxins and then dissolves into harmless, naturally occurring chemicals. And fish in the treated water survive.

At the DNR conference, the Maddoxes and I demonstrated this technique using fish in tanks treated with potassium permanganate and in untreated control tanks. The experts ignored our evidence. But Wasserman must have heard some of what I said. On Aug. 11, he came to Pocomoke City for a public meeting and announced that a committee of experts from the University of Maryland and Johns Hopkins would from then on help with diagnoses.

I couldn't wait for the experts. Just three days later, two Maryland Department of Environment workers who had been working at a fish-kill site came into my office, both with lesions and some memory loss. I sent one of them to my alma mater, Duke University, where further neurological tests matched the water-skier and people from Burkholder's lab. Any doubts I had about the illness were gone.

I provided Wasserman's blue-ribbon doctors with case summaries of many of my patients, along with medical records, wondering whether his specialists would agree with my findings. Would they see what I saw?

They saw it. The pfiesteria syndrome was finally announced on Aug. 29. When we talked later, Wasserman and I realized that we had been like two wrestlers on the mat. As for the question of who had won, let it be said that Maryland has won—by being the first state to respond appropriately to the health threat. Gov. Parris Glendening may have taken some heat when he closed rivers where 20 percent of the fish had lesions, but he was right to do so. It was a triumph, too, for old-fashioned primary-care medicine.

Do I feel vindicated? Yes, indeed. I pushed the state to acknowledge the human health problem, and I presented the first proven cases at the Medical and Chirurgical Faculty of Maryland convention earlier this month. Am I happy? Not yet. There's still work to be done: most of all in persuading scientists and public officials that copper, not nitrates or phosphates, is the culprit—and that potassium permanganate can be used to stop fish kills in our rivers.

–by Ritchie Shoemaker, MD.

chapter 31

Some Thoughts about Treatment and Prevention

September 22

After learning that my appearance on the Today Show had been canceled, I reminded myself that there would surely be more chances to tell the pfiesteria story nationwide. And that hunch turned out to be correct. Within a few days of my escape from New York, in fact, I got a call from Barbara Lippman at CBS News. "48 Hours" wanted to do a show about pfiesteria.

I was especially pleased to take that call, because I thought I had the "perfect case" for their documentary-style program. A student in the Gifted and Talented math program run by The Johns Hopkins University had fallen victim to pfiesteria. He'd been swimming, playing and fishing in the Nanticoke River all summer long. He'd also been performing well in math, while enjoying this summer of "boy heaven."

Then disaster struck. One afternoon in July, after he'd been swimming in some of the backwaters of the Nanticoke, his head began to hurt. He soon developed abdominal pain, followed by acute diarrhea. The next day brought the first lesions. Soon his summer school math scores were taking a steep nosedive.

After the kid had been struggling with the illness for a month, his worried mother brought him to me for an exam. The child had classic pfiesteria lesions on his legs. The lesions were healing, producing the characteristic slight darkening of nearby tissues. His exam wasn't remarkable for much else, however, and his memory seemed sharp.

While some of my pfiesteria patients had developed problems with sequencing and subtracting, this kid's wide-ranging math problem seemed unique. Hoping for answers, I sent him for neuro-cognitive testing at the University of Maryland. Five weeks after exposure, he was still functioning two or three levels below his pre-pfiesteria performance. This toxin was incredible!

Meanwhile, the referral-problems at the University of Maryland continued to mount. Somehow, the boy's history of tumbling math scores had never reached Dr. Grattan. As a result, the child was given the standard mental testing, which produced normal-range results (even though no special math-testing was done).

Enter "48 Hours." What the editors wanted, they said, was to paint a picture of the case from the very beginning. They would track the initial evaluation and the beginning of treatment, then observe any ensuing testing and report on follow-up. Their strategy sounded like it would produce a terrific story—especially if the math scores later went up, as I expected they would.

The "48 Hours" crew soon ran into problems, however. For starters, the testing could not be observed. It was confidential, period. Could they stage a "simulation" of the testing process? No … that scenario would cause the kid's identity to be revealed, and it would have been terribly unfair to subject him to possible derision from his schoolmates, if he were labeled as a "pfiesteria victim" on national TV.

It was an aggravating ordeal. And it ended on an utterly absurd note—when Ms. Lippman called back to say that her crew was "short-staffed," and that the project had been scrapped. I shook my head, and couldn't help muttering to myself: "Prince Charles strikes again!" Without the national media focusing on treatment, I was left alone again, just like being on my favorite dock on the Pocomoke. I couldn't understand how the media had failed to see the vital importance of treatment of PHIS.

I reviewed the empiric regimen for treatment. It made pretty good sense. Empty the gallbladder, bind bile and toxin in the gut, retain toxin in stool and then have it eliminated. The toxin wouldn't be reabsorbed, as happened normally with other bile salts. Deplete the body's load of toxins by having the poison eliminated right down the commode.

The medical strategy seemed quite simple, even if based primarily on speculation and repeated observation. Let's face it: Our knowledge was still woefully inadequate. We didn't have an I.D. on the toxin involved, and we didn't know if it dissolved in fat. Could it exist in bile? All we had were a few patients who'd gotten better, under circumstances that might have been purely coincidental.

I recalled several interesting conversations I'd had with Dr. David Oldach on the subject of treatment. The first time I'd told him about "adding a teaspoon of this, and then mixing it with a teaspoon of that, and then take the dose frequently," he'd responded by marveling at the "incredible placebo effect" that could be expected from such a treatment.

He had a good point. Even a brief survey of medicine throughout the ages shows that the "shaman" has always depended on patient cooperation and patient ownership of treatment, in order to work his cures. And my cholestyramine approach met every "shamanistic" criteria. But the wary Dr. Oldach restrained his enthusiasm for my "shotgun" approach, while pointing out that it left many questions unanswered.

Of course, Dr. Oldach would not be able to put his name or the name of the Maryland research group on my new study. He and his fellow-researchers had their academic criteria on the line with the article they were themselves preparing for Lancet, with Dr. Grattan as the lead author. That piece would report on the cases they'd seen August 22. It would also emphasize the neurocognitive deficits that derived from pfiesteria.

In addition, my own study wasn't "randomized" or "controlled" —and that simply wasn't rigorous science. Before the medical authorities signed on as advocates of the Shoemaker treatment protocol, it would have to withstand the most careful scientific scrutiny.

Dr. Oldach was willing to review the information that I sent him, however. He said he was quite intrigued by the treatment. For a moment, I almost felt that he was tempted to co-author my treatment study—especially since some of my more unusual cases had responded quite well. In the end, however, he demurred. Maybe next time.

I kept my disappointment to myself, and went back to worrying about the plague. If treatment had been the third of my goals, then prevention of illness was my fourth and final one. Having personally experienced the wallop packed by pfiesteria toxin, I had trouble imagining the effect of, say, a massive fish kill in Baltimore's Inner Harbor. Consider: With only a few thousand dead fish in the Pocomoke and fewer than 100 people stricken, the state's entire seafood industry had taken a huge hit.

The political stakes and the potential for a media-fueled panic were enormous. What would happen if fish died in large numbers near the Bay Bridge? How many senators or congressmen would get phone calls if the Potomac were closed because of health issues? Perhaps these kinds of questions were occurring to others—all I knew was that my permanganate theory was now attracting more than casual interest in the media.

Channel 2 in Baltimore and Channel 7 in Washington had already reported on permanganate as a "preventive approach" in the early stages of the bug invasion. But there hadn't been much reaction until Channel 5 in Washington presented a five-minute feature on stopping fish kills with permanganate. Now, however, public response to the idea was beginning to pick up.

The sudden flaring of interest in permanganate produced some bizarre responses from the state scientists. At one point, for example, a working group at the Maryland Department of the Environment declared that the "treatment of entire watersheds with permanganate" would not only be ineffective, but would also wipe out huge numbers of species of algae. What form of logic were the environmental experts using here? I'd never advocated using permanganate to treat watersheds!

Perhaps the same authorities who had "refuted" my copper theory by citing normal copper levels in fish had taken up residence at MDE? Or maybe the reporter who told me about the MDE permanganate-quote was simply yanking on my chain, hoping for a good quote? It was hard to be sure. But a more reasonable MDE response, surely, might have been to point out that the "watershed suggestion" seemed extreme, and required further study.

Interestingly enough, the most important critic of the permanganate approach turned out to be my own wife, JoAnn. She said she couldn't condone putting chemicals into the river, since the ecological impact couldn't be predicted. And her point was well taken. If we wanted to find an effective preventive approach to the pfiesteria fish kills for the next year, we needed to start the research immediately. Obviously, we had to come up with a way to stop any active fish kill that became a threat to adjacent population centers.

At the same time, however, we would have to be very careful to safeguard the human and wildlife populations of our watersheds from inappropriate use of hazardous chemicals.

Still, permanganate deserves careful study. The evidence I had seen showed that it didn't produce long-term ecological detriment. As a matter of fact, Baltimore is already using the substance to eradicate zebra mussels from its reservoirs. Reflecting on this fact, I found myself wondering about the steps that would be required in order to get a license to use permanganate.

First there would have to be an environmental impact statement, with review by EPA, DNR, MDE and Coastal Zone Management. Next, we'd have to schedule testimony from environmental groups. After that, we'd need to set up license fees and schedule follow-up studies. ...

Ah, bureaucracy! Sure, I want to move as carefully as possible on potential forms of prevention. But the fact remains: We need to know now what to do if a big kill erupts for nine straight days in the Severn River—or some other major river—next year. We should be studying permanganate right now, so that it will be available when and if we need it.

Of course, the alternative to prevention of toxin-release into the water and air during an active fish kill is simply to use cholestyramine to treat affected patients. Can you understand why I found myself thinking of Nero fiddling with his fire extinguishers, while Rome burned?

Really, all I wanted was for someone to consider investigating pulse doses of permanganate in a water column. If employed according to the guidelines laid down by Tony Mazzacarro, the permanganate works like a precisely directed bomb ... meaning that it can be limited to areas of active fish kill or active acquisition of symptoms in people.

Bruce Nichols knew about using permanganate to offset rotenone spills. The principles of benefit to the estuary versus risk to the estuary are now over-balanced by the very real risk of aerosol-spread of pfiesteria toxin-causing human illness.

Once the oxidation of organic molecules, like pfiesteria toxin, has occurred, the breakdown products of permanganate include potassium, a naturally occurring ion, oxygen (a naturally occurring gas), and MnO, another naturally occurring compound. Levels of permanganate over ten parts per million kill fish; levels of three parts per million successfully bind toxin and organic molecules without killing fish.

The tests in Shelltown—conducted in tanks that held more than 1,000-gallons—showed that fish could survive nicely with low levels of permanganate, but that once the levels fall, any newly released pfiesteria toxin is just as lethal as it was before the addition of the permanganate. Conclusion: Permanganate is a quick fix—nothing more and nothing less.

As a side issue, how can anyone know if they are in a pfiesteria bloom? Even before lesioned fish appear, the warning signs of burning eyes, hot skin and peppery air announce the bloom. Use the permanganate now!

There's no doubt that permanganate needs further study, or that its effects should be evaluated before it is used indiscriminately. But I know it works. It stops pfiesteria toxin. I'm also convinced that there are no long-term effects, but I can't prove that. (Or at least, not "scientifically.")

As of this writing, the urgent question remains before us: How many people are going to suffer the grim consequences of pfiesteria-poisoning, before permanganate research finally gets the funding it deserves?

chapter 32

Med Chi and the BBC

September 23

No sooner had the Med Chi convention wrapped up its business in Ocean City than I received a call from Margaret Burri. She had just completed her review of the manuscript I'd sent her that described my cases. She said she would forward it to the Maryland Medical Journal editorial group, for whom Dr. Marion Friedman served as editor. Ms. Burri explained that the Maryland Medical Journal was the ideal forum for these cases, since the patients involved hailed from Maryland and I was a Med Chi member.

While pointing out that the journal articles are usually prepared at least a month in advance, Ms. Burri said it was impossible to predict whether or not my article would make it into the next issue. In the interim, she sent my material to Vivian Smith, the writer and editor of the *Med Chi Physician* brochure. This newsletter goes out to Maryland physicians, and the next issue would contain information about my presentation, along with some of my thoughts about pfiesteria. In this way, some information could be published before the article appeared in the Maryland Medical Journal.

Then Dr. Friedman called. He said there would be a place for my article in the November issue of the Journal—but that it needed to be corrected, and the writing improved, prior to publication. Dr. Friedman had read the Washington Post article, and he was convinced that the Journal needed to respond to the pfiesteria issue in a timely fashion. I asked him about publishing my treatment cases, and he was receptive to the idea. He wanted the information prepared and sent to him as quickly as possible, since articles had to go through both peer review and editorial evaluation.

I agreed to the proposal, although I was given no guarantee that what I submitted would be published. But I was hopeful—especially after Dr. Friedman speculated out loud about the possibility that the Maryland Medical Journal might be the first such publication to publish information on both the diagnosis and the treatment of this brand-new disorder known as "pfiesteria human illness syndrome," or PHIS.

I crossed my fingers and went to work. A few days later, the media side of the story took another interesting twist, when the first foreign reporters began to check in. Although requests for interviews from the US networks had ceased after a one-week flurry, their absence was quickly filled by the foreigners.

For starters, Canada Public Radio wanted to do a 30-minute segment on pfiesteria for its new show, "Quirks and Quarks." I obliged by presenting the pfiesteria data—including the factors influencing the bug's growth in areas of environmental degradation due to nutrients and heavy metals complexing with pesticides. I also suggested that pfiesteria and dinoflagellate blooms would probably not threaten our northern neighbor, since Canadian waters are generally colder and swifter moving, with rapidly emptying watersheds. By way of example, I mentioned the 50-foot tides that swept through that nation's Bay of Fundy every 12 hours.

Canada does have its own red tides, however. Nitrate and phosphate enrichment, dithiocarbamates and chlorothalonils aren't a problem—but heavy metals, including copper, often degrade the waters. "Is there an analogy between Canada and the United States?" the interviewer asked.

I did my best to frame a useful comment, but my basic message was that the immense complexity of the problem defied simple, clearcut answers. How could we predict the future of Canada's watersheds, if we weren't even sure of what was happening along the Pocomoke?

Next the Toronto Globe sent one of its top reporters down to cover the story. "Please don't tell me they have dinoflagellate blooms around Toronto!" I said. No, I was told, they didn't ... but Globe readers *do* travel to the United States, especially to Ocean City in the spring. It seemed that many of those readers were eager to hear about pfiesteria.

The Globe interview was a bit of a surprise—but nothing like the shock I got when the British Broadcasting Corporation (BBC) called me for an interview. They wanted to talk with Dr. Burkholder and me, if they could get both of us together. Could I travel in order to meet their reporter, Tom Mangold? He was hoping to interview Rick Dove and Dr. Chris Delaney in New Bern, then quiz Dr. Burkholder in Raleigh, before wrapping things up with me at a watershed near Salisbury Airport.

Just for fun, I left a message for JoAnn at her school. "We are going to London to do a BBC interview. Could you meet me at the Concorde? We'll be back in time for dinner."

In reality, I planned to meet Tom in Lewes, Delaware, where Dr. Burkholder was giving a presentation and could interview us together. The BBC angle on the story was a compelling one: The network wanted to show how environmental factors were contributing to a global problem of harmful algae blooms, including dinoflagellates (of which pfiesteria was only one type).

Right away, I told Dr. Burkholder about my successful treatment of pfiesteria patients with cholestyramine. "Well, give me a bushel-basket full, then!" She was trying to hang onto her sense of humor, but she looked tired. I tried to imagine how many people called her daily, with each one wanting "just a few minutes." Brutal! Still, she told me that her lab was close to isolating the toxin, and her explanation seemed quite convincing. Although several labs—including NIEHS—were working on the problem, I felt sure that Dr. Burkholder's crew would isolate the toxin first.

Amazing but true: The story of Pocomoke and its pfiesteria was now running worldwide, and not just on CNN. With the arrival of the BBC, the bug-saga had developed a truly international spin.

Several weeks later, I was preparing to begin my office hours when my receptionist called my name. "There's a fellow named Tom calling from London," said Bonnie Rose. "Do you want to talk to him?" We both thought it rather remarkable that someone—anyone—would telephone from London.

It was the BBC reporter, of course. Tom Mangold wanted to ask a few more questions, prior to "putting his story to bed." He sounded surprised to learn that I was on the job so early. "Tom," I told him with a chuckle, "I'm afraid that I'm gonna have to put in a lot *more* of these 16-hour days, before we get the pfiesteria bug under control!"

chapter 33

The "Pfiesteria Wars" Continue

September 25

As the national and international news media continued to crank out dramatic stories on the bug invasion, my office telephone was ringing off the hook. And many of the calls were coming in from people who feared that they'd developed pfiesteria human illness syndrome.

Interestingly enough, a high percentage of the calls involved worried residents of Florida—and not just around the active kill sites in the Indian River, either. On several occasions, I fielded queries from the Gulf Coast and the "Blue Water Bay" ... even though no major kills had been observed in these waters, and no lesioned fish.

What did this mean, exactly? It was hard to say. My earlier experience with the Nanticoke River patient had taught me that the presence of lesioned or dead fish wasn't the only criterion that should be employed by those who wanted to avoid getting sick.

In my interview with the *Med Chi Physician*, I'd suggested that one useful form of prevention for travelers might be to call ahead in order to find out if there were any ailing fish on hand. I'd also recommended that people should avoid swimming and water skiing in slack water and backwaters, where the organism seemed to flourish. But as new information about pfiesteria continued to pour in, I realized that this advice was flawed as well—since the new reports strongly suggested that merely avoiding sick fish and stagnant water wasn't enough to guarantee safety from the toxin.

At this point, only one generalization about pfiesteria's impact on human beings seemed valid: You couldn't generalize! Each case seemed maddeningly different in terms of symptoms, duration, cause of infection. And so it was with the commercial diver from Wicomico Creek, who had undergone extensive wet suit-exposure to tainted waters on the job.

The diver had been operating in the Wicomico Creek for several months and had never seen lesioned fish or sick fish. Six weeks later the DNR reported finding fish with lesions upstream from where he was working as well as confirming the presence of pfiesteria ten weeks later.

The diver had experienced an abrupt onset of abdominal cramping, severe headache and confusion about four weeks before the public hearing held by Congressman Gilchrest. He came to see me after that meeting. After listening to his story, I suggested that he drop by my office for an evaluation. He appeared one week later, and when I examined him, I realized that his was a classic pfiesteria syndrome in all respects.

The man's memory was shot; he couldn't remember a single number out of five. His secretory diarrhea had cost him ten pounds and many hours of sleep. His abdominal cramping was so bad that he hadn't been able to work. He also suffered from shortness of breath after even the mildest activity. Although he displayed no rashes, he said his headache was so bad that it would prevent his return to work, unless he got immediate relief.

I started him on the cholestyramine protocol and quickly sent him off for neurocognitive studies. The tests were markedly positive. As a matter of fact, the only thing missing from his roll-call of symptoms was skin lesions. And he was furious ... especially about

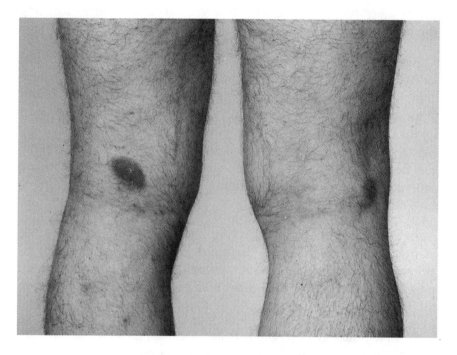

Pfiesteria lives in Virginia too.

the way the DNR workers had driven past him and his dive area in their boats, while conducting their own pfiesteria investigation ... without ever bothering to inform him of the upstream fish kill.

But the DNR investigators had merely been following their own guidelines. Since they hadn't found more than "20 percent" of the fish in the area to be afflicted with lesions, there was no need for a public alert. (Understandably, the diver had a hard time accepting the logic of this curious policy.)

At any rate, it was now quite evident that Maryland State public health policy had failed both the diver and the victim in the Nanticoke River case. Soon I was fielding yet another call from Dr. Marty Wasserman. As it turned out, the media had interviewed both of us about these two cases. Yet Marty had no knowledge of them. We discussed that when I'd reported them to the health department, the illnesses had not been classified as having occurred in waters with 20-percent fish kill. Was this communication problem going to be a new theme?

In short, those two cases simply hadn't met the criteria for investigation. I outlined all of this to Marty, and he asked me to report any new cases I saw to him, regardless of the circumstances. I agreed. My total number of cases was now approaching 50; so far, all had been reported.

In epidemiological terms, managing information about the outbreak was nothing less than a nightmare. For one thing, the public health definition of a case was extremely tenuous. Another major problem was the increasing difficulty in getting patients studied at the University of Maryland. Because of these obstacles, a number of the cases remained unknown to the medical personnel who were working on the disease.

Of course, such lack of coordination didn't surprise me in the least. There was so much "turf-protecting" and "political damage control" going on around the issue that it was a wonder they ever got *anything* done. The whole thing reminded me of what would happen if four people tried to cook a soup at the same time!

A mess. What Maryland had done was to invent a structure for public health policy in order to combat an illness that some people said didn't exist. The State was trying to include experts from rival institutions in Baltimore on one team, and to coordinate health concerns from two different hotlines and at least twelve county health departments—all under the glare of TV cameras, and with a steady bombardment of questions from newspaper reporters. All things considered, the State was actually doing rather well. Not perfect, mind you, but better than could have been expected.

Another interesting development on the public side of the story took place after the Washington Post decided to take an up-close look at some of the problems that were occurring in Virginia. Fish kills had been reported at various times along the Rappahannock and James Rivers, but there were no reported cases of humans having been made sick by exposure to these lesioned fish.

Understandably nervous, the Virginia state officials continued to insist that their waters were safe for fishing, recreational and economic activities. They wanted no part of the "seafood panic" that had put such a big dent in Maryland's economy. All of that changed quickly, however, when the Virginia Fisheries worker mentioned above finally decided to follow Jack Howard's advice—and came to my office for an examination.

In many ways, this Virginia worker's job was similar to the jobs that had been held by the bug-infected Maryland DNR workers. For one thing, he'd been actively involved in monitoring the Pocomoke River—but on the Virginia side—during the second fish kill, back in August. During that period, Jack Howard had vowed to send the Virginian in to see me, since Jack knew that the hapless worker had "been in it."

"It" was pfiesteria, of course, and Jack had called it exactly right. All at once, I found myself treating a third patient from the Old Dominion State ... and a patient whose telltale symptoms could not be ignored by the Virginia state officials, as had happened in Maryland when the DNR workers fell sick.

The Virginian was hurting bad. His memory defects and his

other pfiesteria symptoms were similar to those displayed by many of my other cases. His memory was faltering badly, and he was suffering from abdominal cramping, secretory diarrhea, significant headache and classic skin lesions.

Because of the potential political importance of this patient, I made sure to arrange for medical photographs of his skin lesions. Then I got him started on the cholestyramine protocol. I also urged him to report himself to his supervisors and the Virginia Health Department. Of course, he was worried sick about the possible repercussions on his career, should he go public as a pfiesteria patient. Who could blame him? The record showed that Virginia had been less than kind to those of her sons and daughters who claimed to have fallen prey to the bug in the past.

I decided to call Marty about this one. I knew he'd scuffled with Virginia over the question of whether or not Maryland should share the pfiesteria test data that Virginia's experts wanted to study. Dr. Wasserman doubted the legality of sharing individual case data with the Virginia physicians. I had trouble understanding his position, however, because it seemed that both states had such an obvious interest in cooperating.

Couldn't Maryland share what it had learned with Virginia, in order to prevent huge amounts of needless suffering? Apparently, the issue was more nettlesome than it looked ... because the weeks were passing, and the communication simply wasn't taking place.

Next I asked Marty what I should do about my Virginia Fisheries patient. His advice was simple: He recommended that I become "as big a pain in the ass to the State of Virginia" as I had been to the State of Maryland! This was more of his jovial locker-room talk, but I didn't take offense. I simply assumed that he was instructing me to follow the dictates of my conscience, by reporting my case to the Virginia Health Department. And if the media discovered that we'd loaned out these case histories ... well, we'd cross that bridge when we came to it.

I appreciated Marty's directness and his perception of the case, but I kept trying to imagine what the Virginia Health Secretary was going to do when I started talking about pfiesteria in Virginia. I'd already gotten one anonymous phone call from Virginia suggesting I should keep my "fat mouth shut"!

To no one's real surprise, the Washington Post soon began reporting this story. And when the Virginia Marine Resources Commission representative, Wilford Kale, announced on October 1 that one of its employees had been treated for pfiesteria and was being referred for further testing, Post reporter Eric Wee decided that it was time to print all of the information he'd been gathering for several weeks.

I'd already been burned once on the issue of "patient confidentiality," and I certainly didn't want to risk taking another pounding. During interviews with Wee, I did my best to dance around the issues of "who, what, where, when and why."

But Eric wanted specifics. What to do? In the end, I decided that because Virginia had released some information about the cases, it would be acceptable for me to simply confirm what they'd already made public. However, I firmly refused to disclose the names of any patients. Nor would I discuss sex, age or race. After all, I'd been the treating physician and I'd arranged for photos ... which were okayed for publication, provided that no names were attached.

One week later, my Virginia patient called me and I learned the worst. Virginia was reporting loudly that it had done "additional testing" on him. For starters, a dermatologist had performed a biopsy. And so what, if that particular test had no bearing whatsoever on the nature of the infection or the health of the patient?

The remaining evaluation had been conducted by a neurologist, during an exam which the patient said lasted about five minutes and consisted of exactly 15 questions. No neurocognitive testing had been done. No imaging studies had been performed. No pulmonary functions, no blood work, no CT scan, no PET scan. *Nada.*

Soon after the conclusion of all of these non-studies, the State of Virginia announced its findings: This patient did not have any health problems that had been caused by the river!

But the Washington Post wasn't about to let that statement go unchallenged. Within a matter of hours, the Post bloodhounds were back on the chase, and the switchboards in Richmond were lighting up.

Within two days, the State of Virginia admitted that they had information to suggest that seven individuals were suffering from possible pfiesteria syndrome. Four had already been examined. Eventually, all were found to be normal.

When Eric Wee called me for my reaction, I asked him about the testing. He said that the neurological exam reported by the State of Virginia had consisted of 30 questions. He also confirmed that nothing more had been done to investigate these cases than to conduct routine dermatology and neurology evaluations. Here was another barrage of front-page news for the Metropolitan area readership of the Washington Post!

As the summer dragged slowly on, I still had no clue as to why the two states weren't cooperating. One day I called Dr. David Oldach and asked about the possibility of sending Dr. John Taylor a copy of the preliminary paper that Dr. Oldach's group had written for submission to Lancet. (Dr. Taylor was the head of the Virginia medical team, which was the mirror-image of its Maryland counterpart.)

Dr. Oldach said he thought that sharing the article was a reasonable suggestion—especially since no individual test data had been sent from one state to the other, to his knowledge. I also sent along a copy of my diagnosis paper to Dr. Taylor, who had been demanding cooperation on these cases and didn't understand why Maryland had been so reluctant to share data.

It was a frustrating sequence of events, but I'm delighted to report that this part of the story has a happy ending.

After the controversy over Virginia's allegedly superficial analysis of pfiesteria cases finally calmed down, the two states launched a cooperative effort at information-sharing. Later, in a strongly worded, published letter, Virginia Governor Allen would deplore the failure of communication—while urging Maryland Governor Glendening to join him in calling for open disclosure.

Politics! For a practicing family physician who simply wanted to do what he could to prevent people from catching the bug, the endless posturing and PR-spinning were painful to watch.

chapter 34

Deja Vu All Over Again: Here Comes Another "Blue Ribbon Committee"!

September 25

Somewhere in the middle of the media brouhaha over the origins and health hazards of pfiesteria, I opened the morning newspaper to discover that the State of Maryland had created yet *another* "Blue Ribbon" committee to study the bug-infestation from top to bottom.

"They must be kidding," I muttered to myself as I read the front-page headline. But the brand-new "Blue Ribbon Citizens Pfiesteria Commission" was no joke. Like the state's Blue Ribbon medical panel before it, the Commission would hear testimony and make a report to the Governor. And would the newly launched think tank's recommendations be free of political bias? Of course they would! This time, vowed the latest assemblage of Blue Ribboners, all conclusions and recommendations would be based on methodical, objective review of the data.

Right.

I'm sure I wasn't the only Marylander who had become cynical about the hidden political purposes that lay behind the creation of these august inquisitory panels. And why not? I'd already been thoroughly disillusioned by the political manipulation that had accompanied the first committee's findings. Why expect that things would go any better the second time around? As far as I could tell, both Governor Glendening and his hand-picked pfiesteria advisor, Donald Boesch, Ph.D., had already made up their minds: The plague had been triggered by runoff nutrients, and nothing else. What concerned me was the politicization of the science. I'd heard Dr. Boesch say, and read his quotes in the newspapers in August, that nutrients were *not* too high in the Pocomoke.

I was thoroughly skeptical of this latest initiative. And yet I had a high regard for three of the newly tapped committee members, each of whom enjoyed a solid reputation for open-mindedness and integrity. The trio included:

- **Will Baker**, an executive at the Chesapeake Bay Foundation, who had demonstrated a knack for independent thinking during his many years of campaigning for the Bay. Because he often refused to join the political consensus on environmental issues, Baker was regarded as a watchdog who actually possessed a few teeth.

- **Rick Nelson**, president of the local Farm Bureau, was the representative from Somerset County, and I knew him well. After all, I'd been the Nelson family physician for nearly two decades, starting way back when his college-age children were still in diapers. Given the regional and national attention that would soon be focused on the committee, I found it rather amusing that Ricky and I would be teaming up to deliver key testimony during the proceeding.

  I liked Ricky's bluntness. He told you what he thought—and that was the end of it. I admired that kind of candor, and I didn't believe for a single minute that he would buy into the bogus theory that nitrates and phosphates were the only mechanisms at work in triggering toxic blooms of pfiesteria.

  Of course, I was also quite confident that I could get Ricky to listen to me on the subject of copper ... because if he refused, I'd make him listen to some of the wonderful "Grateful Dead" tapes that his son Chris had been sending me over the years. (Ricky loves country music, and he can imagine no fate more horrible than being forced to attend a concert by the "Dead"!)

- Maryland State Delegate **Ronald Guns** was, to my mind, the most politically influential member of the new committee. Sure, there were some other politically "wired" committee members, but Delegate Guns was the "main man," according to Jan Graham's "Haztrak" Environmental Coalition, a public citizens group that monitors threats to the ecosystem.

As for my own participation in these hearings: Once again, Marty Wasserman had informed me that I would not be asked to join the committee in any formal way, but that I would be permitted to testify at a hearing scheduled for the University of Maryland Eastern Shore on October 2. At long last, I would have a chance to thoroughly air out the copper theory!

My spirits were soaring higher by the day, and for good reason: The Washington Post article had brought me allies from all across the Chesapeake Bay region. For example, Dr. Lester Andrews, Professor of Chemistry at the University of Virginia, sent me a note correcting some mistakes I'd made in the Post article on the subject of permanganate. I called him back, hoping to learn more, and was delighted when he said he wanted a chance to review my data on copper and dithiocarbamates.

When he sent me the results of that review a few days later, I felt even better than I had after the confirmation of my diagnosis of pfiesteria. Here was an authority with academic credentials and international standing who agreed with me on dithiocarbamates ... even to the point of suggesting in a letter that they should probably be banned!

While I was still basking in the glow of this affirmation, Jerry Rosen called (Sept. 26) with some very useful information. Dr. Rosen was serving as the Chair of Pharmacology at the University of Maryland Medical School ... but he soon reminded me of the fact that he'd taught me pharmacology when I was in medical school at Duke. Then he reviewed with me the large number of species of organisms that can survive potential poisoning by copper, simply by excreting it from inside the cells. After the review, he suggested that I call Dr. Irwin Fridovich, Professor Emeritus of Biochemistry at Duke. (I remembered Dr. Fridovich because he had been such an entertaining lecturer.)

Dr. Fridovich told me all about "superoxide dismutase." That enzyme protects cells from oxidative stress, and you won't find it in blue-green algae. The Duke specialist confirmed that both copper and zinc were cleared from aqueous solutions by dithiocarbamates. He also explained how the copper dithiocarbamate complex could penetrate the cell membranes of larger organisms (called eukaryotes) and then inactivate the superoxide dismutase.

Once again, I was thrilled to hear an expert suggest that the "copper theory" might hold water. Here was powerful academic confirmation of the disproportionate impact of copper on lower organisms that lack superoxide dismutase, and the exact mechanism showing how copper dithiocarbamates complex kills higher organisms like rotifers. Dr. Fridovich was quite familiar with the avid binding of copper by dithiocarbamates in the water column.

After that heartening colloquy, I paid a visit to John Hughes, the agricultural chemical salesman for a major regional agricultural firm. John described how copper and dithiocarbamates are used to retard bacterial diseases, especially in tomatoes. He also offered me a professional opinion: At present, there are no viable alternatives to this combination of bacteria-zapping chemicals. But a new class of chemical substances—including genetically engineered compounds that reduce plant susceptibility—are coming out next year. The chlorothalonils are a usable alternative after tomatoes have begun to fruit, but not before. (It's interesting to note that the fungicide most frequently used locally isn't copper sulfate but copper hydroxide.)

After setting the record straight on these subjects, John Hughes challenged my suggestion that planting cover crops of wheat and rye adjacent to streams would deposit copper and dithiocarbamates on the stream banks, where they would then be filtered out into the mud-layer. John pointed out that other fungicides are much more effective than dithiocarbamates for diseases on wheat, such as rust. Fair enough. But I felt encouraged by the fact that there were so many alternatives to chemicals I viewed as toxic. Surely the agricultural-chemical industry could come up with something safer than copper and dithiocarbamates on for use on tomatoes!

While I continued to work on the questions surrounding copper, I found that I was becoming increasingly aware of the analogy of copper and dithiocarbamates to DDT, a chemical product that had been used extensively as an insecticide. DDT had been advertised everywhere as the best and least expensive insecticide on the market. And the argument in its favor then had been a strong one: According to its advocates, DDT was demonstrably superior.

Was DDT truly indispensable? Nope. Once society learned just how dangerous it was, the researchers went to work and soon came up with substitutes that greatly reduced the hazards inflicted on our bird and insect populations. The parallel was obvious: If we could eliminate hazardous DDT with a determined effort, we could certainly put the brakes on our dangerous use of copper in agriculture. I was now more convinced than ever that the use of copper and dithiocarbamates must stop in fields adjacent to watersheds where environmental conditions allowed pfiesteria blooms.

John Hughes also noted that there are many other labels available for use of dithiocarbamates. (The term "labels" refers to indications for safe use.) But one problem with my theory, according to the savvy Hughes, was that the soils where dithiocarbamates are used didn't show significantly elevated levels in the surface assays. No data are available for the subsurface assay. Did the dithiocarbamates penetrate quickly to the lower-level soils? Unfortunately, however, the subsurface is the area of greatest flow for most chemicals that are mobile in soils. What I needed was some sort of index of flow of pesticides, especially dithiocarbamates in soils. Of course, I couldn't prove that subsurface flow of dithiocarbamates increased after a rain event. And I was reminded constantly of the fact that black plastic strips directed dithiocarbamates immediately into run-off.

No sooner had I finished this interesting discussion with Hughes than George Demas called to inform me that $10 million in federal research money had just been earmarked for studies that would look at agricultural implications of the problem of pfiesteria. At last the soil science academic community might begin acquiring the resources needed for an in-depth investigation. Maybe my complaints hadn't been falling on completely deaf ears!

Earlier, I'd telephoned Delegate Guns' office with some suggestions about the upcoming committee sessions, and had been referred to John Woolums, the delegate's counsel on environmental matters. Woolums sent me on to Diane Shaw, the scientific advisor, who would call me soon. I was pleased to hear Woolums say that my ideas had merit and ought to get a hearing.

Intent on following up, I called Dr. Dietrich again on September 29. She provided more information for me regarding copper and runoff from the tomato fields that she'd studied in Virginia. Her description of the dynamics involved differed slightly from the theories advanced by Dr. Gupta.

According to Dr. Dietrich, there were key changes in the water column concentrations of copper that depended on recent rain history, tidal conditions and on "mixing" of stream water that occurred with the tides.

Dr. Dietrich explained that copper is a compound that quickly penetrates into the subsurface, especially in the hydroxide form, along with other organic chemicals added. But copper in the sulfate form (as in animal feeds) is bound by soils faster than in the hydroxide form.

Next Dr. Dietrich stressed to me that the black plastic culture for tomato plants minimizes runoff of nitrates and phosphates. She then noted that organic agents keep copper hydroxide ten to thirty times more soluble in water than copper sulfate. Nor is the hydroxide form as complexed as copper sulfate. One result, she said, is that there can be an enhanced "localized effect" of copper in a pocket of the creek, as well as higher levels in water areas that became stagnant, once the runoff following the rain has stopped.

This was it! Another academic scientist had now concluded that the mechanisms by which pfiesteria can bloom were due solely to the toxic effects of copper and dithiocarbamates. The environmental conditions in creeks spur the pfiesteria bloom, period. There was no need for phosphate stimulation of pfiesteria growth (or phosphate stimulation of algal growth which provides food for pfiesteria, for that matter).

You better believe I was busy that day. After the Dietrich call, I talked to Dr. Robert Brumbaugh, a soil scientist with the Chesapeake Bay Foundation (CBF). Dr. Brumbaugh asked me if I could attend a VIMS meeting the following week at the York River; the agenda would include detailed discussion about pfiesteria in Virginia. Dr. Brumbaugh told me that copper was being reviewed, especially in terms of its possible impact on pfiesteria blooms.

This was an exciting development, of course. But I found myself wishing that the CBF's Will Baker would take up the cause as well. Blunt and outspoken, the no-nonsense Baker offered the perfect antidote to the kind of one-sided testimony that would no doubt dominate the proceedings. Baker could have provided lots of common sense—along with scientific sense, logical sense, hydrologic sense and soil sense!

Next I called Dr. Gupta to help me understand exactly how copper has been increasing in areas of the Pocomoke River and how it could be shown to be the toxic trigger. He agreed to see me the next day.

Diane Shaw soon returned my call from Delegate Guns' office. I sent her every bit of information I had. Her time was limited, so I hurried my presentation a bit. In the end, she didn't seem as convinced as her legal counsel had been.

So far, I still hadn't had a chance to speak directly to Delegate Guns, which I found regrettable. But he was operating in the very eye of the pfiesteria storm, and access to him was limited. I felt frustrated as critical weeks passed with no contact between us, and I never did manage to sit down for a discussion with this key legislative figure.

One day after my presentation to Diane Shaw, Dr. Gupta discreetly suggested that it was futile for people or government agencies to blame each other for the bug invasion. Were his comments aimed partially at me, because of my outspoken opinions about copper and pesticides? I wasn't sure. Dr. Gupta urged everyone to recognize the fact that pfiesteria was now a permanent inhabitant of the local rivers. Because it lives there, he said, we need to learn to control it.

Besides, he went on to point out, you can't isolate the causes of an ecosystem event of this kind. Rather than looking for a lone culprit, why not recognize that there are many factors involved in such sudden growth-spurts of watershed organisms? (I certainly didn't dispute him on this last point—which I'd been trying to make, myself, for the past several months!)

Dr. Gupta was very generous with his help. He showed me how the porewater along a stream provided a yardstick that could be used to measure the amount of copper and other heavy metals deposited in the Pocomoke during the previous five to ten years.

In the areas that Dr. Gupta analyzed, there were clear indications of a slow increase in silt formation, with approximately 1.5 cm per year being deposited. The silt was a time capsule that told the story of copper and other river metals in recent years. And while sampling of the pore water below 7½ cm showed negligible amounts of copper and other heavy metals, the same samples, when taken from the top 7½ cm, reflected the last five years or so of river history. Those samples showed that copper was dramatically increased in porewater.

How interesting it was to learn from Dr. Gupta that the increased amount of copper was highest adjacent to a poultry operation downstream from Pocomoke City! Porewater taken from samples at this site was the most toxic of such samples that Dr. Gupta had collected in either the Pocomoke or the Wicomico during the past several years. This toxicity, enough to kill most biologic creatures, was eliminated when the porewater was treated with EDTA, a chemical that binds and removes positively charged heavy metal ions, including copper.

Here was the missing puzzle piece! The no-till farming method had sent the copper shooting through the water column, until it dissipated in the porewater. The porewater showed increased amounts of copper deposited in the Pocomoke over the past five years, which reflected the changes in the river's chemistry.

This shift correlated exactly with the switchover from traditional methods of tilling land to the no-till approach. In no-till, a small furrow is placed in farmland, allowing seeds to be sown. The furrow is then filled in, after the land has been treated with herbicide, to kill competing weeds. By avoiding deep tilling, the farmer saves a great deal of money and time while preparing land for seeding. An additional benefit is reduced erosion of soil due to wind and water.

The downside was significant, however, starting with the fact that any types of manures or fungicides applied to the land would remain exposed on the surface—with a vastly increased potential for runoff into adjacent watersheds. With tilling, by contrast, the manures or other kinds of chemicals would be mixed into the soil at the root levels and then retained within soils.

As Dr. Gupta's work demonstrated, the effects of no-till farming had caused increased runoff of copper and dithiocarbamates into the Pocomoke River watershed and others like it. The porewater testing indicated that this increase could be shown to have occurred over the past five years. The dynamics worked as follows:

While copper will normally complex with organic chemicals (such as humic acid) over a 12–24 hour period, the use of copper *hydroxide* will keep copper in its cupric, or toxic ion phase longer. And that extended period of "cupric ion load" was enough to cause local die-offs of cryptomonads—the energy-rich protozoan food source for pfiesteria in its amoeba phase. After the shrinkage of its food supply due to copper-infusion, the now-starving pfiesteria would shift its life stage to the zoospore phase, which often became toxic.

The bottom line was crystal-clear. While complexing with dithio-carbamates, the copper disrupted superoxide dismutase *within ten minutes* in organisms such as rotifers, which would normally be capable of resisting the effects of copper, alone. These organisms played a major role in the bug invasion, since they are potential predators for pfiesteria in its smaller, zoospore phase. Wipe them out with copper, and watch the pfiesteria proliferate! At the same time, it was worth noting that the creatures which normally provided food for pfiesteria in its benign phase (the cryptomonads) could be killed by copper directly.

Could anything be simpler, or more obvious?

In spite of the evidence for this theory, however, the State of Maryland DNR wasn't buying—a fact which became maddeningly clear when DNR point-man Dave Goshorn sent me some information designed to show that copper simply "wasn't a problem" in the Pocomoke.

Indeed, according to the "safety criteria" cited by Goshorn, the typical 15-parts-per-million level of copper in the river during the past six to seven years posed no threat at all to aquatic life!

Mr. Goshorn's curious criteria failed to address several of the facts, however. For one thing, toxicity wasn't a problem for the higher organisms that can excrete copper directly to protect super-oxide dismutase. Make no mistake: 15 parts per million is orders of magnitude higher than lethal levels of copper (see appendix) for the primitive prey species of pfiesteria. And indeed, samples of pore-water had not even been collected (a lapse that was met with derision from Dr. Gupta).

The Goshorn sampling data had included sediment on a dry-weight basis, as well as free water samples from the water column of the river. Dr. Gupta had of course insisted that measuring dry sediment was of no relevance ... but even the dry sediment showed levels of copper up to 11 parts per million. Obviously, the argument about high levels of copper in the water column wasn't over!

Aquaculturists such as Jerry Redden (he operates an enclosed aquaculture system for raising tilapia), and Tony Mazzacarro (a farmer of striped bass) remained utterly skeptical about the levels of copper that had been declared "normal" by the State of Maryland.

Both men agreed that any concentration of copper over 0.5 parts per million was harmful to fish. They were convinced that the capacity of organic ligands of copper, including humic acid, was exceeded by such high levels.

After wrestling with the data for days on end, I was now prepared to present my copper theory to the Blue Ribbon Commission. Fortunately, I had several minutes before the hearings in which to discuss my findings with Will Baker. He quickly pointed out that the evidence I would soon present was new to him. Of course, I'd expected some resistance from the Chesapeake Bay Foundation, since their public position was that phosphates levels of .10 and .12—a typical range for the Pocomoke—were high enough to cause algae blooms ... even though such levels were fairly low, when compared to other state watersheds.

After the brief confab with Baker, I went to work. As usual, I talked too fast. I also made the mistake of presenting my theory as if I were testifying, and not by simply reading it. I gave each of the members of the panel a copy of the copper theory. I hoped they would read it, but my heart sank as I saw the stacks of similar reports they were already carrying in their briefcases. (But I was heartened to see Rick Nelson actually reading his copy during breaks in the testimony.)

Rick had provided me with copies of some of the papers that Dr. Burkholder had presented to the panel. One major point that I was able to use from her work was the assertion that the nutritional prehistory of pfiesteria determined its response to phosphates.

Dr. Burkholder's research had shown clearly that if pfiesteria could get all it wanted to eat in its amoeba phase, then the organism wouldn't switch to its toxic phase—even at much higher levels of phosphates. But if the environment didn't contain much prey for pfiesteria, then even low levels of phosphates could set off toxin production. Once again, I found myself applauding some good common sense. The point was that with copper and dithiocarbamates acting on both ends of the predator-prey relationship, these low levels of phosphates—ordinarily harmless to pfiesteria—could become hair-triggers for the toxic phase.

It now seemed clear that preventing runoff (that is, keeping mobile nitrates and copper hydroxide from entering the river) should be a key strategy for preventing incursions by the bug. But such prevention would not be accomplished merely by planting shallow-rooted grasses such as wheat or rye in 10–12 foot swaths along the river edge. In fact, we needed buffers that would combine trees tall enough to block wind with deep-rooted grasses that might be counted on to protect surfaces, as well as deeper-rooted shrubs that would block sub-surface flow.

But how could these wetland buffers become a reality, when so many farmers were engaged in no-till agriculture that brought the treated cropland right up to the river's edge?

Reflecting on all of this, I recalled some of the controversy that had erupted in Worcester County when that municipality had locked horns with the American Civil Liberties Union (ACLU) on the issue of county redistricting. The ACLU understood clearly why no minority member had ever been elected county commissioner. It was simply because the districts themselves reflected local populations containing white majorities.

Redistricting, argued the ACLU, might change all that. By creating a long, narrow district that held more minorities than whites, the chances for minority representation on the commission would surely be increased. This same concept had been used in North Carolina to create a legislative district that was long and skinny. Well … why not employ the same concept to protect the Pocomoke River? Instead of creating a "skinny voting district," why not carve out skinny ribbons of land flanking watersheds, in order to protect them?

An interesting concept, no? Instead of maintaining all those jumbo-sized national parks—think of Yellowstone, or the Smoky Mountains—why not tie together long, slender parcels of watershed-adjoining land that would be owned by the public?

This public land could then be planted with properly designed wetland buffers. The farmer would be compensated for his land, and everyone would benefit—provided that park visitors were not permitted to violate the farmer's privacy.

The Blue Ribbon hearings had been an exciting time for all of us. But things got even more exciting about two weeks later, when Vice President Al Gore came to the Eastern Shore to announce a federal program of loans to farmers. Gore was promising more than $195 million over the next fifteen years, in order to help protect areas of farmland adjacent to watersheds in wetland buffers.

It was exciting ... but I didn't know why the VP was doing the announcing. From what I'd heard, Senator Paul Sarbanes had come up with the original idea, which had also included planting wetland buffers. And indeed, this was the same kind of program that has been used for some time by the Natural Resource Conservation Service in its Conservation Reserve Program. Maybe it wouldn't produce a long, skinny, "gerrymandered" national park ... but the idea was the same. The Gerry Mander National Wetland Reserve! Why not make it economically feasible for the farmer to stop planting directly adjacent to watersheds? Why not build a wetland buffer? It's the only solution that makes any sense, if your goal is to restrict runoff—not just of the small amounts of nitrates and phosphates, but also of harmful pesticides, fungicides and heavy metals, and especially copper.

After scanning the regional press and talking to my pal Ricky, I realized that my presentation had made little impact on the Blue Ribbon panel. Their theme was "nitrates and phosphates, phosphates and nitrates." And if anyone dared to raise the "copper question," the experts advising the commission simply announced: "Nope! Sorry! We don't think so." (Nonetheless, some of my ideas did manage to make their way into the final commission report.)

The "Cambridge Consensus"—Dr. Boesch's alliterative name for his group of state estuarine scientists—regarded my idea as "improbable" ... because even though there might be extremely high levels of copper in the river, the metal was tightly complexed with organic material. I just sighed and shook my head. In the end, all of my intensive literature searches on water column aqueous chemistry, dithiocarbamates displacing humic acids, free ion runoff and related subjects was dismissed. Yet all I sought was a reasonably designed test to see if the copper/dithiocarbamate data that had been collected actually fulfilled the predictions of the model.

The nutrient enrichment theory didn't match the model; there was no denying this blunt fact. But the matter was out of my hands. I'd made my presentation; I'd submitted the data that were logical and merited further review. I was convinced that the "heavy metal concept"—and especially the copper version—had not been given proper review.

But there were bound to be federal-level scientists out there who knew a lot more about copper, and who would listen to me.

It was frustrating, but I did make an impact on the documentation of human health cases from other parts of the country. My notes from these days are full of phone calls from around the country. On September 29, a patient calls from Tennessee to ask about lesions picked up along the Gulf Coast of Florida. (That one sounded like a typical pfiesteria case.) On Sept. 30, a North Carolina caller checks in to describe pfiesteria symptoms that had begun after fishing in Pamlico Sound. Day after day, it was the same story: People wanted to know what the bug was doing to them and their communities.

But the calls weren't all personal; more than once, I received reports of environmental disasters that defied explanation. Example: One day Ken Mills called me from the Rappahannock River area. Ken is an avid member of the Friends of the Rappahannock who had spotted an incredible surge in mortality in turtles. Twenty-two of 42 turtles in a recent survey had been found dead, many with lesions that looked like pfiesteria. There was a kill of fresh water mussels as well.

I sent Ken a copy of my copper theory. And indeed, we had noticed turtles with lesions back in 1996, while examining Pocomoke River fish traps. A number of turtles with bizarre lesions had also been found in April of 1997. These suffering animals had been observed laboring around fresh waters near Salisbury, Maryland. I'd also heard about huge sea turtles being blinded by dramatic growths of "papillomas" (benign skin tumors).

Was there a common theme here? Could we understand the biochemistry, the monstrous biological complexity of these massive infestations? We needed to know more. We needed to get back into our laboratories and work, work, work ...

chapter 35

Blue Ribbon Testimony

September 30

The testimony before the Blue Ribbon Committee took less than 10 minutes. The response to my testimony by the committee was a lukewarm thank you disregard. The impact of my testimony was trivial. The following is a transcript of what I presented to the Blue Ribbon Committee:

Experts have told us that pfiesteria is not a new visitor to the Chesapeake Bay estuaries. Dr. Eric May found it in Jenkins Creek in 1992. Dr. Burkholder has shown that pfiesteria can exist in a variety of life forms, generally classified as an amoeba stage, a non toxic animal stage (zoospore) and as a toxic zoospore. Dr. Burkholder has also shown that the nutritional prehistory of pfiesteria affects its response to enrichment of phosphates and nitrates. With a bountiful supply of blue green algae, cryptomonads and cyanobacteria prey, pfiesteria remains in its large non toxic amoeba form, using engulfed chloroplasts of prey as additional fuel sources. Without adequate nutritional prey pfiesteria transforms into a toxic form at lower levels of phosphate and nitrate enrichment.

Nutrient levels in Bay rivers such as the Rappahannock and Pocomoke are far lower than those in the Pamlico Sound and Neuse River. While the Chesapeake Bay Foundation considers even these low levels of nitrates and phosphates to be too high, the levels are not significantly different from those recorded since 1986, according to DNR data. In the absence of markedly high phosphate levels, which Dr. Burkholder has shown drives pfiesteria toxic zoospore replication, we must not limit our solutions to the pfiesteria problems by only stopping run off of nitrates and phosphates from chicken manure applied to no-till farms. We know pfiesteria can kill fish in non degraded waters too.

We must also acknowledge that there are informed pfiesteria scientists, including Dr. Hans Paerl, who do not agree that nutrient enrichment is the key to pfiesteria blooms. In a press release from the North Carolina Sea Watch, dated 4/28/97, Dr. Paerl and Dr. James Pinckney reported that pfiesteria does not respond strongly to nutrient input. Other dinoflagellates, diatoms, blue green algae, and cryptomonads multiply quickly when nutrients are made available.

DNR data do not show high levels of chlorophyll which would be expected if there were algae blooms from nutrients in the Pocomoke River.

Focusing on phosphate and nitrates only does not provide an adequate model to account for the change in pfiesteria activity in the tributaries of the Chesapeake Bay. I suggest that we expand our perspective on the pfiesteria problem to include the perturbation of biological aspects of predator-prey relationships, the loss of wetland buffers that can block runoff of both surface flow and subsurface flow, and a change to no till farming techniques.

Dr. Gian Gupta has shown a dramatic increase in the amount of copper in the Pocomoke River over the past five years. The Pocomoke River sediment accumulates at approximately 1.5 cm/yr. Sediment samples below 7.5 cm show little heavy metal and copper enrichment. The top 7.5 cm of river sediment show high levels of heavy metals. Dr. Gupta analyzes the water between soil particles (porewater) in the river sediment for heavy metals. Assays of heavy metals taken from dry sediment and the water column (done by DNR) do not reflect day to day changes in copper that is dissolved in water or loosely complexed with organic molecules. Apparent normal levels of copper in the water column, found by DNR samples, reflect approximately 7% of the total copper load (Principles and Application of Aquatic Chemistry, 1993). The rest of the copper is in other forms. These forms are loose ligands of copper with organic acids, mostly humic acid. Those ligands form slowly, taking nearly 24 hours to remove free copper from the water column. Dithiocarbamates, agricultural fungicides, break apart the copper ligands in less than ten minutes. A recent draft of the USDA position paper on nutrient management emphasizes the previously understated roles of copper and dithiocarbamates in the watersheds of the Eastern Shore.

Please remember that copper levels in the Pocomoke River exceed 12 parts per million (not billion).

Dr. Gupta's sophisticated research also shows enhancement of biologic toxicity of porewater in area adjacent to poultry farms. The copper found in the Pocomoke could either come from chicken manure (350 ppm), chicken feed (200 ppm) or agricultural use of fixed copper, a fungicide. Tomato growers apply dithiocarbamates with two pounds of copper per acre every 7–10 days throughout the growing season. Nearly all green leaf vegetables including tobacco, are treated with copper as a fungicide (cabbage is an exception).

Data from Dr. Dietrich of VIMS, show levels of copper runoff exceeding 200 ppb following a rain event from each of four separate creeks tested adjacent to plastic culture tomato farms. Copper is an algicide used commercially in aquaculture. Copper compounds are still used to kill algae in swimming pools as well. It is not unreasonable to suggest that localized copper fluxes could easily kill blue green algae and cryptomonads, nutrient and chloroplast rich food sources for the amoeba phase of bacteria. This selective pressure should shift the equilibrium of pfiesteria's life phases to the zoospore stage.

The selective killing of amoeba prey would be most pronounced in areas of slack water, back water or a boundary area of reduced current, especially after a rain event. The sporadic Pocomoke kills heralding the larger August kills were true to this model of copper run off. Nitrates and phosphates have such a rapid uptake into algae species that localized blooms, manifested by elevated chlorophyll levels, would prevent excessive levels of these nutrients, even in low current conditions.

Copper and other heavy metals are retained within tidal marshes and soil sediments. A rain, especially with flooding, could give an additional pulse of heavy metals just like it could increase run off from fields. The heavy rains of 1996 along the Pocomoke River likely increased copper leachate. Surprisingly, despite the heavy rains, levels of nitrate and phosphate didn't increase in the Pocomoke River. The reduced salinity and lowered pH in the Pocomoke, noted from October 96 through July 97, would have reduced reproduction rates of plankton species not as tolerant as pfiesteria to changing salt and acid conditions.

An additional complicating factor in the analysis of copper levels in the water column is the avid binding of copper by dithiocarbamates in aqueous conditions. This binding dramatically increases lipid solubility and uptake of copper into cells of higher organisms, such as rotifers, known predators of pfiesteria in its zoospore stage. Intracellular copper levels kill higher organisms by disrupting superoxide dismutase, the enzyme that protects organisms from oxidative damage. Without predators, zoospore populations can grow exponentially (bloom), once the sexual reproductive phase of zoospore growth begins.

There are species differences in resistance to copper poisoning. Some gram negative bacteria and yeasts can excrete intracellular copper to survive high levels. Diatoms are quite resistant to copper with cyanobacteria (eaten by pfiesteria) being quiet sensitive. Dinoflagellates are heterogeneous in sensitivity, with some species, (Thoracosphaera) inhibited by 10^{-12} levels, (parts per trillion) of copper and others, including Gymnodinium, surviving 10^{-5} levels (pp hundred thousand). The sensitivity of pfiesteria is not known. Many one celled algae are killed by 10^{-11} copper levels (pp hundred billion). Higher algae forms are resistant to copper at the parts per hundred thousand level. The differential killing of pfiesteria prey would be magnified by low flow current conditions.

Preliminary experiments are underway in my lab to establish killing levels of copper diathiocarbamate complexes for rotifers. I have not found those data in my literature searches. Feeding and swimming of rotifers are slowed by copper alone at 1 ppm. Dithiocarbamates alone do not harm rotifers. The combination of copper and dithiocarbamates kills rotifers in less than 12 hours.

Copper, even in low levels is toxic to many biologic species. Removal of copper from chicken feed, with substitution of a different fungicide is economically feasible according to Dr. Benjamin Lusio, who runs the Poultry Research Division of Cornell Veterinary School. Substitution of chlorothalonils for dithiocarbamates is standard agricultural practice in Virginia. Despite the reported presence of pfiesteria and the similarity of creeks on the Virginia Eastern Shore to the Pocomoke, there are no fish kills adjacent to the tomato farms there where chlorothalonils are used. At low levels of nitrate and phosphate, without excessive copper and dithiocarbamates, there would be biologic controls preventing blooms of pfiesteria. This Blue Ribbon Commission needs to look for simple, reasonable measures to reduce the magnitude of next year's fish kill and next year's sick people.

As an addendum, planting narrow buffers of shallow rooted cover crops would not block subsurface flow of nutrients or heavy metals. High soil levels of phosphates do not correlate with high runoff amounts, as phosphate is tightly bound in soils and sediments. Use of copper sulfate as a preservative in wheat or rye seed would compound our existing problem, as would use of dithiocarbamates to prevent wheat disease such as rust. Wetland buffers must have a mixture of heights to block wind, root depths to block subsurface flow and grasses to prevent surface runoff. Even a ten foot wetland buffer planted along major ditches or creek banks would help reduce nitrate, phosphate and copper run off.

No-till farming practice reduces erosion of soils and reduces cost but exposes surface applied manures and fungicides to wind and water. Tilling improves retention of nutrients at root level, at a higher cost and a greater likelihood of erosion. Instead of tilling wetland edges for shallow rooted cover crops next year, I suggest that the state fund a similar $3 million for Eastern Shore watersheds to plant wetland buffers without manure, copper or fungicides for the next five years.

The principles of correction of the pfiesteria problem in the Chesapeake Bay are applicable elsewhere. Just as Maryland has taken the national lead in health care regarding pfiesteria, so too can Maryland lead the nation in proper diagnosis and treatment of the ecological disease of pfiesteria.

As basic examples, hog manure has over 600 ppm of copper from feed fungicide. Tobacco farms have used copper and dithiocarbamates in agricultural quantities. Florida melon, pepper, tomato and citrus growers use similar agricultural practices. The coastal plains soils of North Carolina, Maryland and Florida are similar. The pfiesteria blooms in North Carolina, Florida and Maryland parallel soil types and agricultural chemical usages.

Let us eliminate excessive copper from our estuarine ecosystems. Since pfiesteria lives with us, I suggest we feed it cryptomonads and not menhaden, watermen or DNR employees.

See Appendices 4 and 5 for additional copper theory data.

chapter 36

Editorial

September 30
Printed in the
Daily Times of Salisbury

Idea Warrants Fair Hearing

In Summation Dr. Ritchie Shoemaker of Pocomoke City believes copper is linked to the fish kill problems. His theory should be honestly and objectively evaluated.

Dr. Ritchie Shoemaker is mounting a lonely crusade in the Shore's pfiesteria crisis. Having had his theories on the cause and effects of pfiesteria met with reaction ranging from polite skepticism to outright ridicule, he can be forgiven for feeling a little like Columbus taking on the Flat Earth Society.

We employ the analogy because Shoemaker, like the fellow who insisted the world was round, has been proven right once, and could be again. And he's proud enough of his previous accomplishment and certain enough of his ideas that he won't be easily deterred.

Here's a man whose ideas warrant a fair hearing.

Shoemaker, a physician in Pocomoke City, believes it is copper, not nutrients, causing the mysterious microorganism to attack fish and make people sick in the Pocomoke River. He thinks the copper content of fungicides used on farms along the Pocomoke plays a dual role in advancing pfiesteria's deadly attack.

First, he theorizes, the copper kills food that pfiesteria feeds on in its non-toxic state, forcing its transformation into a deadly predator. Second, he believes the copper destroys the phytoplankton that eats pfiesteria once it evolves into its toxic state.

So far Shoemaker's copper theory has been widely doubted by state officials, members of the scientific community and a host of others who have their own ideas about what triggers pfiesteria's toxicity. Tests dispute Shoemaker's findings of unhealthy copper levels in the river and research suggests nutrients are the prime suspect.

But two things give Shoemaker credibility.

The first is it was Shoemaker who determined something in the Pocomoke River was making people sick, even before the presence of pfiesteria was confirmed. His successful campaign to prove pfiesteria was hazardous to humans forced the state to assign the crisis a greater sense of urgency.

The second thing that gives Shoemaker credibility is, with so much still unknown about pfiesteria, his educated guess is as good as anybody's. Until someone conclusively determines what's behind the pfiesteria outbreak, there are no wrong answers, only suggested areas of study.

Some researchers have joined Shoemaker in studying his copper theory and lent his ideas credence. Vindication may, once again, await.

Meanwhile, there are plenty of people—some of whom once dismissed Shoemaker as a crackpot—with good reason to hope he's onto something.

His theory would take some of the heat off the poultry farmers who are being blamed for allowing excessive nutrient runoff to despoil the river. It may offer a comparatively easy and painless solution—just remove the copper from some fungicides, Shoemaker says—to a disaster some see as rife with economic, environmental, political and regulatory ramifications.

And it would lessen the sense of despair among those who are convinced it could be years before the river's delicate ecological balance is restored, if ever.

Given that, some may embrace Shoemaker's latest theory only as a matter of wishful thinking. But he has demonstrated once he knows whereof he speaks; it is for that reason everyone with a stake in the pfiesteria crisis has an obligation to listen to what Ritchie Shoemaker has to say.

chapter 37

Publish ... or Perish!

October 1

One of the most perplexing aspects of the pfiesteria invasion was its unpredictability. As the news media had pointed out again and again, people were often getting sick from the bug in areas where no fish kills had occurred. The commercial diver, for example, had been felled after working in the Wicomico Creek, where the fish seemed perfectly normal. And then there was the strange case of the boy who'd been stricken after exposure to the waters of the Nanticoke River, where the fish also appeared to be thriving.

Those two medical mysteries—and several others like them—raised a provocative question: What criteria should be established for determining the safety of a waterway?

While I was chewing on this puzzle, I got a phone call from a fisherman named Norman Tarr. (He said he had no objection to having his name mentioned in interviews.) Tarr explained that he'd been catching menhaden in Chincoteague Bay, located on the ocean side of the Eastern Shore. He also noted that he'd never worked in Virginia waters, but only in Maryland's.

Tarr's story was disturbing. He claimed to have seen a number of fish with bizarre lesions caused by a worm called "lernecia." This inch-long parasite bores a hole in fish (including menhaden), eventually killing its hosts. But Tarr had also spotted some other lesioned menhaden, which appeared to display the classic symptoms of pfiesteria. Some displayed anal vent burns, while others exhibited ugly sores where flesh had been eaten away.

Although fish-lesions can be caused by many different agents, the ones described by Norman Tarr sounded identical to those I'd earlier noticed during the low-level fish kill in the Pocomoke River. The state health authorities were soon alerted by District Conservationist Bruce Nichols, and the DNR officials moved quickly to examine these new lesions. They soon pinpointed the lernecia, however, which brought an immediate halt to the investigation.

Meanwhile, I was doing my best to help Norman Tarr, who appeared to be a very sick man. But the ailing fisherman didn't have a lernecia syndrome. In fact, he was struggling with all the symptoms of pfiesteria-triggered human illness. His headache was unbearable, and his abdominal pain, cramps and diarrhea seemed identical to symptoms I'd observed in other pfiesteria patients. Norman's memory was also deeply affected.

On my recommendation, Norman adopted the protocols for pfiesteria treatment immediately. Were his symptoms self-limited? Maybe. But neither of us was willing to wait two months to find out.

Two weeks after beginning the treatment, Norman had recovered. But his case would never be investigated by the State of Maryland's medical team. Was the state's reluctance to examine his illness linked to the fact that the bug had attacked him only a few miles from the huge Ocean City summer resort?

I could understand the economic and political motivation for trying to keep Ocean City out of the headlines. But ignoring history—and also biology—just didn't make sense to me. I felt frustrated, because I knew that if the state didn't investigate Norman's illness, I'd have no way to prove that he'd gotten better with my

MCS protocol. Still, it was a great joy to see my pal recover his good health and his high spirits.

Norman's case was pivotal, in my view, because it showed that the bug could strike in the Eastern Shore's inland bays. And if that happens again during the summer months, his case will serve as a compelling example of how human beings can be harmed by swimming in such areas as the Chincoteague Bay, which is located almost in the shadow of the big Ocean City tourist hotels.

After describing Tarr's painful illness in detail, I outlined my treatment protocol for Todd Shields of the Washington Post. He was especially interested in the fact that no other clinician had tried anything to treat PHIS. My results seemed quite positive, and I was half-willing to believe that I'd accomplished a scientific breakthrough. There was no way I would back off on treating PHIS.

I talked to Shields on October 3, and figured that his story would soon appear. When it didn't, I began to wonder what was going on. After all, Salisbury Times reporter Doug Hanks had done a solid, convincing story about treatment. What would explain the Post's silence? This was a great American newspaper with a terrific reputation for integrity! Wasn't this the paper that had broken Watergate? Puzzled, I asked myself if there might be something wrong with my data.

A few more days passed ... and then I started getting calls from other scientists whom Shields had interviewed. Suddenly, the picture seemed clearer: The Post reporter was simply doing his homework, and I needed to remain patient.

Next I got an interesting call came from Dr. Frank Johnson at National Institute of Environmental Health Sciences (NIEHS), located in Research Triangle Park near Durham, North Carolina. Dr. Johnson was in charge of the huge federal research grant that had been earmarked for studying the pfiesteria outbreak.

I should set the record straight by pointing out that I'd worked at NIEHS as a college undergraduate involved in the "Stay in School Program." I'd had a marvelous time doing molecular biology research on DDT under the supervision of Dr. Jud Spaulding—and I quickly mentioned this fact to Dr. Johnson.

Much to my surprise, they turned out to be best buddies. (Their relationship was a great example of the "small world syndrome" that dominates academic science circles.)

At any rate, I sent copies of my work to Dr. Johnson for his use in the Environmental Toxicology Program at the Research Triangle—and I hope that researchers there are binding dinoflagellate toxin with cholestyramine, even as you read these lines.

Progress! Within a few days, I learned that Dr. Donald Schmechel had also received a copy of the materials I'd sent to Todd Shields. Dr. Schmechel thought the info had come from me, but it was clear that reporter Shields was still doing his background work.

Next I sent copies of my work to Dr. Sherwood Hall at the FDA. Much to my surprise, Dr. Hall had already dispatched one of his staff members, Paul Eilers, to Shelltown. There he met Jack Howard, one of my PHIS patients. Moving fast, I sent more copies of the material I'd gathered to Doctors Poli, Delaney and Schmechel.

Then I called Marty Wasserman at his office, and found him closeted with one of his top aides, Georges Benjamin. I asked Marty what he thought about my treatment successes. His suggestion was, "Why don't you move to North Carolina?" I puzzled over this enigmatic remark for some time. Was he implying that since Virginia had a resident "gadfly" hard at work behind the scenes, and producing some good results, North Carolina might very well benefit from the services of Ritch "The Mouth" Shoemaker?

Or was this Sphinx-like question Marty's way of suggesting that since Maryland had little interest in my treatment protocol, perhaps it was time to carry my crusade to another state?

A mystery! Responding, I called Dr. Schmechel and spoke to him in some detail about treatment. He quickly pointed out that without neurocognitive testing before and after treatment, it would be difficult to show complete improvement in a patient. And yet Dr. Schmechel considered the treatment promising enough to suggest we write it up for the authoritative New England Journal of Medicine.

It was an interesting suggestion ... but the medical professionals I most wanted to reach were in Maryland. And the Maryland Medical Journal had offered me the chance to present my cases through Med Chi. How could I send these treatment cases to another medical journal—especially if the article were to include a co-author who hadn't participated in the treatment?

While I mulled those questions, I sent the treatment protocol paper to Vivian Smith and Dr. Marion Friedman. Even if the specialists from the Blue Ribbon team of physicians didn't want to sign on as co-authors with me (and even if I missed my remote chance at appearing in the New England Journal), I wanted to make sure that I had a chance to present the text in formal proceedings.

Dr. Friedman, editor of the Maryland Medical Journal, still sounded enthusiastic about the project. He asked me to send it to him for review by the MMJ editorial staff.

My spirits sank a few days later, however, when the editorial staff of MMJ made it clear that they didn't like my paper. It had been too hurriedly prepared, they said, and some cases had been added at the last minute. The criticism hurt even more when I discovered that the rough draft—not the final version—of the paper had been circulated for review. The article was returned for correction.

The reviewers had been especially critical of the use of Milk of Magnesia as a stimulant for gallbladder contraction. They noted the absence of modern data to support my gall bladder treatment. My paper, however, had not focused on the usefulness of Milk of Magnesia to treat sluggishly contracting gallbladders. It was actually about using cholestyramine to bind a toxin ... in a process that would alter the rate of recovery from pfiesteria from "no improvement" after four weeks or more to "rapid improvement" with medication.

What to do? I fretted for a few days, then removed the stuff about MOM-stimulated gallbladder contraction, and submitted the paper again.

Of course I was the first to admit that my paper wasn't "hard science" in the traditional sense. My study wasn't controlled, for one thing. No pfiesteria patients had been given placebos. The study wasn't double-blinded, either. These criticisms were certainly fair, but I thought they missed the main point—which was that cholestyramine might very well help a physician treat a patient who couldn't remember where he'd parked his car.

My favorite criticism was the one that upbraided me for failing to present the structure of the toxin. True enough: I certainly hadn't accomplished that. *That* immense undertaking will have to await the far-off day when the various dinoflagellate toxins involved in fish kills and human illness can be accurately identified. But the point I wanted to make was a simpler one: We needed treatment protocols to help the victims of this illness! Sure, using cholestyramine was scientifically premature. Without analyzing the toxin in a test tube, I couldn't possibly be 100-percent certain that my treatment worked.

But the record showed clearly—indisputably—that it worked well enough for those who followed it. And if re-exposure occurred, as in the case of Jack Howard, the treatment would still be there waiting for victims. Let's face it: The bug lives here now. And I was ready to treat the human illness that it caused.

As I reviewed the struggle over this new treatment, I couldn't help comparing it to the way in which penicillin treatment of pneumonia had evolved. While the scientific debate about penicillin continued, one fact became strikingly clear: The first few patients with pneumococcal pneumonia who had been treated with penicillin were still alive—despite the fact that the "basic science" that described penicillin binding proteins, sero typing of pneumococcal strains and inhibition of cell wall synthesis remained incomplete.

As time passes, the validity of that analogy will be determined.

After I resubmitted my treatment paper with corrections for the third time, the MMJ editorial board reached a "split-vote decision" to publish it, which pleased me a great deal. At last the medical professionals would hear the news about this new treatment!

Challenging the "conventional wisdom" about public health problems is always an uphill struggle. For that reason, I'm a great fan of Dr. Lynn Grattan, who remains one of the heroes of Maryland's battle to convince other states to recognize the neurocognitive deficits caused by pfiesteria.

Without backing off, Dr. Grattan kept insisting that her sophisticated tests were a valid tool for "fingerprinting" pfiesteria. And when Virginia finally got around to doing the proper neurocognitive testing—which confirmed that two of my patients were "real" pfiesteria cases—Dr. Grattan was vindicated along with me.

As the U.S. Centers for Disease Control experts begin their federal-level investigation, which is just now starting to unfold (long after Maryland Senator Barbara Mikulski called for their involvement, by the way), Dr. Grattan's pioneering work will serve as a necessary guideline.

Dr. Grattan had shown that many of her test subjects could improve their neurocognitive scores over a three-month time period. But does it really take three months to recover from the pfiesteria syndrome? My patients know it doesn't!

The treatment paper turned out to be quite controversial, with some of the experts asking: "Why publish treatment for a self-limited illness?" I also heard rumors that my work was being attacked as "not being original."

Apparently, members of some standing in the academic-medical community hadn't agreed that the paper should be published. And those reservations caused a delay in publication. Dr. Friedman decided to wait for a broader base of support for my work. It was one thing to publish a diagnosis article, he said, but quite another to maintain that I could treat a persistent illness from pfiesteria, an ailment that lasted more than four weeks and recurred with re-exposure to affected water. (The State had insisted that there was no "persistent" illness.)

Dr. Friedman soon found the support he needed, however, and the paper was scheduled for publication in the February 1998 MMJ. Describing the squabble over publication, Dr. Friedman pointed out that doctors had been arguing with each other "since time began." He also predicted that my article would continue the pfiesteria debate among physicians.

It seemed clear to me that Dr. Friedman had taken a medical stance that transcended politics. Since I felt certain that my treatment protocol was sound, I remained convinced that publication would offer primary care physicians a basis for helping patients sickened by pfiesteria, during the years immediately up ahead … even as the researchers continue their attempts to isolate the toxin.

(Please see Appendix 6 for more treatment data.)

chapter 38

Dr. Shoemaker Goes To Washington

October 29

After several grueling rewrites, the final draft of my pfiesteria article had been delivered to the editors of the Maryland Medical Journal. Good riddance! What I needed now was a bit of R&R. I needed to sit in a canoe for a while and watch the autumn leaves scutter across the rippling surface of the Pocomoke.

No such luck. No sooner had I wrapped up the journal article than the phone rang again. This time it was the Family Practice News (FPN) on the horn. Would you believe that they wanted to "do a story" on pfiesteria?

The International Medical News actually publishes six different medical news magazines, and the plan was to write a feature on the human illness aspects of pfiesteria that could run in all six periodicals. Scheduled for publication on November 19, the feature would include photos of lesioned legs, along with a detailed description of treatment methods. The editors said they planned to run a front-page photo of me—along with an accompanying backgrounder that would describe how I had pushed the State of Maryland to adopt a realistic strategy for combatting the plague.

After agreeing to the interview, I found myself hoping that the FP News would also try to obtain some quotes from my good friend Marty Wasserman. I hadn't heard much from him recently, although I'd done my best to keep our dialogue going ... mainly by asking all of the Virginia and Delaware health officials who crossed my path to "be sure to say hi to Dr. Wasserman for me!"

While the FP News project went forward, I was warming up for yet another public forum on the subject of pfiesteria. This time the sponsor would be the Anacostia Watershed Society, and the meeting would take place during the first week of November. I would represent the medical community on the panel, while Dr. Tom Simpson spoke for the State of Maryland. The EPA Bay Program was sending along Bill Matuszeski, and we would also be hearing from Rick Dove, the environmental activist who'd called the world's attention to pfiesteria in North Carolina's Neuse River. (Talk about rounding up the usual suspects!)

The panel members were heavyweights, no doubt about it. For one thing, Maryland Agriculture Secretary Riley was about to resign his agricultural post—which meant that if Governor Glendening won reelection, Dr. Simpson would be the logical choice to replace him. For his part, Mr. Matuszeski was in charge of $30 million in grants that were developed after the pfiesteria problems began.

Rick Dove was a remarkable conservationist who had enjoyed a great deal of success as the "Keeper" of North Carolina's Neuse River. The concept of appointing one individual to "guard over" the health of a watercourse had actually begun on the Hudson River in New York, after that stream was increasingly threatened by the huge populations that surround it.

The "Keeper" concept soon caught in America, and today there are 22 rivers enjoying the careful attention of their protectors. (Most of these troubled streams can be found on the East Coast.)

Rick had spent more than six years warning people about the pfiesteria threat near Pamlico Sound. Ironically enough, however, he now found himself being drowned out by the media attention that had been focused on Maryland, with the arrival of the plague along the Eastern Shore. Now it was the Old Line State that was receiving the attention, the credit and the megabucks (via grants, anti-pollution programs and research initiatives).

But Rick Dove had been there first—and I was eager to meet him. I wanted to thank him for his great contribution, and to shake his hand. There was no way I was going to miss this symposium ... although I did find myself wondering why they had to schedule it on the same day that had been set aside for the 20th-year reunion of my medical school graduating class!

First things first, however. As the day of the conference approached, I was informed that The American Society for Microbiology—led by Robert Hall, Ph.D.—also wanted me to make a presentation. That symposium would take place one day before the Anacostia Watershed Society's get-together. So now it looked as if I would be appearing before both groups. (Maybe I'll make the 25th reunion of the Duke Medical Alumni!)

Before I could begin assembling my data for these two appearances, however, I got a call from a hospital-based, infectious disease expert who wanted me to address the medical staff in a Virginia suburb of Washington. Suddenly, pfiesteria had gone from being a media curiosity to being a key subject for medical education. Soon the director of a primary care residency in Newport News, Virginia, was also requesting some of my time: He wanted me to make a "grand rounds" visit to his unit.

The director's spin on the pfiesteria issue was an interesting one; he was convinced that I was a primary care physician who had seized the opportunity to make a giant leap forward in the progress of medicine, rather than merely plodding along. He wanted his young physicians to see that they could make medicine progress as well. He pointed out that since our knowledge continually changes, and since physicians practice medicine day in and day out, the physicians are required to adapt to change by learning new things on a daily basis.

I admired the director's enthusiasm, but I felt reluctant to make a presentation on pfiesteria in a state that had not yet acknowledged the presence of a bug-related human illness syndrome.

Soon it was time to depart for Washington. As always, JoAnn was full of good advice: "You're going to Washington, and you'll be meeting with important people, so you should look the part. You need a suit, black shoes—and a haircut."

I didn't own a suit, however, and I certainly kept no shiny black shoes in my closet. Why should I dress up in a monkey-suit in order to make a presentation about a disease threat in the Chesapeake Bay region? Did I really have to dress up in formal attire, in order to deliver an effective talk?

Yes, I did. Deep down, I knew that I still felt uneasy about the notorious "sports shirt photo" that had been snapped during my appearance in Annapolis ... a picture, you may recall, in which the governor and the other dignitaries were clad in elegant-looking suits, while I wore a gaudy sports shirt! (See back cover.)

All right, all right. If I had to wear the "proper" clothes in order to get a "proper" interview, then that's what I'd do.

Along with making my presentation in Washington, I was also hoping to carry my message to Maryland's U.S. Senator Paul Sarbanes. The Med Chi's Gene Ransom and Sarbanes aide Lee Whaley had put their heads together on this, and they had arranged the appointment. I was hoping against hope that the senator would help me reach beyond these state-level scientists who were downgrading my copper idea to national figures who might be willing to help.

I knew that I'd earned some credibility on the human health issues, and I was planning to use it as a lever in the struggle to convince someone with national power to recognize that nutrients weren't really the problem—and that focusing on nutrients only was both shortsighted and misguided. At any rate, Senator Sarbanes had agreed to see me on Friday, November 7, at 11:45 a.m.

I had also been attempting—but without much luck—to set up an interview with Vice President Gore. I had hoped he might want to take a look at my data ... but the refusal letter I received let me know that he didn't. (Bonnie Rose suggested that I save my turn-down letter from the Vice President's office: "It's better to have asked and been turned down, than not to have asked at all.")

The vice president's response to my query was disappointing, but I didn't waste time fretting over it. The chance to address the American Society of Microbiology, Washington DC branch, was a chance to present my ideas of causation of pfiesteria blooms to a top drawer level of talented scientists that had a national reputation. It turns out that Dr. Jeff Beers, acanthamoeba researcher, had read the Post article and had recommended me to Dr. Hall.

I was thrilled to say yes to this proposal, because I had enormous admiration for both Robert Hall and his fellow-researcher, Sherwood Hall (no relation). The two Halls worked next door to Dr. Beers. Talk about a scientific trio!

I was intrigued by Dr. Robert Hall's suggestion that I organize my presentation in several different areas. Why not explore scientific questions about pfiesteria, and medical questions about diagnosis and treatment of the related human illness syndrome? Why not also address the political complexities of the issue, along with the philosophical implications of my rather unique situation as the first healer to report a brand-new disease?

Good plan! As Dr. Hall explained it, the researchers who attended these Microbiology seminars were interested in the arcane and the abstruse. They wanted to hear the inside dope on what it was like to cross the unexplored frontier of new medical knowledge.

It was an exciting prospect, and I was eager to oblige with another slide-show extravaganza that I hoped would answer their questions.

As you might expect, I was feeling pretty euphoric about having been the first to diagnose and treat this new disease. Here was a chance to make a contribution—the kind of contribution I'd dreamed about so often in medical school. I burned with enthusiasm and energy on this topic, and so it shouldn't have been very surprising when some of the news media labeled my excitement as "pure ego." I saw it differently, of course. I didn't expect non-scientists to understand. For me, the diagnosis had provided one of those exceedingly rare moments in scientific research when the daily drudgery of the endlessly repeated practice of medicine and experiments is interrupted by the exultation of a sudden discovery; "Eureka!"

Hitting a home run to win the game, spotting a nearly extinct red-cockaded woodpecker in the Pocomoke forest, watching a child begin to breathe again after a penny had closed up an airway: For me, these moments capture the "natural high" of living and practicing medicine. The newness added meaning to my career as a physician. And so it was with the pfiesteria "discovery": Suddenly, I was moving across unknown terrain and dark waters, struggling to untangle a scientific enigma.

I knew there would be some highly regarded scientists listening to my talk about pfiesteria. For starters, Dr. Beers was a researcher with an awesome reputation. Yet he was also a bit of a "sandbagger" … a perfectly unassuming, low-key fellow who just happened to rank as the world's leading expert in cyclospora, cryptosporidium and acanthamoeba. It was an extraordinary experience, to share a meal with him, while listening to his thoughts on the "troubling" photos he'd studied of the amoeba phase of pfiesteria.

"Free, living amoebas—some toxic, some not—look no different than the photos of pfiesteria amoeboid forms that I've seen," noted the expert. "A lot of those [pfiesteria] forms look familiar to me."

"Jeff, tell me," I asked, "is there an 'over-diagnosis' going on here?" Were we in fact over-emphasizing the life forms of pfiesteria, and thus confusing it with something else? It was an interesting problem in biology, no question about it.

I also learned more about the famed researcher Sherwood Hall at the meeting. It seems that he'd found a way to clear pfiesteria amoeboid stages and cysts out of sediment, by using oysters. But the toxic phase of pfiesteria *ate* oysters, leaving behind only an empty, open shell. If we could keep pfiesteria from going toxic, oysters would surely help control pfiesteria populations!

The scientists were receptive to my talk. Even better, I managed to slow the presentation down a bit—instead of zooming from A to Z, as had happened all too frequently in the past. I also felt a little better about my wardrobe ... since I'd worn the nice new suit, tie and new shoes that JoAnn had recommended. (Of course, I'd managed to leave the shiny black shoes behind in Pocomoke—and was forced to pick up a new pair on the way to the conference.)

Soon after the talk, I got a call from Mike Fincham at Maryland Public Television. He was assembling a story on pfiesteria, but his approach was different. Affiliated with Maryland Sea Grant at College Park, Fincham was hammering together a long documentary. He'd already interviewed Dr. Burkholder and would sit down with Rick Dove after questioning me.

Since my hotel in College Park was located near his studio, Fincham said he'd pick me up. He even offered to drive me to Senator Sarbanes' office for my appointment, scheduled for later that day. And I was glad for the ride—since I lacked both umbrella and raincoat, and would have been drenched on this rainy November day, while searching for the Hart Senate Building on Capitol Hill.

Mike turned out to be affable, easy to like. I was feeling a bit tense as we got started, and worried aloud: "Look, I have to meet Senator Sarbanes at 11:30. Do you need much of my time?" I wasn't used to such a lengthy, documentary-style interview. Mike was thorough, and he'd already assembled more background information than most reporters would have considered essential for this kind of story.

I did my best to answer everything. But I badly needed a break —a chance to call Dr. Rufus Chaney again at the USDA in Beltsville. He's the world's top expert on the environmental chemistry of copper in aqueous solutions. I'd left messages for him, and he had called back once.

Again and again, I'd been told that Dr. Chaney had key information that would support the copper dithiocarbamate theory. I wanted to talk with him before I met with Senator Sarbanes. No such luck, today. Later Dr. Chaney was indeed a fabulous source of information about copper in water that I needed and that the state scientists didn't have.

Michael casually suggested that he would bring his camera along as we went to Senator Sarbanes' office. Right, I thought, bring a camera along—go ahead and destroy any credibility I might have had with the Senator!

But Michael waved my anxiety away. "I'll be nice. I'll ask, and if they say no [to the camera], that's fine. I'll still wait for you and give you a ride back. Actually, I've still got a few more questions, anyway!"

The Hart Senate Office Building is a beautiful marble facility capped by a soaring atrium. I couldn't believe what was happening. There I was, dressed up in a monkey-suit, with a cameraman on my shoulder. And here was Senator Sarbanes, shaking my hand and smiling: "Ritchie, it's nice to see you again. I want to walk that trail that you built."

But the senator's staff looked pained, when Michael asked if he could film Senator Sarbanes shaking my hand. They finally agreed, but Michael was forced to hurry. I apologized to Charlie Stek, the Senator's aide. He simply shrugged: "Water under the bridge."

With the photo op out of the way, the Senator wanted to know what I had to say. His two top aides were in attendance. He also wanted to know what I'd done to resolve the copper issue with Dr. Boesch. "I've spoken with him, sent him information and testified before the commission," I told the senator. "The opinion of the Cambridge Consensus is that my idea is improbable."

"Are any other scientists supporting your position?" was the next question.

I told him that many did, but added: "The problem is that the Cambridge Consensus didn't acknowledge what dithiocarbamates do to organic liganding of copper in a runoff situation in a water column." Then I reviewed the scientific data and emphasized the lack of data supporting the nutrient theory.

"Even if copper and dithiocarbamates aren't the whole answer, most assuredly, focusing on agricultural runoff is a short-sighted prescription for failure to understand how pfiesteria acts in a food chain." I told Senator Sarbanes that if we ignored methods of reproduction of phytoplankton and their prey and predators—while also failing to examine how human contributions to an estuarine habitat change its ecology—we would be forced to accept a pfiesteria theory that failed to meet the test of the scientific evidence.

Next the Senator asked if I were opposed to no-till agricultural methods.

I told him that I felt no-till could work—provided there were adequate wetlands buffers in place to retain nutrients, heavy metals, agricultural chemicals and fertilizers. Such buffers would prevent runoff into ditches, guts, creeks, rivers, swamps, lowlands and the Bay. "The Governor's buffer plan," I said, "doesn't provide for anything more than grass-type crops, which can only block surface flow."

"My proposal is for establishing vegetated wetland buffers," Senator Sarbanes said. "Send me your data on your buffer ideas, along with documentation that a national level of scientists support your idea. I have to go now." Before he left, Senator Sarbanes looked intently at me, shook my hand, and said, "Show me you are possibly right. I will do everything I can to help you."

He asked me to send him my information, and to list some things he could do to help. "My $750,000 grant program is perfectly suited to grass-roots organizations of dedicated citizens like yourself. If you find high-level scientific backing for your theories let me know."

These days, I keep a picture postcard from Senator Sarbanes mounted on my office wall, along with hundreds of postcards my patients have sent me over the years. I put the picture of the Senator and his wife in the top row. I also have a program from the Pocomoke Chamber of Commerce dinner at which I was named Citizen of the Year in 1993. (Senator Sarbanes had been the speaker that night.)

I wanted Sally to come with JoAnn and me to hear the Senator give a talk. But little Sally was sick. She obviously couldn't travel, and JoAnn stayed home to take care of her. But Sally penned a note in her fourth-grade handwriting, telling the senator that she was sorry she couldn't come. Still, Senator Sarbanes was welcome to come and meet her and her horse anytime!

The Senator wrote a nice note back to Sally, and it's now on my office wall with all the others.

Later that day, I filled in the rest of the documentary footage for Michael Fincham. We drove back and forth across Capitol Hill in the rain, while he alternately interviewed me and took background shots. I tried my best Jimmy Stewart imitation on him, but it wasn't very good. (Dr. Shoemaker—and not Mr. Smith—had gone to Washington!)

Still, I was quite pleased that I'd been able to make my point in the nation's capital. There is a human health problem from pfiesteria—and there is also a cure. There's a real—and not a confabulated—explanation for blooms of pfiesteria. There's also a way to stop active toxin production.

But could I convince the State of Maryland that all of these things were true?

chapter 39

Showdown at the
Anacostia Watershed Society

November 7

After several weeks of careful preparation, I was now geared up for what promised to be an extremely interesting and controversial public meeting on the subject of pfiesteria in Maryland. As you might imagine, I was eager to try and prove my case in front of the attendees at the Anacostia Watershed Society forum—by hitting them head-on with the reams of hard scientific data that I'd been gathering for months on end.

I knew it wouldn't be easy, however. Wherever I looked, these days, public officials seemed determined to mislead the public about the true scope of the human health threat presented by pfiesteria. That threat was still being put behind economics and politics in North Carolina and Virginia, for example, where public officials were stonewalling furiously. Maryland seemed to be doing a little better, and was actually setting national example for its willingness to conduct open discussions of the illness factor.

But the Old Line State was still blaming nutrients for causing blooms of pfiesteria. Obviously, the state was doing its best to protect the millions of dollars tied up in seafood commerce, along with lots of political careers. Understandable, maybe—until you realized that the health of thousands of human beings was still at risk.

Anyway, I did my best. But with only fifteen minutes to tell my story, I wouldn't be able to present all of my environmental information. Instead, I concentrated on telling the crucially important story of the diagnosis of PHIS. Yes, it was true; I'd been in the right place at the right time. And I yearned to tell this audience about some of my Eastern Shore patients, and how they'd been helped by my pfiesteria treatment protocols.

Tommy East was working hard again, for example, and feeling strong; he seemed to have shed both his cough and his persistent diarrhea. Jack Howard was also doing better (provided that he took his "MCS" before wading into Pocomoke pfiesteria blooms). Lori Maddox was also improving, and almost back to normal. Make no mistake: The true value of the pfiesteria work was the return to normal health of the watermen.

Greatly heartened by these success stories, I was pleased to be joining Dr. Simpson, Bill Matuszeski, Rick Dove and Robert Boone (the President of Anacostia Watershed Society) in an overheated, non-functioning lecture room on the campus at College Park. About 75 people showed up for the proceedings—not bad for a night of torrential rain.

On the way from a nearby restaurant to the auditorium, I decided to ask Tom Simpson some more questions. (He had heard my presentation at the Gilchrest meeting.) Tom explained that he wasn't in possession of my DNR data yet; all he had was a copy of the Blue Ribbon Commission report, which had been released two days earlier. As we talked cordially, it seemed to me that we'd read two entirely different sets of water-quality test results. What I knew to be normal was abnormal to Tom. And indeed, the Blue Ribbon numbers—as relayed to me by Simpson—suggested that percentages of nutrients were soaring off the charts in the Pocomoke.

"Like a 60-percent rise in phosphates?" I asked.

"Exactly," he replied.

I just shook my head. It was hard to believe that my "renegade" copper theory was being derided, although supported by solid evidence ... while the so-called "nutrient theory" was being propped up by manipulated statistics!

All at once I was remembering my course in statistics in college. What was it the professor had said? Oh, yeah: If you don't have the numbers required to prove a theory, simply crunch them a bit and come up with a "trend" by using a percentage. No doubt about it: The most effective way to lie with statistics is to use percentages.

That "60 percent rise in phosphates," by the way, was the 0.10–0.16 outrage that Rick Nelson had complained about. (Remember: 0.16 was still "normal"—even if did represent a rise of 60-percent.)

The presentation went well, however. Both Bill and Tom noted that of all the environmental problems facing the Chesapeake Bay (rainfall, acidity, temperature, presence of fish, population, location and nutrients), the only one that could be controlled by government intervention was the nutrients. (Was there a connection here?) Tom talked at length about phosphate-based nutrient-management practices, and Bill focused on the dynamics of the huge watershed that is the Chesapeake Bay.

Their presentations were certainly interesting, but I remained unconvinced. If water-borne phosphates and nitrates were the problem, I wanted to see the unmanipulated data to prove it. For several months now, I'd been making that same point. But as the Watershed Society meeting drew to a close, it seemed quite clear that those crucial numbers would never be found.

chapter 40

Let the Copper
Tests Begin!

November 10

It was mid-November now; Thanksgiving would soon be upon us. As I prepared to celebrate the holiday with my family in Pocomoke, I could look back on several months of solid achievement. At the very least, I had accomplished my primary goals: to make clear to both the government and the citizens of Maryland that pfiesteria caused human illness—and that my treatment methods could be counted on to blunt its harmful health effects.

So much for the positive side of the story. On the negative side, I still felt frustrated by my inability to convince the State of Maryland's medical and scientific brass about the accuracy of my "copper theory." And that hurt. More than ever, I remained convinced that the State's unwillingness to discuss using permanganate as a major weapon against the bug was a short-sighted, even reckless public health policy.

But maybe it wasn't too late, after all. In a last-ditch bid for support, I rang up Dr. Fritz Riedel at the Academy of Natural Sciences again, and made another impassioned plea for my theory. He was courteous, but said he needed more information. Fair enough: I quickly phoned the dithiocarbamate expert, Dr. Jonathan Phinney, and asked him to call Dr. Riedel. Dr. Phinney praised my thesis and offered to supply Dr. Riedel with lots of data.

At this point I was also exploring the possibility of landing a state or federal research grant for further study of pfiesteria. Dr. Riedel had pointed out that the EPA Bay Program usually made grants to scientists who'd done Bay work in the past. That sounded a little ominous. I thought immediately of the "Cambridge Consensus" of State-level biologists. I told Dr. Riedel about Senator Sarbanes' encouraging words, and that I also had the support of Glen Eugster, the former director of the EPA Bay Program. Dr. Riedel agreed that these were powerful allies. When it came to nailing down grants, he said, "Senators help. EPA heads help. Maybe we can do something!"

Another strong possibility also loomed, at this point: If Senator Sarbanes and Glen Eugster would agree to write letters, perhaps the Academy could test the copper theory. Funding was the obvious obstacle, however; without sufficient dollars, there would be no testing.

Next Dr. Riedel sent me a three-page letter outlining strategies for testing my theory. For starters, he was eager to determine if copper-enrichment of runoff actually took place after rain events. This would be a key first step, he said, and it had already been taken successfully in Virginia by Dr. Dietrich.

After that, Dr. Riedel hoped to measure dithiocarbamates in estuarine water. As he pointed out in his letter: "We can reasonably expect to be able to demonstrate high concentrations of lipophilic Cu [copper] complexes *if* [emphasis added] they occur." Here was some real progress. And it didn't hurt that Dr. Phinney soon called Dr. Riedel, at my request, with the news that he'd be willing to take part in this project at some level.

I liked what I was hearing. I also agreed fully with Dr. Riedel's recommendation that biomonitoring for copepods, rotifers and other micro-zooplankton should be carried out in the Pocomoke. Why not ask Dr. Richard Lacouture to add a few Pocomoke locations to the list of "biomonitoring stations" that formed the heart of the MDE and EPA Bay program? Among other vital tasks, those stations perform the analyses, counts and measurements of the phytoplankton that would be crucial for this study.

It was an exciting prospect. If copper-dithiocarbamate toxicity were a real factor in pfiesteria blooms, Dr. Lacouture could document it by showing changes in rotifer population (for example) before and after rain.

Unfortunately, however, Dr. Riedel did not regard my copper theory as the most likely explanation of the bug invasion. He often cited Dr. Magnien's work, which predicted that a blackwater system such as the Pocomoke's would deliver added nutrients to trigger algae blooms. These would attract filter-feeding fish, and these in turn would fuel pfiesteria blooms. I disagreed, of course ... and soon sent Dr. Riedel a copy of the water-quality testing that showed no rises in chlorophyll a. I still felt this was the weakest part of Dr. Magnien's theory. Where was the chlorophyll?

The oxygen tests and the nutrient tests didn't support Dr. Magnien's idea. Those data were damaging, but the chlorophyll levels were the fatal flaw. If the data don't fit the model, then the model must be wrong. But maybe there were some chlorophyll data that hadn't been published? That was an important possibility, because the published numbers documented only two increases in chlorophyll. These two tests had been performed August 6, 1997. But two other tests on August 6 had turned up negative—and the levels were once again normal on August 7.

A *real* algae bloom would produce chlorophyll levels over 500 and sometimes over 1000. A trivial rise of chlorophyll levels in the Pocomoke River from 40 to 60 meant nothing.

Dr. Riedel might not agree with me yet, but I was pleased to learn that he was now willing to run the tests. At last, my request had been granted! A study would be performed that analyzed levels of copper, phytoplankton and dithiocarbamates. All I'd ever wanted was to see this kind of testing accomplished—and now it looked as if that vital step was about to take place.

Greatly heartened by these new developments, I was absolutely thrilled when the results finally came in on my daughter Sally's Science Fair experiment. Her careful water sampling and testing demonstrated clearly that levels of copper such as in the Pocomoke river water column would slow down rotifer movement—but that copper alone wouldn't actually kill the rotifers. Nor did normal water column levels of dithiocarbamates, when acting alone, wipe out the tiny creatures.

But guess what? When Sally combined two parts per million of copper with one part per *billion* of the dithiocarbamates in a test vial, the rotifers were killed *within five minutes*.

Sally's fine work later showed that 500 parts per million of copper, alone, or one part per million of dithiocarbamates, alone, would kill the rotifers in less than an hour. And those were the maximum levels of poisons that the river would be forced to digest in a runoff situation. Nice job, Sally!

After reviewing Sally's experiments with her, I was bursting at the seams with fatherly pride. And my spirits soared even higher a few days later, when I learned that Dave Oldach would address a group of local physicians in Salisbury on November 11. As a lecturer on pfiesteria, Dr. Oldach possessed impeccable credentials; he'd been trained at Hopkins, Massachusetts General Hospital and the University of Maryland.

I'm convinced that if powerhouse researchers like Dr. Oldach will only incorporate some of my primary care data and theories into their own observations, we'll quickly get a handle on the bug.

"Ritchie," David said to me during one of our conversations, "if your copper theory holds up, it would be a grand slam—because it would offer a direct remediation solution. That is very interesting. I will be in touch."

Among the many top-notch researchers, politicians and media reps I met during my year-long pfiesteria odyssey, three stand out in particular.

- Dr. David Oldach has the credentials and skills to solve the pfiesteria human illness problem with academic certainty.

- Dr. Lynn Grattan never wavered in her application of neuro-cognitive tests, even though they were initially criticized by public health officials from at least four states.

- Congressman Wayne Gilchrest will no doubt provide the policy leadership required to guarantee a thoughtful, broad-based environmental policy that will treasure wetlands and rivers as living parts of our ecology.

Secure in the knowledge that my pfiesteria theories were about to be tested in earnest, I could now turn to some long-postponed chores that needed attention before the snows of winter arrived. I needed to dig in some winter trees and move some mulch! And I also needed to hug my wife and show my daughter that I was still her dad, after so many nights spent making speeches or writing journal articles.

I was more than ready to return to my professional life as a country doctor—and to my private life as an ardent naturalist who feels most at home when he's holding a canoe paddle or a shovel in his hands.

My year-long journey across the "dark water" of the Pocomoke had taught me a great deal about biology, about state politics, about the news media. I had learned volumes about how our noisy, often inefficient political system really works, when great questions of public health policy suddenly loom large.

As I bowed my head in gratitude over our Thanksgiving turkey, my prayer was that those lessons would make me a better doctor … and an even better defender of the river that JoAnn, Sally and I have grown so much to love.

chapter 41

Onward to the Science Fair!

November 11

Although I didn't want to admit it, there was no longer any doubt that pfiesteria had changed my life.

At first I refused to concede the fact that I was now spending most of my free time giving talks and writing articles—as opposed to paddling the canoe, working on the Nature Trail, or joining my family on leisurely hikes through our pastures and wooded wetlands.

I didn't want to admit that perhaps I'd grown a bit too serious—even a bit churlish at times—about my "crusade" to bring the "truth of pfiesteria" to the good citizens of Maryland and the Mid-Atlantic region.

During the course of a highly stressful year, I'd learned how to successfully ignore most of those who were warning me against the dangers of "obsessing" on the topic of the bug.

But when my 13-year-old daughter, Sally, told me that she thought I'd changed … that's when I knew I had to sit up and listen.

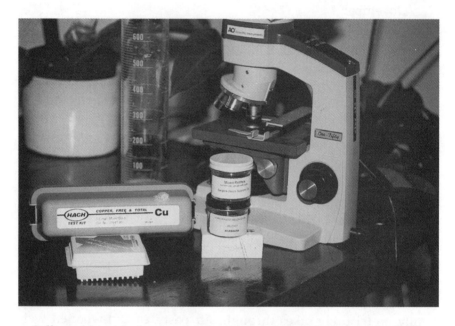

Sally and I watched as low levels of copper killed blue green algae. The combination of dithiocarbamates and copper killed rotifers quickly.

As always, Sally was kind but direct. She didn't pull her punches, as she explained how I'd changed during the past year or so. For one thing, noted the perspicacious Sally, I hadn't built anything for a while. And "we hadn't taken any pictures recently either." When is this extra work going to be over?"

She'd nailed me cold. Suddenly, I found myself wondering—half-seriously—if my mild case of pfiesteria had caused some permanent brain damage. Had the bug wiped out my memories of sitting in the canoe, or sinking my hoe into the rich black soil along the river's edge? Like the mythical Antaeus, I had always drawn my life's energy from the earth. But now I was a creature who wore new suits and shiny black shoes ... a driven man who had nearly lost touch with the river and the wetlands that had once provided his spiritual sustenance.

I was in danger of losing my psychic balance, and I knew it. Slow down, Ritch! Still, I wouldn't have traded that high-energy year for anything. I didn't regret the time I'd spent weighing issues and arguing with politicians. Nor was I sorry about all the hours I'd put in researching gastrointestinal physiology in carrion-eating birds, and studying the molecular biology of DNA replication in blue-green algae. I was also glad I'd worked so hard to understand soil science and aquatic chemistry.

Most of all, I was happy to have learned that one individual *can* make a difference—not only in the scientific community, but also in economic policy, political policy and yes, world opinion.

I was pleased with myself for ignoring some of the slams I'd received, and delighted that some people were saying I'd done "brilliant scientific work," while making "outstanding contributions to medicine." It was good to hear that my activism on this issue was regarded as a textbook example of how a primary care physician can interact with the academic community for the benefit of all. When I heard my name used in sentences along with primary care physicians who had worked with other new illnesses, such as the Hanta virus, it was deeply gratifying to know that I'd been able to contribute in this way.

I felt that my involvement with pfiesteria had probably reached its end, however.

What a joy it was, when I asked Sally if she wanted to go for a walk in the woods and take some pictures "just like we used to do." What greater thrill can a dad enjoy than watching his daughter grow intellectually and emotionally?

My part in this saga appears to be winding down. But I don't think the pfiesteria story is over yet. Not while some of the politicians continue to insist that "nitrates and phosphates" are the cause of the pfiesteria problem, even as they attempt to make public policy on that basis.

With all due respect, I simply think they're wrong.

Make no mistake: The pfiesteria issue isn't going to vanish along the Pocomoke River—just as it has not vanished in North Carolina. I sincerely hope that my treatment protocol will help prevent lasting disability from pfiesteria toxin. Now that we know what to do, more patients can be properly diagnosed and treated.

My task now is to make sure that other doctors know how to treat the disease after they recognize it. Public health departments will need help from practicing physicians, in order to make intelligent decisions about water quality and water safety, without resorting to arbitrary criteria like the "20-percent fish kill." Yes, much work remains to be done.

Perhaps the most useful thing I can do is pass along what I've learned about the story of pfiesteria—not just to my daughter, but also to young people like the student from Round Hill High School in Virginia, an enterprising young biologist who told me she wanted to do a "science fair project" on copper and permanganate.

Would I help her? You bet I would. I'd do everything I could ... to help her learn how to think for *herself*!

chapter 42

The Otters Return

November 24

It was the week before Thanksgiving. The State had closed its monitoring station at Shelltown, after announcing that the water was too cold for pfiesteria. The creeks were open again, and seafood sales were booming. Meanwhile, area farmers were suddenly confronting a host of new rules designed to better control the use of manure as fertilizer.

I couldn't blame most of the local farmers for feeling wary and suspicious. If the rumors they were hearing turned out to be accurate, all new restrictions on fertilizer would be made by "regulation" as opposed to "legislation"—which meant that the bureaucrats who promulgated them would be operating outside the media scrutiny that attends most law-making.

Alarmed and angered at the prospect, several of our local legislators had vowed to fight any laws that placed onerous burdens on agriculture.

Although the weather had certainly turned colder, I wasn't convinced that we'd actually seen the last of the pfiesteria threat for the year. For one thing, Jack Howard's eyes looked red again, and he was describing another bloom in the Pocomoke—an outbreak that he said had taken place in the dark, soft bottom of the warm shallows. Jack had spotted more lesioned trout and perch there, although the menhaden had already migrated south. Apparently, the dormant pfiesteria cyst wasn't so dormant after all.

As I fretted over Jack Howard's physical condition, I was also preparing to examine a student at the University of Virginia who would be traveling to my office in a few days from Charlottesville. The young woman was reportedly struggling with lesions and other symptoms, after vacationing on the Rappahannock during the previous Labor Day holiday weekend. Her mother seemed distraught, and for good reason; no physician had been able to diagnose the daughter's ailment. Was I about to inherit yet another "Virginia case"?

It was going to be a busy week. Along with the suffering UVA student, I was also scheduled to consult with a swimmer from Neptune Beach, Florida, during the next few days ... provided, of course, that this pfiesteria victim could remember how to find my office on Market Street (his memory was shot). This poor unfortunate had already taken every lab test in the book, with the exception of Dr. Grattan's "neurocognitives."

What was going on here? The more I thought about this patient's symptoms, the more they seemed to resemble those of a North Carolina man who'd been left virtually disabled after fishing in North Carolina. (Rick Dove had told me all about that disturbing case.) The two cases sounded so alike that I found myself ready to recommend cholestyramine therapy for the tormented Floridian, even in the absence of neurocognitive tests and/or a PET scan. Would my homegrown cholestyramine protocol help him or hurt him? If he had PHIS, it would help him. And if he wasn't really suffering from pfiesteria human illness syndrome, I would probably be able to tell him that.

As the days passed and I did my best to help these struggling patients, I was pleased to learn that the Maryland Medical Journal had published my article on pfiesteria diagnosis. It was also gratifying to read the just-published stories that were now emerging in Family Practice News, Internal Medicine News and Skin and Allergy News. My mug-shot showed up on the front pages of all three publications!

Another pleasing moment occurred when Dr. David Oldach called to wish me and my family a happy Thanksgiving. Was he calling for polite chitchat—or did he want to talk about pfiesteria? Either way, I was delighted to hear from him, and to learn that he was working hard with a team of dinoflagellate researchers now. A group from Norway had even sent him some DNA samples, while marine labs in several locations were sharing resources with his team.

David described how he was finding dinoflagellate DNA in water samples and on fish. That sounded pretty exciting to me—but it was just the first step in locating key sequences of pfiesteria DNA. David sounded tired, but satisfied, and understandably so: What a fantastic accomplishment he and his colleagues had achieved!

While the scientists argued about whether the fish were attacked directly by the bug—or only by its toxin—Dr. Oldach's lab had actually *found* dinoflagellate DNA on the fish! I was absolutely thrilled to know that he would keep me up to speed on what he and Dr. Morris (another key player on the research team) were doing day by day, as they fought the battle to pin down the physiology of the bug and its nasty toxin.

Soon after the publication of the MMJ article, I was informed that Virginia officials had finally acknowledged that two of my four Virginia pfiesteria patients who had taken Dr. Grattan's neurocognitive tests were now officially classified as victims of pfiesteria human illness syndrome. (Two confirmations weren't the same as twenty—but these weren't "zero" cases, either!)

After six months of relentless struggle to bring the human illness aspects of pfiesteria to public attention, I was now feeling rather hopeful about things.

One morning I woke up to find melting frost glittering like some fabulous jewelry beneath the mellow beams of the late autumn sun. Smiling serenely, I watched the sunrise glowing through the forest canopy that surrounds our Pocomoke homestead.

What a show! Soon I saw a platoon of whistling swans flying overhead, their wings forming a sleek-looking "V" and their calls almost magical. Then a kingfisher came swooping in, and his rattling call echoed around the pond. Look out, bluegills! An osprey sailed high overhead, then hovered and dove. No luck. It perched in a leafless red maple, waiting.

I was thrilled to see three river otters in our pond! They frolicked as always, then climbed onto a dock and rubbed their noses on the boards and each other. I cranked off some eager photos, even though the light was low and the film slow. The snorts and grunts of the otters sounded so musical! All at once I felt very grateful. After thinking about lesions and devoured flesh and dead animals for so long, it was wonderful to see how the river still supported the life that animated these marvelously playful otters.

Thanksgiving! The blonde hair of Sally and JoAnn was backlit in the morning sunlight. They had seen the otters, too. What a glow. The morning felt metaphysical ... and I had every faith that an answer to the pfiesteria problem was at hand.

chapter 43

The "Nutrient Theory"
Takes Another Hit!

January 5

After spending a solid nine months on the front lines of the Great Pfiesteria Debate, I was forced to conclude that although I still believed in the integrity and value of science, I'd completely lost my faith in the political process.

My disillusionment was based on the gradual realization that the officials who ran Maryland's political establishment were far more interested in managing public relations than in dealing with the truth about pfiesteria blooms. The blunt fact of the matter was that the state-released information appearing daily in the newspapers simply didn't hold up. And yet it was rapidly becoming the "conventional wisdom"—the ruling set of attitudes and assumptions—that would determine the state's response to the invasion of the bug. Some people might actually believe that Eastern Shore agriculture caused the pfiesteria blooms.

Having worked on the problem from the very beginning, I found it painful to watch the Glendening administration launch a public relations blitz based on the flawed Pfiesteria Commission report ... with its wrong-headed recommendations on everything from insisting that nutrients fueled pfiesteria blooms to placing strict controls on agriculture. And Gov. Glendening was adamant: Farmers must obey new laws regarding manure use, and would be given only a few years to adapt to new, phosphorus-based land management practices. State inspections and fines would be mandated for non-compliance.

As you might expect, the protests from the Ag community were loud and long. Traditionally distrustful of government, the farmers of the Eastern Shore were furious at this draconian set of proposed regulations. How dare the bureaucrats tell them what to do!

Their resistance was perfectly understandable ... especially given the shoddy science that underlay the "nutrient theory" of pfiesteria. Having thrown the sound logic of "modus ponens" right out the window, the Maryland Senate had rushed to propose a set of punitive actions and rigid regulations that seemed likely to make matters even worse (a somewhat milder bill soon emerged in the House of Delegates).

It was all quite irrational, even bizarre. How could the politicians get away with this? How could a non-existent algae bloom, supposedly triggered by a "horrendous" runoff of nutrients (though watershed nutrient-levels were unchanged!), be blamed for the pfiesteria fish kills? Where was the proof of a rise in chlorophyll levels? No chlorophyll, no algae blooms, no nutrient theory.

Madness. While the public debate roared non-stop, one of the few voices of calm reason belonged to former Maryland Governor Harry Hughes, who was now serving as Chairman of the Pfiesteria Commission. With an impeccable reputation for "telling it as it is," Hughes pointed out the obvious: Even if agricultural runoff didn't fuel pfiesteria blooms, there were still too many nutrients in the Bay—and curbing them with new laws was a good idea.

At last, a figure with some real political clout had stepped forward to acknowledge that the "pfiesteria controversy" was merely a smokescreen for those who were intent on reducing agricultural nutrients in the Bay.

Understandably, the Chesapeake Bay Foundation quickly announced that it would support the governor's bill. This made sense, since the CBF had long sought stricter controls on agriculture in order to "save the Bay." Indeed, the CBF had earlier given a major public service award to Dr. Burkholder for her "outstanding science." Her work epitomizes the ideals of science. But the CBF had taken to quoting her at length, whenever faced with a challenge to the "nutrient theory." In fact, her work had become a giant lever with which the state brass controlled public perceptions about pollution in Bay waters.

Let me be clear about this: If the intent of the proposed nutrient-control laws had been to reduce pollution along the Chesapeake watershed, I would have signed on happily. But to insist that new manure laws would prevent pfiesteria blooms was just plain wrong. For one thing, I'd watched up close while the Pfiesteria Commission's scientific data had been cynically manipulated. I'd also felt firsthand the effects of the ferocious "political spin" that had been put on the medical issues of diagnosis and treatment of pfiesteria. And now here we were again, with public policy being shaped on the basis of distorted information.

Still, it was heartening to see a ground swell of skepticism about the nutrient theory beginning to take shape in the academic community. It wasn't a tidal wave yet, but more and more of the academic scientists were beginning to ask searching questions about the "predator-prey hypothesis" as a possible explanation for the sudden surge in illness-causing toxin. The role of heavy metals and toxic pesticides in stimulating blooms was an idea that wouldn't go away. It was raised with increasing frequency. Suddenly I wasn't alone in demanding that the proper research be carried out as swiftly as possible.

The political wrangling over pfiesteria became quite evident in January of 1998, during a public meeting in Salisbury. Representing the State of Maryland were DNR Secretary Griffin, Secretary Nishida of the Department of the Environment, and the new Secretary of Agriculture, Bud Virts. Along with Dr. Donald Boesch, they would make brief statements.

More than *800* concerned citizens showed up to listen to the politicos, and to make three-minute comments of their own, if they so desired. The audience seemed polite, if rather angry, and the proceedings remained civil ... except when a speaker from the Sierra Club was shouted down for proposing a "manure tax" on chicken farmers.

Rick Nelson and I attended this political sideshow together. I'd promised JoAnn that I would keep my mouth shut. That lasted about 30 seconds, until the first politician began sounding off about how perhaps "a few people were sickened by pfiesteria." Of course, Rick and I had been through this same public drill many times. We'd heard it all before ... yet we feared that if we halted our crusade against the political truth-twisters, no other voices would arise to challenge them.

There was a long line of people waiting to get into the hall. Surprisingly, Secretary Griffin wound up standing in line next to Rick and me. He greeted us cordially, and seemed comfortable with the bantering that went back and forth. Then Mike Howard arrived out of nowhere, and his presence eased any remaining tension. I asked Mr. Griffin if he'd seen my manuscript, *Pfiesteria, Crossing Dark Water*, and he looked surprised. He wanted a copy, and I was happy to report that the book painted him in complimentary colors, for the most part.

Still, I wasn't going to pretend that I didn't have major problems with the nutrient theory. Griffin listened and said he was "keeping an open mind" on the subject. He pointed out that he had to find a mechanism for monitoring that would protect both our population and our waterways. Right now, he noted, that mechanism depended on looking carefully at watersheds, while paying special attention to agricultural runoff, low tidal flushing and estuarine conditions.

Had he seen the USDA maps of ground water vulnerability indices for pesticides? These maps showed that the highest levels of toxic pesticide indices in the Northeast were located between the Nanticoke and Pocomoke Rivers, with the second-highest areas around the Neuse River in North Carolina, and the third-highest near the St. John's in Florida. And the St. Lucie River area in Florida wasn't far behind. Of course, these were also the areas of greatest pfiesteria activity! Was all of this a coincidence? Causation?

Besieged by other questioners, however, Secretary Griffin moved on without addressing the problem of the pesticides.

Still, I thought I was onto something with these maps. Following a suggestion from the always helpful Glenn Eugster, I had called a very interesting woman named Margaret Maizel, who worked in a Washington, D.C., environmental think tank known as the National Center for Resource Innovation.

Yes, Maizel knew all about the pesticide factor … and she quickly suggested that pfiesteria hadn't showed up in our backyard merely by coincidence. She noted that the "ground water vulnerability index" had been created by the federal USDA—not the State of Maryland—and that it was a terrific measuring stick, because it described movement of pesticides and dithiocarbamates into watersheds based on soil types, soil slope, rainfall, erosion, percolation and pesticide solubility. These indices were plotted by counties across the U.S.

In the end, Maizel's maps would serve as my most powerful weapon in the ongoing battle against the nutrient theory. (Just about everyone who looks at the maps ends up exclaiming: "Wow!")

The maps that Griffin hadn't seen reveal the incredible density of toxic pesticides in the subsurface flow (ground water) in areas of fish kill. (The maps also coincided perfectly with the "skip areas" along the East Coast.) Suddenly that familiar phrase, "If you can see it on the land, you know it is in the water," had taken on a whole new depth of meaning!

The pfiesteria culprit wasn't manure—it was pesticides. Copper was a major factor too, poisoning not just the Pocomoke, but also the Chicamacomico, the Neuse, the St. Lucie, and countless other waterways.

Another interesting map plotted areas of very low leaching (or high retention) of pesticides. Now, the kill sites had almost no soils with low leaching ... meaning that the killer-pesticides in areas where fish had been wiped out were readily washed into ground water, in subsurface flow, and eventually into the rivers. When it rained, pesticides leached. Or, as had happened in Florida, when water from the Lake Okeechobee was diverted into the St. Lucie River, it took along pesticides, herbicides, and copper in industrial quantities.

The skip areas in Georgia, South Carolina and the Great Dismal Swamp area had a much higher density of low-leaching soils. Pesticide use in these areas meant more retention of pesticides in the soils, and less washing into the water. And indeed, the areas north of the Neuse (and especially near Elizabeth City, N.C.) contained so much organic material in the soils that they were actually capable of catching fire, like the peat beds of Britain. No wonder we didn't see kills in skip areas; the predators of the zoospores weren't poisoned there!

The maps were a marvelous tool. Unfortunately, however, they didn't list individual categories of pesticides. I had good evidence to show that dithiocarbamates were a particularly toxic estuarine poison, but that chlorothalonils weren't (if worry about cancer wasn't bad enough). What a powerful blow this was to the nutrient theory!

High ground water concentrations of pesticides were being found in the same areas where pfiesteria was killing fish and hurting people—while low concentrations of pesticide runoff, areas with a low vulnerability index, were found in the skip areas.

I held my breath when I opened the water quality test reports from the South Florida Water Management District. Sure enough, the copper levels were unbelievably high, from 20 to 200 ppm! Finally, the decisive proof had arrived, from a region that was outside of Maryland's political control. And that proof had matched the predictions of the "predator-prey toxic hypothesis"!

Perhaps the answer to the pesticide problem lay *inside* the plants, and not *on* them? John Hughes had told me about tomato plants that were genetically engineered to resist attack by fungi and bacteria. Still, it's important to remember that in nature, everything is food for something else. If a fungus couldn't eat the tomato plant, maybe a nematode would ... except that this wouldn't be a *normal* nematode! In fact, the genetically altered tomato plant would have helped to create a brand-new ecological niche.

It seemed like a lot of hassle for the sake of a "perfect tomato." Why not simply avoid eating the blemish on the ordinary fruit? Or better yet, why not find a way to convince people that blemishes on tomatoes gave magical health benefits, as with ginseng, gingko leaf extract or chrysanthemum leaves? (And don't forget that those nasty-looking "yellow" chickens usually taste much better than their snow-white counterparts!)

As Rick and I listened to the government speakers, we stared at each other in disbelief. Was my heavy-metals-and-toxic-pesticides-theory really a "myth," as Richard Eskin had been overheard calling it? The theory seemed perfectly logical to anyone willing to consider the evidence. So why did each speaker at the gathering make a point of saying something negative about the theory?

Maybe they hadn't seen the maps, either.

"For a theory with nothing behind it, they sure talked a lot about it!" groaned my friend Rick.

I nodded. "I've just about had it with these public political pronouncements," I told him. "Maybe we should hold our own 'public meetings'! If the public only had more information, maybe we could all stop pointing the finger at agriculture."

Rick Nelson clenched his jaw. "I've got about the same amount of spare time as you do, Ritch, which is none. But I tell you what: If you can get some discussion going, I'll be glad to tell everyone what really happened on the Pfiesteria Commission.

"I'll also tell 'em just how ridiculous all these new regulations are gonna be!"

chapter 44

Research Begins in Earnest ... Finally!

March 15, 1998

Having helped to form a tiny non-profit watershed protection organization—the Pocomoke River Alliance (PRA)—
in order to build a nature trail, I was eager to see if we could turn
the alliance into a research organization to nail down a small study-
grant from the $750,000 that had been routed to the Chesapeake
Bay Alliance. These monies, part of the federal funding for the
Chesapeake Bay Program that had been sponsored by Maryland
Senator Paul Sarbanes, were designed to help researchers better
understand the complex chemical and biological forces that were
at work in pollution-triggered disasters like the one involving the
bug.

While I wanted to learn if our application would bear fruit, there
was time to field a very interesting call from Glenn Eugster. He'd
been reassigned to a higher-level post at the EPA in Washington, as
it turned out, and now he wanted to re-establish ties. Glenn has a
special place in his heart for the Pocomoke. He'd helped us to get
the PRA established, a few years earlier, and he'd also worked hard
to help bring the "Beach To Bay Trail" project to completion (along
with Senator Sarbanes and many others).

Glenn told me that he'd been following the pfiesteria story in the newspapers, and that he thought he might be able to help. As a matter of fact, he'd dug up a funding source that was providing money for small towns that wanted to stage "public forums" on the topic. Was I interested?

You bet I was. Once again, it looked as if I might benefit from the "right place, right time" scenario that had helped me so often in the past. As far as I was concerned, you couldn't find a better funding-organization for a forum than the EPA!

Glenn went on to point out that there was plenty of additional grant money out there for studying the bug. And those funds weren't tied exclusively to science and medicine, either; at least some of the dollars would be spent on studying the "anthropology of human response" to pfiesteria, along with its impact on the heritage of a watershed. Suddenly there was money, money everywhere ... when all I had ever wanted was to eliminate copper and dithiocarbamates!

Convincing the public of the need for taking that step would be a long, uphill struggle, however. For one thing, formal testing of those two substances was still notoriously incomplete. The EPA reviews all agricultural chemicals only once in every 12 years (although the dithiocarbamates were scheduled for an early review). Is there any doubt that the EPA system for analyzing these hazardous chemical substances is woefully inadequate? Maybe if I sent the agency a few hundred thousand dead rotifers—killed by copper and dithiocarbamates after a "rain event"—we could finally get those two poisons regulated out of our coastal plain soils!

After I finished fuming with frustration about a system I couldn't budge, I received some very promising information from John Hughes, who had learned that a new generation of chemical fungicides was nearly ready for production—and that it might one day eliminate copper and dithiocarbamates, since it relied on a new breed of lethal agents. That sounded encouraging ... but I couldn't help thinking about what happened every time a drug company came up with a "new, safer, better antibiotic." At first, the doctors

would use this new "toy" with great delight: TRY NEW CEPHAK-
ILLITALL: ONE PILL FOR EVERY GERM KNOWN TO MAN!

Guess what happened next?

Sooner or later, some bizarre bacteria that wasn't killed by the
wonder-drug would begin to flourish. And then—just as in the case
of pfiesteria, which seemed impervious to fire and ice, and was
controlled only by feeding rotifers—the surviving bacteria would
reproduce at skyrocketing rates, producing yet another "bug invasion"! (Are we going to end up with world epidemics caused by
germs that are resistant to every antibiotic? A chilling thought!)

I couldn't forget, either, that DDT was still being manufactured
and sold … even if it wound up being used almost exclusively in
Third World countries. Once upon a time, DDT had been "new,
safer and better," as well.

These were monstrously complicated ecological issues, of course.
But for right now, my goal was a much simpler one: I merely wanted to convince the State of Maryland that pfiesteria blooms are tied
to biologic principles. Accordingly, I sat down and planned three
research projects to be coordinated by the PRA.

Dr. Gupta had already agreed to take on the first study, which
would involve his porewater experiments at the fish kill sites of the
Pocomoke and the Chicamacomico. His work was based on the fact
that the porewater—the water between particles of sediment in the
mud of the river bottom—is a fundamental factor in the ecology of
phytoplankton.

As you no doubt recall, the amoeba phase of pfiesteria doesn't
swim freely. It lives, eats and dies on top of the river bottom. There,
creatures such as blue-green algae bridge the gap between a higher
oxygen level in the water and a lower oxygen level beneath the
mud's surface. Indeed, these ubiquitous blue-green algae have often been described as the "first plant life form" to have taken up
residence on Planet Earth. In those early epochs, of course, oxygen
wasn't present in the atmosphere. If it were, the blue-green algae
would have been killed quickly.

As long as the mud which houses the algae remains undisturbed, the algae will survive—until it can be eaten as a favorite food by the amoeba phase of pfiesteria. (My own image of the process features a fat, contented cow who grazes placidly on fresh, succulent grass.)

Stir up that mud, however, and you better watch out. Now the chemicals trapped in the porewater are released, and the algae are quickly wiped out. Pesticides also emerge from the porewater, even as the oxygen wallops the blue-green algae.

The vital importance of this low oxygen/high oxygen boundary has been discussed by Hans Paerl, among others. It is here, along the thin line that separates life and death for the food of amoeba, that the pfiesteria blooms are born. Just as I'd speculated way back in July: The answer was in the *mud*!

Remember: In the water atop the mud (the water column) swim far fewer numbers of species of phytoplankton, when compared to the number of creatures that creep in or on the sediment. These free-swimmers must move fast to escape from predators ... or they must hide in the mud, where they are then devoured by the slow-moving vacuum cleaner that is the amoeba phase of pfiesteria.

It's important to realize that any toxic chemicals washed into the water (such as copper complexed with an organic acid) will eventually settle into the mud. As they sink toward the porewater, however, the chemicals can damage the creatures in the water column. In addition, the chemicals can be stirred up out of the sediment, back into the boundary layer of the water column, in times of turbulent flow or tidal surge. Back and forth with the tides after a heavy rain, the killing goes on.

Obviously, it will be necessary to identify toxic chemicals and pesticides in porewater, in order to confirm my predator-prey theories. And Dr. Gupta's important research proposal, if funded, would provide the hard data required to evaluate the "toxic" theory. Except for Dr. Gupta's, I'm not aware of any studies that have ever looked at the toxic impact of copper and pesticides on these systems.

The second proposed study would consist of mapping the submerged soils of the Pocomoke and the Chicamacomico. George Demas (soon to Dr. George Demas), had plotted the Sinepunxent Bay, near Ocean City, back in 1997. That bay featured an incredible diversity of soil structures, soil types and chemical makeup, and it demonstrated that underwater soils are every bit as diverse as those found on dry land.

George had been working with Dr. Martin Rabenhorst at the University of Maryland's Department of Soil Sciences. And Marty agreed that a full study of the submerged soils would make a lot of sense. He and George were equipped to do the detailed analyses that would be necessary to define the soil structure and chemistry associated with pfiesteria blooms. By layering a porewater map over a soil map, we could build data that would begin to give a total ecological profile of pfiesteria's habitat.

The third research experiment is an important one, but it might not get done this year. That survey would attempt to determine if the pfiesteria cysts were located at the kill sites. And if not, where did they hide? Would a cyst be found at the boundary layer of oxygen—or covered with silt in the porewater?

Dr. David Oldach had continued his collaborative work with some of the top microbiologists around the world. But these days he was working directly with Dr. Parke Rublee who had worked with Dr. Burkholder as well. And the necessary DNA research on pfiesteria was well underway. So far, as David explained, the team had been able to identify pfiesteria DNA "base pairs" in water.

"Could you find pfiesteria DNA in river sediment?" I asked.

"Probably not, at least not yet. There would be inhibitors. We don't know enough about the DNA in the cyst phase."

Discouraging. But the good news was that our sediment samples could be frozen and preserved for later study. The DNA assays could be done later, as well. As fast as David and the collaborative team was proceeding with the DNA technology, I was convinced that it would be just a matter of time before we could overlay a third map—showing sites of DNA in the sediment—over the first two, in order to vividly illustrate the importance of sediment type, porewater toxicity and pfiesteria at documented kill sites.

The land use maps that Margaret Maizel sent me, a new treasure store of pertinent information, showed a bright red line along watersheds that exactly matched the sites of fish kills in the Chesapeake Bay. "Palustrine emergent land" was found in the few spots of kill on the Rappahannock and James Rivers as well as the active kill areas on the Eastern Shore. Lighting up in red, too, were areas of the Potomac, Patapsco and Patuxent Rivers. If porewater in those rivers had toxic chemicals, then the next outbreaks of pfiesteria were likely to occur there in 1998. Did the state scientists know those watersheds were at risk?

After endless hours of study and writing, the grant applications had finally been mailed. Groaning with fatigue, I promised JoAnn that this was "absolutely" my last research push. By now, a large cadre of established scientists from top institutions was working hard at figuring out the true source of the pfiesteria blooms. These bluechip workers in the scientific vineyard couldn't be intimidated by the politicians ... and they were quite willing to attack the state's sacred "nutrient theory," based on their findings.

For now, I could return safely to my medical practice and my family ... secure in the knowledge that if the top scientists did drop the ball, "The Mouth" could always return to the field of play!

But I assumed that The Mouth would no longer be needed, because some of the most gifted scientists in the world were now doing the kind of accurate, well-thought-out research that this crisis so urgently required.

Finally!

chapter 45

A Funny Thing Happened On the Way to the Forum

April 1, 1998

☐ **Sponsored by Salisbury State** University and partially funded by the EPA, the public forum on pfiesteria was now rapidly approaching. Titled "What You Haven't Heard About Pfiesteria But Need To Know," the widely publicized event would consist of three different presentations. After several weeks of careful discussion, conservationist Bruce Nichols and I planned the presentations as follows:

- First, we would make a presentation that severely downgraded the "nutrient theory";

- Second, we would expose the utter lack of logic in the new state-mandated directives that had been issued to farmers;

- And third, we would do our best to present a reasonable, carefully designed cropland management plan, based on solid biology principles and agricultural fundamentals.

While Nichols and I prepared for battle, we were reading some very interesting pfiesteria stories out of North Carolina, where the State Department of Health had interviewed callers to a "hot line," along with a few other residents, before concluding that pfiesteria wasn't a "serious health issue." Their controversial finding had been reported in the regional newspapers, however, and not in a peer-reviewed medical journal.

The reports out of the Tar Heel State quickly set me to thinking about the enormous hurdles my "treatment article" had faced, before it was finally okayed by such a journal. Good luck getting the NC study published! I was smiling ... but I also felt some anxiety, as I asked myself how far a state public health department would go in order to minimize the importance of pfiesteria as a human health risk.

Somehow, the situation kept reminding me of an airplane's best defense against anti-aircraft guns. If the pilot sent out so much "chatter" that the enemy radar couldn't "lock on," then the threatened aircraft would probably survive. Well, you can be sure that our public seminars had been designed to lock on—and with what we hoped would be explosive results!

Whenever I looked at the field of play before me, I was greatly encouraged by the way that Dr. Richard Halpern had battled Virginia's Department of Environmental Quality in 1992. Against all the odds, Dr. Halpern had won!

In a scenario that would soon be repeated in Maryland, the DEQ had focused its energies on the extensive farming operations that were taking place around Harrisonburg, Va. Predictably, the "nutrient theory" had been dragged out, as state health officials pointed at concentrated densities of cattle, hogs, chickens and turkeys—while insisting that their manure had to be polluting first the Shenandoah, then the Potomac, and then finally the Chesapeake Bay.

As it turned out, however, the DEQ was unable to prove its case; in this instance, the farming community's "best management practices" seemed to be working quite effectively. Because Dr. Halpern had gained lots of experience in the Virginia battle, I was looking forward to his appearance at our forum.

It's important to remember that nutrient levels in the Potomac were running slightly higher than those in the Pocomoke. And my question was a simple one: When pfiesteria lowered the boom on the District of Columbia later in 1998 (I'd had only three D.C. patients with symptoms in 1997), would agriculture get the blame? Or would some of the officials point a regulatory finger at the Blue Plains sewage plant near Washington ... a facility that funnels 15 million pounds of nitrogen into the Bay per year? Remember that every time it rains, the Anacostia sewage treatment facility (near Washington) experiences a flood. Was this mixture of storm water and sewage really helping the Chesapeake?

Another high point of the approaching forum would surely take place when Rick Nelson told us what really had happened during the Pfiesteria Commission hearings. His take on the proceedings was a highly critical one; he felt convinced that the commission had staged a carefully orchestrated review of nutrients, nutrients, nutrients—instead of conducting a truly open, scientific forum. Rick seemed to know a great deal about the political pressure, political agendae and political posturing that had ruled the sessions.

Understandably enough, Bruce Nichols said that he intended to leave his official "USDA hat" at home during the presentation. He hoped to speak from the heart about the biology of wetlands and watersheds. He also hoped to bring logic back to the regulatory control of agriculture, by using his experience and insights to help everyone involved make some sense of nutrients and best management practices.

Bruce had seen—up close and personal—what banning fertilizers on buffer cover crops had done. (This was the concept advocated by the Chesapeake Bay Foundation.) That idea made sense, but only superficially. "Just don't put any nutrients at the water's edge!" That sounds reasonable, doesn't it? Sure ... until you remember that cover crops are supposed to take phosphates out of the soil and into their roots, stems, leaves and seeds. Harvesting a crop would lower phosphates, thus mitigating "damage" caused by phosphate-rich chicken manure fertilizer.

The cover crops (wheat, in this case), sounded like a great idea. But once again, a closer look revealed problems. The young plants emerged looking thin, yellowish, sickly. Why? You guessed it: These cover crops, planted on best management practices lands, were nitrogen-deficient! Somebody ... please come fertilize these young plants before the snow geese arrive to feast on such a slow-growing crop!

Always the ecological sage, Bruce had noticed that human attempts to manage abundant wildlife often ended in failure. Whether the experiment involved rabbits in Australia, wild hogs in the Smokies, horses in the American West or Canada geese on golf courses, the results were almost always the same: a disaster.

Thankfully, biological "rescue attempts" had enjoyed a somewhat better fate. Whooping cranes, bald eagles, and even the famed Maryland rockfish had all benefited from the protections afforded by legislation designed to protect their food, cover and habitat. And these laws made good sense: If we really wanted the red cockaded woodpecker to return to its normal range here, we'd have to stop cutting down the mature loblolly pines that provided its habitat.

As for the pfiesteria problem ... why not simply declare the rotifers and the copepods to be endangered species? Then we could point the finger at anything that threatened them—such as copper and dithiocarbamates—and insist that it be banned! Might as well put the cryptomonads on the endangered list, too, and shut down the use of the heavy metals that attacked their fragile systems.

As the day of the forum drew nearer, I was pleased that Dr. David Oldach would be making one of the presentations. To nobody's real surprise, he and his outstanding team were now able to identify pfiesteria DNA in sediments. David was quick to give most of the credit to his fellow-investigators, but I didn't allow myself to be fooled by his modesty. I knew his contribution had been enormous, and I was eager to hear the whole story behind this fantastic collaborative achievement.

George Demas would be sharing seminar time with David. Outfitted with a brand-new Ph.D in soil science, Demas had been working hard to map sediment types of submerged soils in the bay area. Both Delaware and Maryland wanted him to work elsewhere, but we badly needed him right where he was. After all, a road map to soil types was the first step on the information highway of pfiesteria residence in sediment, silt and the mud of the Pocomoke and Chicamacomico Rivers.

My own seminar at the forum would be a straightforward description of the diagnosis of PHIS, followed by some commentary on the treatment of persistent PHIS. Once again, I would rely on my medical work to supply credibility.

Here was one more opportunity to hammer home an obvious point: The nutrient theory didn't make sense. The state's own water-quality testing showed that! There was simply no doubt that the heavy metals could and did kill phytoplankton. The pesticides presented an awesome threat to water quality, and it seemed clear that they were the common link that connected worldwide explosions of toxic blooms of dinoflagellates and other previously non-toxic life forms.

The pesticide maps were quite impressive. Was it really a coincidence that the places marked by highest ground water vulnerability indices for pesticides just happened to coincide with areas of pfiesteria kills?

Even as I was looking forward to discussing all of these matters at the forum, however, the telephone rang. It was the head of public relations at Salisbury State U. And the reason for the call? Simple: All at once, the university had decided that it could not formally sponsor the forum! (And so what if most of the details of time, location, speakers, travel arrangements and publicity had already been arranged?) The word "sponsor" didn't mean "endorse" to me, but the political connotation was the same.

I could hardly believe my ears. What was the university telling us? According to the brass, we would be allowed to hold informal "discussions" on campus at the standard cost for the use of

University facilities… but the University Cabinet had suddenly decided that the political hot potato of pfiesteria should not be caught by a state institution of higher learning!

What a pity. Our forums were informational and scientific. We weren't a political advocacy group. And what about the DNR conference that had been staged at SSU, back in August? Was that a "political event"? No, said the university president … the DNR confab had been organized and paid for by state government.

I just shook my head. But my mood improved considerably, a few days later, when I received a letter (March 25) announcing that Med Chi had selected me for its Laughlin Award for distinguished authorship and contribution to medicine through my original writings in the Maryland Medical Journal. Maybe the battle was beginning to turn? Maybe some important folks were actually starting to listen?

Somehow, I'd gone from being a kooky country doctor to the award platform at Med Chi.

Reflecting on this strange turn of events, I found myself remembering my Haitian patient way back in 1981. He'd been suffering with an "AIDS-defining illness," back before we even knew about AIDS. The common theme at that time was an ominous one: It centered on the possibility that something had triggered a weakness in the human immune system that allowed previously non-virulent germs to kill people. Had there been a breach in the "slime layer" of ordinary germ-protection? The invader, of course, was later determined to be the HIV virus.

The more I thought about it, the more it seemed that we were grappling with a kind of "environmental AIDS" along the Pocomoke. Consider: A non-toxic dinoflagellate suddenly begins to wreak havoc on an estuarine ecosystem—after the "immune system" formed by local predators and prey in the watershed is poisoned by our chemicals! A striking analogy, no? So far, science has been working on finding a protective AIDS vaccine for 15 years, without success.

How long will it take to develop a restorative vaccine for an estuary? And how many people will be injured by pfiesteria toxins before an organized, unpoliticized scientific effort emerges to correct the problem?

I hope it won't be 15 more years.

chapter 46

Confirmation
From Florida

April 15, 1998

The research team was in place now, and seemed likely to be funded. All at once, I was feeling pretty good about my part in the Great Pfiesteria Debate of '97—and especially after hearing some dramatic news from Florida about pesticides. Here was the proof of my missing link!

The long-suspected connection between pesticides and pfiesteria had become quite evident in the Sunshine State in recent months, after blooms of dinoflagellates began to appear in the St. Lucie River. As expected, the blooms were accompanied by large numbers of lesioned fish of all species, most of which had been chewed up by secondary invaders.

Interestingly enough, Ray Maddox had been quoted in the Jacksonville newspaper, way back in early September: "If you have a few lesioned fish now, you've got a hell of a spring coming."

Already, newspapers in Bradenton and West Palm Beach were raising the specter of human illness. The South Florida Water Management District was also being bombarded with criticism about water channeled from Lake Okeechobee back into the St. Lucie

River estuary. A quick look at the local economy showed that a few nearby cattle farms did produce manure (but not in feed lots) that went into the water—but this level of beef production was far below the amount of cattle-raising that had taken place in the 1960s.

A closer survey showed that the rich black soils near Lake Okeechobee produced three crops of irrigated vegetables per year. Numerous truck farms fed the nation a steady supply of tomatoes, cabbages, peppers, parsley, you name it. All of these leafy vegetables required pesticides, fungicides and herbicides to flourish. Did they need heavy metals like copper, as well? Yes, indeed, this is agricultural country now.

Of course, the bacteria that grew on vegetables in Florida weren't slowed down by cold weather. Peppers, for example, were attacked by a variety of southern plant germs. And the best protection? You guessed it: a lot of copper and dithiocarbamates.

Even a brief glance at the pesticide (agricultural and domestic) map was enough to trigger alarm. The same areas of the St. Lucie river that had copper levels over 20 ppm (and some areas topped 200 ppm) also showed a bright green wall of chemical bug-killer encircling West Palm Beach, indicating a high "pesticide index." The map made it clear that the substances being washed into the St. Lucie watershed were nothing less than a prescription for pfiesteria blooms ... or maybe the blooms of a similar dinoflagellate with an unpronounceable name, such as cryptoperidiniopsis.

As always, the greatest damage would occur where fresh water collided with salt. Where the fresh water from the Everglades joined the salty water of the Indian River—look out! The Indian River Lagoon is an obvious at-risk site, too. The St. Lucie kill site this spring is now occurring near Stuart, located just north of Jupiter Beach.

That name rang a bell for me. Back in September, I'd received a phone call from a troubled Colorado Springs woman who had fallen ill with a typical case of pfiesteria illness syndrome, after spending some time vacationing at Jupiter Beach.

But why had the dinoflagellate (or crypto) attack taken place just now? Had it been triggered by the heavy rains that were supposedly the legacy of *El Nino*? Were they using any new pesticides or herbicides in the region, or was it just runoff of pesticides and herbicide retained in organic soils?

The answer to that "why" question began to appear with the Whitbread Round the World Yachting Race. In a move designed to coincide with this world-class sailing event, the Florida Institute of Marine Sciences was hosting a symposium on oceans, environment and education. Would I participate in a video conference with Dr. Tom Jones from Salisbury State University? We would talk about pfiesteria, and rightly so: lesioned fish were commanding headlines all over the Sunshine State, even though "pfiesteria" per se hadn't been blamed yet.

These days Tom Jones is serving as interim Dean of the School of Sciences at SSU. And although he knows a great deal about copper in our Eastern Shore watersheds, he hasn't been a supporter of my toxic-pesticides-and-heavy-metals-theory. Still, he shares some of my strong reservations about the nutrient theory—and he's equally troubled about the lack of chlorophyll and the normal nutrient and oxygen levels in the Pocomoke.

I was grateful for the pesticide maps because they made him examine my theory more carefully. And he was rather startled to learn that what I'd written for the Pfiesteria Commission wasn't what he'd read! The missing data-link was the availability of agricultural chemicals that could shift the balance of aquatic communities of life forms—not in runoff, but from subsurface flow (ground water). As we parted, I could see the scientific wheels turning in Tom's mind, and they were an exciting thing to watch.

What I badly needed, at this point, were water quality data that would show normal nutrients and chlorophyll levels, along with high copper and high dithiocarbamates in the St. Lucie River. Those were the crucial litmus tests, if I hoped to prove that my model of predator-prey relationships—as disrupted by copper and fungicides—was an accurate depiction of the unholy recipe for toxic dinoflagellate blooms of all kinds along the East Coast.

Fat chance, Ritch. Based on what had happened in Maryland and Virginia, it seemed likely that such data would be declared "confidential" the moment the media uproar over the "bug invasion" began in earnest. Surely Florida would follow Maryland's lead in refusing to perform tests for dithiocarbamates—an especially disappointing outcome, given the fact that the Old Line health researchers had already botched their copper tests, according to the world-class expert, Dr. Gupta.

Oh, well. *Here goes nothing,* I told myself, *just another afternoon of making pointless phone calls, when I should be working in the flower beds.* But I went to work ... starting with a quick call to the main office of the Natural Resource Conservation Service. Once again, I found myself sitting endlessly on "hold" ... and then being referred from one office to the next.

After several hours on the phone, however, I finally managed to find a responsive ear. It belonged to a graduate student in biology who was working at a water quality monitoring station, and the student listened thoughtfully to my pleas for water quality data and my explanation of why I needed it.

"Your idea makes a lot of sense to me. The fish lesions down here do sound similar to what you describe ... but you should talk to Anne Forstchen; she's running the investigation by the Florida Department of Environmental Protection."

I made the call immediately, expecting a brush-off by a secretary (or maybe the ubiquitous voice mail), but I got a nice surprise: Anne herself answered, and then listened carefully to everything I told her.

"Your ideas are interesting," she said. "I do remember an article on high levels of copper in the St. Lucie. I don't have the water quality data here, but Paul Millar from the South Florida Water Management District could help you. Say, where can I get a copy of those pesticide books? I'd love to read your manuscript, and I'll get back to you."

Progress! Paul said he had the data I wanted. And, no: The nutrient levels weren't high. (Phosphates were less than 0.10 and nitrates less than 0.5.) He advised me to call Richard Pfeuffer, the SFWMD pesticide expert. Best of all, Millar quickly agreed to arrange for 20 years' worth of data to be sent to me immediately, and not a moment too soon: The April 30 forum was only two weeks away!

While I waited on tenterhooks for the precious data, there was time to catch up on a few other pfiesteria-related developments ... starting with the very interesting petition that I found in the Whitbread Yachting information packet. That document, which was being circulated near Stuart, Fla., adjacent to some fish kill areas, announced in booming tones: "We want action. No pussy-footing around will be tolerated."

When I did some digging into the origins of this broadside, I soon came upon one of the organizers of the citizens protest group, Jean Hearne. Jean listened hard, then sent me on to Brian Killday, a researcher at Harbor Branch Oceanographic Institute in Fort Pierce.

Killday turned out to be a remarkably candid and helpful source. He understood the political problems involved, and the need for discretion. He explained that no "gag orders" had been issued yet —although the he warned that the bug was already a red-hot issue in Florida.

"Ritchie, I can help. This whole area is going crazy. It's one town meeting after the next, and no one is eating seafood. Everybody's blaming the SFWMD for dumping all that fresh water from Lake Okeechobee into the St. Lucie River. The river looks like Yoo-Hoo [a chocolate drink]."

By now, of course, it was quite clear that El Nino had deluged South Florida. The earthen dikes of Lake Okeechobee were being pushed to the max, and the high water had forced the authorities to raise the gates of the drainage dikes. Full of fungicides, insecticides, herbicides and heavy metals, the runoff from the rich truck farms was rushing into the Atlantic via the St. Lucie. The Everglades had been overwhelmed by the endless precip, and now the water was surging out of the swamps without being properly filtered.

In Florida, the construction of the dike system compounded the pollution problems immensely. Back in Maryland, remember, the water control structures in our ponds are designed to control depth by venting surface water. But the U.S. Army Corps of Engineers had constructed the Florida dikes to vent sediment and bottom water. Keeping the dikes clean in that way made sense ... but it also meant that porewater got dumped, and not surface water.

Richard Pfeuffer was sitting on a treasure trove of information, and I was thrilled to learn that my ideas made sense to him. He was supremely knowledgeable—and the phrase "copper chelating fungicides" wasn't Greek to him, as it had been for so many state scientists in Maryland.

"Down here, we measure our agricultural chemicals extremely carefully," said Pfeuffer. "The ETU levels [breakdown products of dithiocarbamates] were always undetectable in water—even in run-off situations."

I did my best to contain my growing excitement. "Would you be willing to measure ETU levels in porewater at a kill site? We've got enough funds to pay the $80 that each test costs."

The seasoned pesticide expert replied: "Well, come to think of it, we *do* have a few positive tests, with levels between 20 and 80 parts per billion. But those must have been lab errors. Any ETU level of more than 10 parts per trillion is too high."

"Richard," I told him, "those *weren't* false positives. Those tests are the proof!"

A few days after this disclosure, there was more news on the Florida copper and fungicide front. New data from the St. Lucie indicated that copper levels in some areas of the river were over 200 parts per million. One concerned caller told me that the crabs next to his dock were as "copper-colored as an old penny."

Any doubts about my theories were being washed away with 8,000 cubic feet per second of Okeechobee overflow water—a deluge that also carried tons of silt, huge amounts of fungicides and heavy metals in porewater.

While I was still reeling with euphoria, Brian called again, in order to point out that the *El Nino* rains and high water had brought an unwelcome visitor to the orange groves. The Phytophthora fungus, aka "brown rot," had threatened hundreds of square miles of orange trees, and rapid treatment had been required.

Instead of using metalaxyl—a safe, slow-acting systemic fungicide that has worked very well for tobacco farmers in North Carolina —the orange growers were forced to resort to using fast acting copper and dithiocarbamates. And the predictable fish kills had begun promptly in the March of 1998, following intensive deployment of the fungicide in February. Now copper levels had topped 200 ppm. in the river. But what about the dithocarbamates? Richard Pfeuffer promised to locate the new data.

All at once, my argument looked much stronger. After all, nobody denied that blue-green algae and cryptomonads were killed by copper—or that copper and dithiocarbamates wiped out rotifers. Both chemicals had been present in the St. Lucie just before a major fish kill ... while the nutrient levels remained normal, along with the chlorophylls.

What about human health problems in the land of oranges and sunshine? Brian said he knew of six people with rashes and flu-like symptoms, and a reporter from Stuart soon confirmed the presence of these cases.

"Ritchie, I've read your manuscript," said Brian. "It could be the script for what's happening here now. Two nights ago, a state health official announced at a public meeting that there was no human health risk from pfiesteria. She didn't say 'crypto'—she specifically said 'pfiesteria.'

"The state dragged the *main* channel of the nearby Indian River and found only seven lesioned fish out of 2,000. Real estate values are down and charter boats are idle. It's *deja vu!*"

I talked fast. "I need a doctor who can help us, Brian. The health issue will come next, and we must be ready to help sick patients. Can you find us a family doc who might be willing to take on this battle? He's going to have to know everything!"

Within a matter of days, Brian had located David Bright, M.D. This physician was also an avid kayaker. He loved diving and fishing, along with the environment and his job as a family doc. Dr. Bright listened to my story at great length, and he sounded intrigued by it.

"The illnesses I've heard about don't sound as severe as your cases," he soon told me. "Maybe 'crypto' will turn out to be more benign than pfiesteria. But it's interesting that ciguatera, another dinoflagellate toxin disease, also begins with neurologic abnormalities and finishes with gastrointestinal symptoms. Maybe these dinoflagellate toxins all act in a similar manner."

During a break in our discussions, David inquired about my own medical training. When I described my resume, he did a double-take. "You began at Duke in '69? So did I! Remember Dr. Bonk in Chem 1?"

As it turned out, David had graduated with me in 1973. I guess I'd been isolated in some DNA lab, and hadn't gotten to know him. Or maybe it was David who was buried in a lab. He had studied with Dr. Fridovich about free radicals and superoxide dismutase. And then he'd gone on to med school at the University of Maryland. Small world, for sure!

I left our talk with the hope that he would "take on the job" of telling Florida the truth about pfiesteria, when the first sick patients began to show up in consulting rooms.

I knew now that the solutions for this problem weren't going to come from the CDC or the state scientists. Even worse, research grant money for the University of Maryland team was being held up by squabbles with a University of Miami team, and Dr. Burkholder's lab was being cut out of needed funding. Turf issues? Academic issues? Jealousy? Why hadn't Dr. Grattan's article been published yet? Questions ...

All this posturing! Political statements, Health Department guidelines, academic rivalries, panicky populations of tourists: Who needs these pointless distractions? Can't we shut down some of the static —and instead find a substitute for the copper-chelating fungicides that are so frequently employed near our watersheds?

If the politicians wouldn't listen to my views about predator-prey relationships and toxic pesticides and heavy metals, maybe they'd listen to Dr. George Simmons, professor emeritus of biology at Virginia Tech. Dr. Simmons is a renowned authority on aquatic ecology and fecal coliforms.

"Ritchie, your ideas are the cutting edge of this issue," the Virginia expert told me candidly. "I agree with you completely. The problem is that we've disrupted the aquatic community of organisms with agricultural chemicals. We've removed the filtering mechanism of biologic controls that in turn permits amplification of population. ..."

What a battle! Yes, it's been an exhilarating—and an exhausting year—to say the least. But I know I've got to keep on fighting. I've got to keep on struggling day in and day out for the health of the folks who inhabit my little corner of the Chesapeake, and in the hope that the truth will eventually emerge in this vitally important public issue.

Meanwhile, there's another reporter on the line (he wants "just a few minutes") ... and two patients are waiting for consults in my office ... and another HMO "recertification packet" just arrived, weighing at least twenty pounds. ...

Lord help us. When is this story ever going to end?

Edgar Hall, Muskrats, Dead Grasses

April 20, 1998

I was groping for answers. What should we do to safeguard our estuaries? Imagine my relief when a Pocomoke old-timer named Edgar Hall agreed to give me a hand.

Hall had seen everything around here and done just about everything, too. While he might sell you a car or life insurance, Edgar was most at home in the marshes and woods of the Pocomoke.

He was an old-fashioned outdoorsman used to seeing foxes trot and owls hoot as if he weren't there. He trapped, too. Muskrats were a source of food and pelt—if you didn't mind walking an icy marsh at 4 a.m. to set and harvest your traps. Edgar explained that the cold water "numbs your hand" so that the cuts from the sharp ice "don't matter much."

"It would be nice if some of you pfiesteria experts could tell me what's happened to the marsh grasses," Hall growled at me. "You go take a look at Pitts Creek, where the Hollands used to trap 800 muskrats in a winter. There's nothing left of the grasses over there now, not even a tump, and not a muskrat in sight."

As it turned out, JoAnn had taught two of Edgar's grandchildren in kindergarten. The old man's daughter, Sharon, was also a teacher at JoAnn's school. And I'd had a lot of fun in my cooking columns, while bragging about the culinary skills displayed by Edgar's wife, Ruth. (She's a local cooking legend, especially when it comes to preparing wild game such as raccoon and muskrat.)

Here in the Pocomoke region, the river and the marshes provide productive habitat for the muskrats, whose vegetarian diet consists of aquatic roots and tubers, cattails, bulrushes, spike rush and a major food-staple that grows in our ponds: water iris.

Muskrats are persistent little rascals. I'd done my best to control our first crew of rodents (after they devoured our water lilies) by building wire fences into dams, digging out cattails and trapping. (A DNR expert had showed me the proper trapping-methods.) But I'd also managed to trap a few of JoAnn's favorite water birds— not good. So I was glad to learn that Edgar had decided to help me understand muskrats. Learning about the dead grasses was an unexpected extra.

In ponds such as ours, muskrats are a frequent nuisance. It's not just that they scarf up every plant in sight. Their tunnels and root-feeding holes also undermine bank structure ... creating booby traps big enough to break a horse's cannon bone.

The DNR allows property owners to trap muskrats year-round in order to offset the damage done by this nuisance species. From a larger perspective, however, it's important to note that muskrats provide important habitat for turtles and other marshland creatures. Like pfiesteria in the rivers, muskrats live in our ponds now; they won't be leaving anytime soon!

I looked forward to my visit with Edgar Hall, because I was concerned about the fact that so many muskrats were now appearing in our ponds. Were they in flight from the pfiesteria-tainted waters around Shelltown?

You've probably heard the saying: "Still waters run deep." So it was with Edgar Hall. He didn't talk much—but when he did, people listened. Edgar's knowledge of the river and the marshland went back a lifetime.

It was alarming to hear him describe how he'd trapped 275 raccoons in 1996—but only 75 by late fall of '97. And the muskrats seemed to have vanished completely from his stretch of the river, as well. I couldn't help wondering: Had our rodent-jammed ponds become an "Ellis Island" for Edgar's "tired, poor, and huddling" muskrats?

"I walked that marsh near Beverly [just upriver from Shelltown], and found just two muskrat holes," said a mournful-looking Hall. "Then I walked 30 more minutes and found no more. Why, it used to be that we would set 200 traps a day there!

"Whatever's killing those grasses starts on the inside of the marsh, not along the river's edge. No grasses, no muskrats—it's as simple as that."

Listening to him, I quickly reviewed the history of the region. The marsh grasses, especially Spartina, had started to die off about five years before: why? Was no-till agriculture once again the culprit? Remember that under this agricultural system, all materials spread on the fields are soon exposed to wind and rain. And the pesticide maps showed clearly that soils high in organics would retain agricultural chemicals.

I knew that heavy metals were stored in marshes, but what about herbicides? If retained herbicides were washed into the marsh under flood conditions, they would stay there. Did these chemicals kill the grasses? Of course, the tides scoured the shorelines, removing runoff chemicals from the soils—but the interior of the marsh, without flushing, has now become barren. And it won't be long before invasive plant species (like herbicide-resistant phragmites) take over.

Phragmites, like similar nuisance plants (kudzu, for instance) that now flourish in the south, don't provide food for our native animals—which suggests that their numbers will soon grow out of ecological balance.

Listening to Hall, I found myself wondering if the changes in our estuarine habitat, with the disappearance of spike rush, were also driven by weed killing herbicides from farms and lawns that were also killing grasses in marshes. I tried to imagine the consequences, if our marshes were in fact being destroyed by agricultural herbicides. Widespread erosion would be one result, and the loss of buffering and botanical filtration another. Then the heavy metals and the retained pesticides would be leached into the porewater of the rivers. All too soon, our swamps, wetlands and marshes would be stripped of their natural defenses.

In a way, I was rather pleased that our own ponds still contained enough vegetation to support a burgeoning population of muskrats. Perhaps a balance of nature would emerge here, without the need for wires, traps and cattail-digging. We'd have more muskrats now (a muskrat bloom!), but soon would have more owl babies, perhaps more foxes. ...

The grim question loomed: Was this ecological system out of balance? With Edgar Hall's help, I'd come to understand enough about our ecosystem to know that habitat means food, cover, and breeding sites. And what I was witnessing along the Pocomoke was a change in that habitat—a change driven by effects of chemicals on the ecologic community in submerged soils.

What do Pitts Creek, Shelltown, the Neuse and the St. Lucie have in common? Answer: Not enough rotifers, not enough marsh grasses—and probably not enough muskrats.

Thank you, Edgar Hall. Although I know he will never be invited to a "photo-op" with the Governor, I was convinced that this gentleman could tell us more about our threatened habitat than most scientists.

"You have to be sure to leave no mark on this runway," he had told me more than once, while describing how the muskrats scooted along their marshland burrows, and how they were spooked away from them by any disruption of their lairs. "The rat runs along the edge here, see? He can sit here protected from owls and hawks, while he eats. Don't let him know we were here!"

But the muskrat's habitat had been dramatically changed now. The invaders had arrived in earnest—in the form of foreign-looking grasses and pfiesteria. Edgar Hall understood that ... and he knew the reasons why. At seventy years of age, he was articulating a perfectly reasonable wetlands policy.

"You will have pfiesteria here until you die, if you let it live. Stop killing the creatures that control it.

"Leave no mark," warned Edgar. "Let no one know you were here!"

What the Media Said

July 17   *Daily Times of Salisbury* (Daily Times)
          Doctor floats theory on fish lesions-copper.

July 18   *Daily Times of Salisbury*
          State politely nixes doc's theory.

July 18   *Daily Times of Salisbury*
          Clean up of Bay behind schedule.
          Reduction of nitrogen and phosphates by 2000.

July 19   *Daily Times of Salisbury*
          Number of afflicted fish on the decline.
          DNR trawls show 1% of 3296 fish.

July 26   *Daily Times* Letter Walt Benton
          Our best rivers are dying.

July 31   *Daily Times* Letter Max Chambers
          Reducing nitrates and phosphates removes algae
          essential for oyster larva production. Cleaning the Bay
          has become sterilizing the Bay.

Aug. 3   *Baltimore Sun*
          First sick fish now sick people.
          Announcement of River Associated Rash and Illness
          Center; Waterskier.

Aug. 5   *Daily Times*
          Delaware tests waters in Indian River, Lymphocystis,
          not pfiesteria blamed for causing lesions on rockfish.

Aug. 5   *Daily Times*
          Man hospitalized for skin lesions DHMH says no corre-
          lation between pfiesteria toxin and ill health in humans.
          The river is safe if common sense used.
          This is my first patient I've directly correlated to the
          river, but I don't feel it will be the last.

Aug. 6   *Worcester County Messenger* Special panel meets at
         Salisbury State.
         Tourism is harmed.

Aug.6   *Baltimore Sun*
         Hopkins, University to examine eight watermen.
         Ritchie Shoemaker says six to eight patients constitute a
         cohort.

Aug. 7   *Daily Times*
         Fish kill forces river warning, State says 2000 fish killed.
         Jack Howard says 100,000. There are a lot of seagulls just
         gorging themselves.
         Dave Goshorn DNR Biologist.

Aug. 7   *Daily Times*
         Maryland's top doc says stop the hype.
         CBF says use bleach after exposure but bleach can cause
         harm.

Aug. 8   *Daily Times*
         Pocomoke shut down. The fish kill continues, people not
         heeding warning.

Aug. 8   *Baltimore Sun*
         Pocomoke partially closed off.
         Life cycle of pfiesteria reviewed. Delaware doing more
         tests. Wayne Gilchrest involved. Additional patient
         reported.

Aug. 8   *Washington Post*
         Fish kill prompts closing of part of Pocomoke River.
         Reports finding dead fish on bottom of river, seagulls
         eating fish, questions pfiesteria causing illness passing
         through food chain.

Aug. 9   *Baltimore Sun*
         Algae may be fish kill culprit. Burkholder gives tentative
         diagnosis.

Aug. 9   *Washington Post*
         Pocomoke problems hurting more than fish.
         Tourism down.

Aug. 9 *Daily Times*
Pfiesteria top suspect in fish kills.
Senator Sarbanes and Mikulski will tour the river.
Meeting at Log Cabin 08/11.
Wayne Gilchrest announces $120,000 coming. Senators announce $400,000 coming.

Aug. 11 *Daily Times*
Few solutions to river woes. Fish sales, shrimp sales, crab sales down everywhere. We are dealing with Mother Nature. There's not much you can do about it. Donald Boesch, Ph.D. who also says researchers have not turned up a substantial increase in nutrients going into the Pocomoke and the problem may be something entirely different.
There is no certain evidence that pollution of the Pocomoke River is causing an outbreak of pfiesteria.

Aug. 11 *Daily Times*
Poultry waste suspected cause of river problems.
Rick Nelson says we get kind of tired that every time something's going on in the water they look at the land and point their fingers at farms.

Aug. 12 *Daily Times* Letter
Larry Knudsen, Innkeeper, fear mongering, for whatever purpose, is deplorable.

Aug. 12 *Washington Post*
US wades in to assess human risk of Pocomoke fish kills.
Senator Mikulski wants CDC detectives. Senator Sarbanes announces $2 million appropriation to upgrade sewage plants in Snow Hill and Pocomoke. Chicken manure is one possibility among many leads, says LT Governor Townsend. Will Baker calls for large chicken companies to take responsibility for manure. 600 million chickens raised on the Eastern Shore.

Aug. 12 *Baltimore Sun*
Pocomoke will be reopened 8-3, toxin is gone. NOAA allocates $250.000 in emergency funds. Agriculture runoff blamed.

Aug. 13 *Daily Times*
Some fishermen find lesioned fish upriver from Snow Hill. Others don't.

Aug. 16 *Daily Times*
Delaware samples positive for pfiesteria from Indian River and Indian River Bay. There is no correlation (between pfiesteria and human illness) as of yet.
Greg Sylvester, M.D., Delaware Public Health Department.

Aug. 17 *Baltimore Sun*
Pfiesteria most likely caused illness, Donald Schmechel M.D., confirms waterskier as a case.

Aug. 18 *Daily Times*
Guilt By Association Dr. Schmechel's Reports.

Aug. 18 *Daily Banner*, Cambridge Maryland Dr. Schmechel's Reports.

Aug. 19 *Baltimore Sun*
Technicians ill after work in Pocomoke.
Baltimore Sun, River's woes go upstream tourism, seafood consumption down.

Aug. 20 *Washington Post*
Three Maryland workers sick after contact with Pocomoke.
Number of sick people rises.

Aug. 20 *Worcester County Messenger*
Pfiesteria could be cause of workers health problems. Dr. Morris team is coming.

Aug. 20 *Somerset Herald*
Officials confirm pfiesteria.

Aug. 20 *Daily Times*
         Researchers ill after river contact. DHMH officials say
         Pocomoke is still safe. Second patient from Pocomoke is
         being evaluated at Duke University.

Aug. 20 *Daily Times*
         Turtles with lesions reported (found in April!!).

Aug. 22 *Daily Times*
         NASA joins Pocomoke investigation.
         $7000 portable weather station to aid in correlating
         changes in the Pocomoke with kills.

Aug. 23 *Daily Times*
         Doctors study river's tie to illnesses. 13 patients seen,
         20 different media organizations on site.

Aug. 27 *Daily Times*
         Farm runoff will be investigated. Dr. Tom Simpson say
         there is no established relationship between agriculture
         runoff and the micro organism.

Aug. 27 *Daily Times*
         Researchers isolated and purify a water soluble toxin;
         Dr. Burkholder finds the toxin can withstand 170
         degrees heat for two hours.

Aug. 27 *Daily Times*
         Fish kill extends upriver officials downplay number
         of dead fish (again).

Aug. 27 *Daily Times*, Extent of danger from fish uncertain.
         Dr. Wasserman acknowledges that officials can't be
         certain there is no serious threat to human illness from
         pfiesteria. There will be answers to those questions
         sooner rather than later.
         He says experts believe people can contract various
         illnesses if they come into contact with the toxin.

Aug. 28 *Daily Times*
         Menhaden die of low oxygen content in a small creek
         on the ocean side, Accomac County.

Aug. 28   *Baltimore Sun*
Angler's find fish with lesions far from Pocomoke River. CBF suspects pfiesteria active elsewhere.

Aug. 29   *Baltimore Sun*
New urgency in hunt for cause of fish kill. Aeromonas blamed but throughout the Bay never have so many fish been caught with sores and lesions.
Warren Klawans is quoted, John Viars and patient from Chester River too.

Aug. 29   *Daily Times*
Officials extend Pocomoke advisory for second time this week upriver, now to Rehobeth, 5 miles from Pocomoke City.

Aug. 30   *Baltimore Sun*
Today section, trouble in the water, overview of seafood, agriculture and the public meeting at log cabin.

Aug. 30   *Washington Post* front page
Governor Glendening says tiny organism has caused health problems. Turnabout in state position is now complete. Next battle is to save the seafood industry.

Aug. 30   *Daily Times*
Governor closed portion of Pocomoke River. Front page.

Aug. 30   *Baltimore Sun*
Fish kill organism harmed 13.

Aug. 31   *Baltimore Sun*
Fish toxin affects brain. Front page Memory loss common exposure, common symptoms convinced medical team that the pattern of health problems was convincing.

Aug. 31   *Daily Times*
Medical teams pursues sick fish mystery.

Aug. 31   *Washington Post*
Truth and consequences. The PET scans convinced Governor Glendening to act.

Aug. 31 *Washington Post*
A key question was how to minimize problems when you tell the truth.

Sept. 1 *Washington Post*
Maryland officials eat seafood making point. Feast near Pocomoke held to allay fears. Metro edition showed Marty with a home brew; that photo left out of local edition.

Sept. 2 *Baltimore Sun*
River's woes go upstream tourism, seafood consumption down.

Sept. 3 *Somerset Herald*
Pfiesteria held responsible for health problem, watermen knew cause of illness.

Sept. 3 *Worcester County Messenger*
River is closed, may be harmful to people.

Sept. 4 *Daily Times*
People feel effects of Pocomoke River includes photo of swimmer misidentified as water skier.

Sept. 4 *Daily Times,*
Additional fish kill on Pocomoke River.

Sept. 5 *Daily Times*
MD's burden near $300,000, costs of pfiesteria test up to $20,000 are rumored.

Sept. 5 *Baltimore Sun*
Officials let watermen retrieve gear, reimbursement planned.

Sept. 6 *Daily Times*
State will reimburse watermen.

Sept. 6 *Baltimore Sun*
Maryland briefs doctors on micro organism, coverage of Med Chi convention, lists me as the first to treat patients suffering from pfiesteria illness.

Sept. 6   *Sun Journal* New Bern N.C.
Hundreds of people have told Rick Dove about being sickened by Neuse River fish kills. NC concedes that exposure to waters involved in fish kills can hurt people. Stanley Musik tries to cast doubt on Maryland's data. Dr. Burkholder flatly states that pfiesteria toxin affects mammals.

Sept. 6   Raleigh News and Observer, panel to investigate pfiesteria response, calls the Chesapeake Bay the backyard playground for many Washington power brokers.

Sept. 7   *Jacksonville Times Union*
Are we next?
Photos and story on pfiesteria in Florida, presents copper and permanganate.

Sept. 7   *Baltimore Sun*
Chicken waste linked to toxin in Pocomoke. No link was presented.

Sept. 8   *Baltimore Sun*, Del Wilber (Quoting Marty Wassserman)
"He just pushed us to recognize the problem. He didn't really understand what our limitations were. I have a great deal of respect for him. He's a very dedicated physician."

Sept. 10   *Worcester County Messenger*
Seeking source of pfiesteria outbreak. Photo of Dr. Wasserman, Governor Glendening, Dr. Burkholder and me, cropped to eliminate me. My hand with its distinguishing middle finger, glasses and blue document pouch are easily seen. Copper theory text is facing Governor Glendening.

Sept. 10   *Daily Times*
Maryland steps up pfiesteria monitoring. Lesioned fish reported by many local fisherman, especially in Tangier Sound.

Sept. 11   *Daily Times*
Kings Creek, tributary of Manokin closed.

Sept. 11   *Washington Post* Front page
New fish kill found miles from Pocomoke. State workers use gloves, boots, rain suits, goggles and respirators.

Sept. 12   *Daily Times*
Manokin outbreak weakens; photos of state workers in full biological warfare gear on a boat. White House now involved. Maryland Congressman secure $7 million in aid.

Sept. 13   *Washington Post*
Farmers fear hasty reaction to fish kills.

Washington Post front page
Sick fish (50 to 75%) discovered in Rappahannock. Virginia's policy is at odds with Maryland. Virginia is acting like NC, hoping the problem will just go away.

Sept. 13   *Baltimore Sun*
Farm runoff rumor started. Proof sought that agricultural nutrients caused fish kills. Local legislators now fight in state senate over agricultural restrictions.

Sept. 13   *Salisbury Times*
Human toll mounts in pfiesteria outbreak. 17 more patients examined by medical team. Nanticoke River harbor kill not confirmed.

Sept. 14   *Baltimore Sun*
Sewage plants slow to upgrade front page.

Sept. 14   *Washington Post*
Rejects bird's link to fish kills. Governor will appoint a Blue Ribbon Commission, headed by former Governor Harry Hughes. What is happening on the ground impacts chicken farmers. What is happening in the watershed.

Sept. 14   *Washington Post*
Angus Phillips allaying fears of pfiesteria. Review water exposure and illness.

Sept. 15 *Daily Times*
Fish fighting losing battle. Chicamacomico kill starts.
Congressman Gilchrest public meeting at Pocomoke
High School.

Sept. 16 *Washington Post*
Microbe symptoms found in 15 more. Dr. Morris confirms additional cases. Virginia says no health hazard
from pfiesteria. Governor says cut the hype. Virginia
will take a scientific approach. Governor Glendening
says there is a sense of urgency in Virginia's outbreaks,
Virginia's Dept. Health Commissioner Gordon is openly
skeptical of Dr. Morris group of researchers. Maryland
won't share data with Virginia. No one in Virginia is
sick. Pfiesteria was found at Kings Creek.

Sept. 16 *Daily Times*
Scientist believe pfiesteria has been around a long time.

Sept. 16 *Daily Times*
Gilchrest assures shore farmers Chicamacomico is not
surrounded by poultry farms. Kill in Chicamacomico
was 100 yards wide and five miles long, says Jack
Howard.

Sept. 16 *Baltimore Sun*
Pfiesteria tests positive in Kings Creek. Blue Ribbon
Commission appointed at Gilchrest's meeting, several
residents grumbled during state officials' presentations.
But nearly all applauded Dr. Ritchie Shoemaker, a local
physician who first treated local residents sickened by
pfiesteria.

Sept. 17 *Baltimore Sun*
Enemy may be Governor's friend, Dr.Shoemaker says
Glendening's response provides a model for other
Governors, instead of trying to suppress it, Governor
Glendening got up and said there is a human health
problem, that took a lot of courage.

Sept. 17 *Worcester County Messenger*
Hundreds at meeting on Pocomoke River.

Sept. 17   *Somerset Herald*
            Crisfield Chamber of Commerce cancels fish fry.

Sept. 18   *Washington Post*
            Watermen say Rappahannock should remain open.

Sept. 18   *Washington Post* front page
            One scary, mysterious microbe. Review of Dr.
            Burkholder's lab.

Sept. 18   *Baltimore Sun*
            Pfiesteria is latest of micro organisms to infest waters.
            Global dinoflagellate problem.

Sept. 18   *Baltimore Sun* front page
            State's closing of rivers justified, medical teams says
            NIEHS has committed several hndred thousand
            dollars for continuing research.

Sept. 18   *Daily Times*
            Fish chaos may help Governor.

Sept. 19   *USA Today*
            Pfiesteria fears, microbe causing concern on Maryland
            Shore. National media covers story too.

Sept. 19   *Washington Post*
            Virginia confirms pfiesteria, not ready to close river.
            Virginia Dept. Health Commissioner says Rap-
            pahannock is certainly a safe place to swim and
            fish.

Sept. 20   *NY Times*
            Governors pledge to join fight against microbe
            killing fish. Maryland is on the offensive to bring
            other states, especially Virginia in line regarding
            pfiesteria.

Sept. 20   *Daily Times*
            Governor team up to fight pfiesteria. PA and North
            Carolina sends a representative; WV, Virginia,
            Delaware, Maryland send Governors.

Sept. 21   *Patriot News* Harrisburg, Pa.
            No sign of pfiesteria in Pa.

Sept. 21   *Washington Post*
Glendening nets political points with bold moves on pfiesteria outbreak. Politicians jockey for position, more waterways suspected.

Sept. 21   *Washington Post* Outlook article see text

Sept. 22   *Daily Times*
Rockfish sores stem from weakness. Another fish stress story. Isopods blamed (this time) invading after a bacteria attacks the fish skin.

Sept. 23   *Washington Post*
Glendening seeks timely pfiesteria study. Dr. Burkholder gives the commission a lesson in pfiesteria. Animal waste, chicken manure is blamed immediately. Rick Nelson asks for tests to identify sources of nutrients in the river. No reasonable answer was given.

Sept 23.   *Daily Times*
Pfiesteria Commission hears testimony. Most of the testimony focused on nutrient pollution and its effect on pfiesteria.

Sept 24.   *Worcester County Messenger*
Governors meet about river fear issues, health report, Dr. Shoemaker's cases, reports and theory.

Sept. 25   *Baltimore Sun*
Scientific sleuths prove pfiesteria harmful to man.

Sept. 25   *Daily Times*
Copper theory presented. Secretary Griffin says nothing to theory at all. Shoemaker says I have heard that tune before.

Sept. 25   *Salisbury Times* Doug Hanks
Without people like Ritchie pushing and prodding, we might not have come to the conclusions we did as rapidly as we did.

Sept. 30   *Daily Times* editorial
Copper idea warrants fair hearing. See text.

Oct. 1   *Worcester County Messenger*
State seeks federal help in fighting pfiesteria. Secretary
John Griffin still hasn't Seen any significant amount of
copper in the Pocomoke River (!!) You've got two good
eyes but still don't see is a featured lyric on a local radio
station.

Oct. 1   *King George Journal*
Virginia reprints Washington Post article.

Oct. 3   *Baltimore Sun*
Illness indicate pfiesteria spread. Two new cases
originate from unclosed rivers.
Seven new cases from the Chicamacomico. Wicomico
Creek and Nanticoke River not closed.

Oct. 3   *Daily Times*
Shore Farmers tell state panel to get facts, my copper
presentation is supported by many, see text.

Oct. 4   Governor Glendening orders reopening of Pocomoke
Rivers. People get sick earlier. We can not go on sick
fish any longer. We've got to go on sick people said
Shoemaker.

Oct. 4   *Washington Post*
Pfiesteria crisis is past, Pocomoke is reopened. Virginia
continues to stall. Two more cases being reviewed.

Oct. 9   *Baltimore Sun*
House oks $3 million for study, monitoring of pfiesteria
outbreak.
(EPA)

Oct. 4   *Baltimore Sun*
Pocomoke reopened, probe of two cases ongoing. The
waterskier won't go near the water. Members of the
Wicomico Yacht Club, near the area of the diver's
activity, saw school of lesioned menhaden but won't
talk to a Sun reporter.

Oct. 8   *Daily Times*
Pocomoke M.D. finds pfiesteria illness cure.
MCS protocol presented to the media.

Oct. 8   *Daily Times*
State officials blame parasite not pfiesteria. Lernecia
was in the Chincoteague Bay but what made Norman
Tarr sick was the pfiesteria that was there too. Bruce
Nichols received this and additional report of lesioned
fish from a second waterman.

Oct. 8   *Worcester County Messenger* present theory in full detail.
State reopens Pocomoke.
Farmers testify at meeting the commission is totally
political.

Oct. 9   *Washington Post*
After tests on four patients, Virginia discounts microbe threat. Virginia tries to rule out pfiesteria. I am
critical about the Virginia public line. They say that
their superficial testing is enough to rule out pfiesteria.
Chesapeake Bay Foundation joins the criticism.

Oct. 9   *Daily Times*
Florida to assemble pfiesteria task force. That State
will be ready for next years fish kill. Virginia pfiesteria
tests from their DNR are negative. There are no human
health effects from pfiesteria in Virginia waters, said
the Virginia Health Commissioner. Additional tests
done by Harold Marshall from Old Dominion University were positive for pfiesteria on samples taken
from both the Rappahannock and the Great Wicomico
River.

Oct. 10   *Daily Times*
Scientists, including Dr. Burkholder and VIMS asked
a House subcommittee on Fisheries, Conservation,
Wildlife and Oceans for additional funding to work
on the pfiesteria problem. Poultry industry officials say
that strict regulatory controls can destroy the poultry
industry on the Eastern Shore.

Oct. 19   *Salisbury Daily Times*
Al Gore announces $200 million grant for a massive
Chesapeake Bay restoration project. The Bay project
will be the first in the nation to come under the USDA
Conservation Reserve Enhancement program.

Oct. 19   *Daily Times*
Scientists write to stop microbe. Maryland, Virginia,
and NC will share medical data.

Oct. 24   *Baltimore Sun*
Special article Awash in uncertainty. Tim Murray, the
diver from the Wicomico Creek is featured as is MCS
protocol.

Oct. 24   *Worcester County Messenger*
Commission votes against chicken house building
moratorium. Rick Nelson says farmers rotate crop
fertilization. Dr. Shoemaker again shows that the
nitrate and phosphate as was said previously by Dr.
Boesch, are not too high. No algae blooms can be
documented.

Nov. 11   *Daily Times*
Restrictions lifted from an shore waterways. Chica-
macomico opened 11/1/97, Kings Creek 10/17/97 and
Pocomoke River 10/3-97.

Nov. 12   *Daily Times*
Fish kill may be other microbe. Jack Howard is correct.
There are at least three different dinoflagellates and
probably at least three different toxins. Karen Steidinger
Ph.D. from Florida's DNR, has proven that the pfiesteria
from the Pocomoke River are similar species to pfiesteria
piscicida. Maybe the difference in exposures and
illnesses in Maryland and North Carolina are due to
different toxins. Just when we thought the problem was
complicated enough.

Nov. 12   *Worcester County Messenger*
Same story as above.

Nov. 17 *Somerset Herald*
A new poultry litter compost system is demonstrated.
Manure is a resource; it will be used.

Nov. 20 *USA Today*
Rodney Barker, Author of *And the River Turned to Blood*,
feels vindicated by what Maryland did.

Nov. 21 *Skin and Allergy News* have photos of Virginia Marine
Police workers and MCS protocol.

Nov. 21 *Internal Medicine News*
Fish eating microbe may affect humans has story,
photos, and MCS protocol.

Nov. 21 *Family Practice News*
My photo is on front page with story, MCS protocol,
and quotes from Dr. Wasserman.

Nov. 21 *Daily Times*
People making news. Jack Howard joins Dr. Ritchie
Shoemaker and Ray Maddox as the local pfiesteria
celebrities. If the State DNR would just pay Jack what
they promised all would be improved.

Nov. 21 MMJ article, Diagnosis of Pfiesteria Human Illness
Syndrome published.
Feb. 1998 MMJ article, Treatment of Persistent Pfiesteria
Human Illness Syndrome published.

Safe Seafood

Maryland Secretary of Health, Dr. Marty Wasserman and his wife Barbara are coming for a Sunday seafood feast. Marty wants to show uncertain seafood eaters in Maryland that eating seafood harvested from outside the closed portion of the Pocomoke River is safe. JoAnn and I just want to have a nice dinner with a fellow physician and his wife.

Mayor Lippoldt will come, as well as Bruce Nichols, Bonnie and Bob Rose, Don Malloy and Alan Bickling, CEO of McCready. TV cameras and newspaper reporters can come too at no extra charge.

Major Mike Howard caught beautiful trout from the Pocomoke Sound; together with some Sally clams and baked rockfish Shoe-style, some crabcakes will show the media just how good life is on the Pocomoke.

Marinate trout fillets, with butter, lemon, dillweed, coriander, black pepper and garlic. Leave uncovered in the refrigerator overnight, spraying lightly with vegetable oil if the meat looks too dry. Wrap well in tin foil and cook over a medium grill for 15 minutes.

Find two nice rockfish fillets (when is it legal Mike?). Marinate, like the trout, with a splash of white wine to cut the oily taste. Lay in an open broiling pan. Brush on Rick Nelson's Vidalia onion sauce, surrounding the fillets with fresh tomato quarters, match stick zucchini and green onion rounds. Top with parmesan, sesame oil, thyme, fennel, ginger and paprika, bake thirty minutes; don't turn.

Add a tomato-basil-feta salad with Italian dressing, Bonnie's famous broccoli salad, JoAnn's fresh bean casserole, munchies, dip and a fruit bowl. This dinner is going to be spectacular!

Now the crabcakes. Separate two pounds of fresh backfin, remove cartilage. Sprinkle with the fine crumbs of two handsful of oyster cracker saltines. Slosh on two whole eggs, whipped. Mix in three, no make it four, dollops of mayonnaise (not low fat). Add a dash of Old Bay, chervil, dry mustard, black pepper, cumin and garlic. Mix gently. Mold into 4 oz. cakes, loosely firmed. Bake in the same oven as the rockfish until brown, about thirty minutes at 375 degrees.

As the media watched, this meal came together, as did our friendship. While Marty and I had been saying different things about human health issues and pfiesteria, he showed courage to reverse his position publicly and act promptly to prevent additional cases of toxin related human disease. With no hard feelings, the crabcakes tasted even better.

—by Ritch Shoemaker

What Marty Wasserman
(and a few others) Said

Aug. 3   Caitlan Francke, *Baltimore Sun*
He hopes to get a cluster of people with similar symptoms to study.

Aug. 6   Dennis O'Brien, *Baltimore Sun*
We are absolutely not blowing this off. We are going to address this problem, but we're going to do it thoroughly and carefully.
No concrete link has been established between the watermen's illnesses and whatever caused lesions on fish.

Aug. 7   *Salisbury Times*, Jon Bentz
There are groups on the periphery that are making it very difficult for us to do our jobs. Some are actually getting in our way with some of the information they've been feeding to the public for which they have no evidence.
No evidence links fish sores to human illness. The Pocomoke River is safe if common sense precautions are taken. We don't want to scream fire in a crowded theater.

Aug. 8   *Baltimore Sun*, Dail Willis
There's been no definite evidence yet, (fish lesions and human health) we are being cautious.

Aug. 9   *Baltimore Sun*, Dail Willis
We're one step closer to solving this problem and looking at this dilemma. We're right in the beginning of uncovering a mystery here.

Aug. 9   *Daily Times*, Doug Hanks
I believe in the next few weeks and months we will
solve this mystery.

Aug. 12   *Baltimore Sun*, Dail Willis
The reason we're opening the river is we don't believe
a toxin is remaining in the water.

Aug. 12   Angus Phillips, *Washington Post*
We are in the middle of a real life mystery and we don't
have the answer.

Aug. 19   *Baltimore Sun*, Dennis O'Brien
We are very concerned about what the watermen and
others are telling us and we are aggressively seeking
answers.

Aug. 20   *Washington Post*, Todd Shields, Dr. Diane Matuszak
We can't draw any conclusions at all until the state
study is complete.

Aug. 23   *Daily Times*, Jon Bentz, Georges Benjamin, M.D.
We're attempting to get data to establish a baseline
study. We'll use that information to work with health
departments to develop a treatment strategy.

Aug. 30   *Baltimore Sun*, Rob Hiaasen quoting Dr. Wasserman
8/11/97 at Log Cabin meeting There is no acute
medical danger with what seems to be going on in
the Pocomoke.

Aug. 30   *Washington Post*, Todd Shields
We are no longer skeptical after PET scans and
research teams findings reported.

Aug. 30   *Daily Times*, AP Staff
There is a likely link between pfiesteria and people
working on the water.

Aug. 31   *Baltimore Sun*, Caitlan Franke
Medically we had been skeptical. Now the situation
has been reversed.

Aug. 31   *Washington Post*, Charles Babington
A key question was how to minimize problems when
you tell the truth.

Sept. 1   *Washington Post*, At our house, The message we've sent from day one is that fish that don't have lesions, fish that haven't died in fish kills, are safe to eat in Maryland. If it was unhealthy, I wouldn't be doing this. Its safe for us, it is safe for the public and safe for the kids.

Sept. 8   *Baltimore Sun*, Del Wilber
He just pushed us to recognize the problem. He didn't really understand what our limitations were. I have a great deal of respect for him. He is a very dedicated physician.

Sept. 13   *Washington Post*, Charles Babington
Maryland's reaction is entirely appropriate. We are erring on the side of caution. When they (Virginia) get health problems, they'll react the way we did. North Carolina for years didn't recognize health problems and now they're (N.C.) looking at our research.

Sept. 18   *Baltimore Sun*, Marcia Myers, re closing rivers supported by medical team I can't impress how profound, how important and how much of a concern this kind of funding is during battle with Virginia regarding river closures.

Sept. 19   *Washington Post*, Eric Lipton re Virginia saying Maryland studies are inconclusive We have the advantage of examining patients at the time they show profound memory deficits. They were substantiated by neuro-cognitive tests and they were consistent with previous reported problems in North Carolina lab workers exposed to the microbe.
We do not want to have additional people suffering.

Sept. 28   *Salisbury Times*, Doug Hanks, Without people like Ritchie pushing and prodding, we might not have come to the conclusions we did as rapidly as we did.

Sept. 21 *Family Practice News*

Dr. Shoemaker was indeed antagonistic at the beginning of the investigation into pfiesteria. Yet he was key in pushing the public health department along and in helping it be responsible to Maryland's citizens. I remember waking up one night and thinking I wish Ritchie would go away but he's been what doctors should be: patient advocates and well trained in science. I have to applaud his persistence.

Dr. Shoemaker also is working with other state health departments, helping to move and guide them along. (This was my favorite Marty quote. Of course I am helping other health departments).

References

(September 30)

1) "Chicken Manure Analysis, Somerset County Extension Service" 05/02/97

2) *US EPA Analytical Report DPI Chicken Feed* 04/19/95

3) *Potential For Nuisance Algae Blooms in Lower Neuse River Estuary* NCD RCD 12/90 Project 90–15

4) Lewitus, Burkholder, May, *et al*, "Discovery of Phantom Dinoflagellate in Chesapeake Bay Estuaries" Vol. 18 No. 2: pp. 373–78, 6/95

5) Burkholder, *et al*, "Phantom Dinoflagellate As Causative Agent in Estuarine Fish Kills" *Nature* 358 (6385): pp. 407–10, 07/30/92

6) Noga, *et al*, "A New Icthyotoxic Dinoflagellate: Cause of Acute Mortality in Aquarium Fishes." *Veterinary Record* 133 (4): pp. 96–7, 07/24/93

7) Phinney and Bruland, "Effects of Dithiocarbamate and 8-Hydroxyquinolone Additions on Algal Uptake of Ambient Copper and Nickel in South San Francisco Bay Water." *Estuaries* Vol. 20 No. 1: pp. 66–76, 3/97

8) Glasgow and Burkholder, "Insidious Effects of Toxic Estuarine Dinoflagellate on Fish Survival and Human Health," *J. Toxic and Env. Health* 46: pp. 502–22, 1995

9) Griffin, *et al*, "Iron and Trace Metals in Tidal Marsh Soils of The Chesapeake Bay," *Soil Sci. Soc. Am. J.* 53: pp. 1010–1019, 1989

10) Gupta and Karuppiah, "Toxicity Identification of Pocomoke River Porewater," *Chemosphere* 33, No. 5: pp. 939–960, 1996

11) Graden *et al*, "Copper Activated Transcription Factor in Candida Species," *Biochemistry* 35 (46): pp. 14583–9, 1996

12) Rauch *et al*, "Copper Inducible Transcription Regulation in E. Coli," *Microbiology* 143: pp. 1191–202, 1997

13) Brand *et al*, "Reduction of Marine Phytoplankton Reproduction Rates by Copper and Cadmium," *J. Exp. Mar. Biol. Ecol.*, Vol. 96, pp. 225–250, 1986

14) Gupta *et al*, "Impact of Point and Nonpoint Source Pollution on Pore Waters of Two Chesapeake Bay Tributaries," *Ecotoxicology and Environmental Safety* 35, pp. 81–85, 1996

Lethal Levels of Copper
(September 30)

Pfiesteria	unknown	
Cryptomonads	1pp	10 Billion
Blue Green Algae	1pp	Billion
Cyanobacteria	1pp	Billion
Thoracosphaera (Dinoflagellate)	1pp	Trillion
Gymnodinium (Dinoflagellate)	1pp	Hundred Thousand
Other One Celled Algae	1pp	100 Billion
Rotifers	Unknown; (were not killed by 15ppm in Pocomoke River)	
Rotifers with Dithiocarbamates	Alive	
Rotifers with Dithiocarbamates and Copper Together	Dead	

Treatment of Persistent Pfiesteria Human Illness Syndrome
(October 1)

This is the manuscript sent to the MMJ.

Abstract

Patients with exposure to pfiesteria toxin have developed an illness syndrome (PHIS) characterized by skin lesions, headache, myalgias, conjunctival irritation, bronchospasm, abdominal pain, secretory diarrhea, recent memory loss and difficulties with number sequencing. Not all patients demonstrate all features of the syndrome. The natural history of PHIS shows improvement in symptoms without treatment in most patients. This paper reports successful treatment with cholestyramine of five patients whose symptoms persisted for over one month. These patient were self referred to a special clinic, the Pocomoke River Rash and Associated Illness Center, opened 8/6/97 in response to the need for a central facility for diagnosis of human illness acquired from pfiesteria.

Until the pfiesteria toxin(s) are isolated, characterized and laboratory diagnostic tests are available, physicians must be able to recognize PHIS and intervene when symptoms, particularly memory loss and diarrhea, cause significant impairment in daily activities.

There are no precedents for treatment of pfiesteria or any dinoflagellate toxin related human illness reported in the literature. The successful use of cholestyramine reported here may provide a model for understanding dinoflagellate toxin physiology in the human body.

This paper reports an uncontrolled observational study only. When identification of toxin is completed a basis for properly controlled studies will be available.

Ritchie C. Shoemaker, M.D.

TREATMENT OF PERSISTENT
PFIESTERIA-HUMAN ILLNESS SYNDROME

Treatment of human illness caused by pfiesteria toxin (PHIS) has not been reported in the medical literature. The diagnosis of acute human illness acquired from exposure to pfiesteria toxin in the wild has only been made (1) and confirmed recently (2). Acquisition of human illness from intensive laboratory exposure to pfiesteria was reported by Dr. JoAnn Burkholder's group at NC State in 1995 (3). Since the initial reports of PHIS acquired in the wild, the Pocomoke River Rash and Associated Illness Center affiliated with the Edward McCready Hospital in Crisfield, Maryland has evaluated nearly 50 patients with acute, recurrent and chronic exposure syndromes. For this report, symptoms lasting more than four weeks with or without recurrent exposure to pfiesteria inhabited water are called persistent.

A cohort of five patients with a clinical diagnosis of persistent PHIS were treated in a non randomized, uncontrolled manner. The marked clinical improvement in these patients within two weeks prompted this preliminary report. Confirmation by properly controlled scientific studies is not likely to be forthcoming until the toxin of pfiesteria is identified.

The Pocomoke River, located at the lower portion of the Eastern Shore of Maryland, is a tributary of the Chesapeake Bay. Beginning in October 1996, commercial fishermen working the Pocomoke began experiencing new symptoms of recurrent conjunctival irritation, unusual skin rashes, recurrent cough, loss of recent memory, headache, crampy abdominal pain and watery diarrhea. These symptoms coincided with the netting of fish with necrotic lesions. Menhaden were most commonly affected. All species of fish were affected. The lesions were similar to those noted from other waters including the Neuse River in North Carolina with low levels of pfiesteria toxin forming zoospores. Not all the fishermen were sickened; most had several but not all of the illness symptoms. No deaths occurred.

Similar symptoms developed acutely in three patients with brief exposure to the river (water skiing, swimming) one week before a major fish kill 8/6/97. Four cases of PHIS were found in Maryland Department of Environment employees, who were working in the water during an active fish kill. The State Dept. of Health organized a multi disciplinary team of University physicians to examine a group of 13 patients with symptoms on 8/19/97.

Consistent abnormalities on neurocognitive testing, similar to those seen in a least one of the NC State laboratory workers were found. PET scans done on five of the identified patients showed global reduction in glucose uptake. Maryland acknowledged the human health risks from pfiesteria, in part based on the severity of the neurocognitive impairment not obvious on clinical exam. The political and economic consequences of Maryland's actions were magnified partly because no effective treatment strategies were available other than closure to public use of selected rivers by the State. The public avoidance of consumption of seafood of all types was in part due to fear of contracting an untreatable illness.

The use of cholestyramine as a treatment for persistent PHIS was developed by the author after the repeated observation by the author that individuals who had an acute PHIS syndrome with secretory diarrhea, which was treated successfully with cholestyramine, also had a concurrent improvement in headache, memory loss, and rash and cough. Treatment lasted two weeks, continuing longer for those individuals with recurrent exposures. All patients were given 1 tsp of Milk of Magnesia upon arising, 1 scoop of cholestyramine mixed in juice four times a day.

Case #1

56 year old female MDE worker was on a boat sorting lesioned fish from non lesioned fish during an active fish kill 8/8/97. She had the abrupt onset of conjunctival irritation, cough, headache, wheezing, and a burning sensation on her exposed skin. The skin subsequently vesiculated and desquamated. Because of impairment of memory she was referred by the author to Donald Schmechel,

M.D. at Duke University 8/18/97. Neurocognitive studies were markedly abnormal. Treatment of nasal congestion and bronchospasm with inhaled steroids and bronchodilators improved symptoms minimally. PFT showed FVC and FEV-1 each reduced to 50% of predicted. Memory loss continued.

Treatment of 1 scoop cholestyramine with 1 oz. of 70% sorbitol (to prevent constipation) QID began 9-17-97. By 10/3-97 PFT improved to FVC 98% predicted and FEV-1 70% predicted, with nearly full restoration of memory.

Case #2

47 year old male fisherman had recurrent episodes of conjunctival irritation, cough, wheeze, headache, memory loss and severe abdominal cramping beginning 10/96. He stopped work on the river 5-97 with improvement in eye and lung symptoms. His memory loss and cramping persisted. He returned to the river 8/11/97 assisting DNR in investigation and monitoring of fish kills in many adjacent water ways. His symptoms recurred promptly. Treatment of cholestyramine, 1 scoop QID begun 8/30/97. By 9/6/97 his symptoms abated markedly. Patient returned to work in pfiesteria inhabited waters, his symptoms returned.

Case #3

33 year old white male waterman was healthy until 10/96 when he developed abdominal cramps, watery diarrhea with occasional incontinence, chronic cough, 40 lb. weight loss and headaches. He was treated for pneumonia six separate times 10/96–7/97, memory impairment documented on neurocognitives, PET scan was abnormal.

Patient was treated with inhaled steroids, bronchodilators and clarithromycin with cessation of diarrhea and improvement of in lung symptoms correlating with closure of river. Memory loss continued. With re-exposure to the river his respiratory symptoms and diarrhea recurred.

Cholestyramine and sorbitol treatment begun 9/797. He continued to have river exposure. At follow up 10/2/97 his memory loss
was dramatically improved. He continued on low dose cholestyramine with a multiple vitamin. He uses bronchodilators rarely, as
needed. Repeat neurocognitive exam showed improvement.

Case #4

32 year old commercial diver had extensive wet suit exposure to
water later shown to have pfiesteria on the Wicomico Creek. He
has the gradual onset of cramps, diarrhea, skin lesions, headache
and memory loss beginning 7/97.

Treatment with cholestyramine and sorbitol begun 9/25/97. Neurocognitives done 9/26 were markedly abnormal. Patient had symp-
tomatic improvement within 3 days though patient could tell when
dose of cholestyramine was wearing off by recurrence of abdominal cramping. At follow up 2 weeks later patient was asymptomatic
and had returned to work.

Repeat neurocognitive exam showed minimal improvement only.
Patient continues to work in area water ways. He uses 2 scoops of
cholestyramine daily.

Case #5

44 year old male Virginia Marine Fisheries worker had extensive
exposure to the Pocomoke River beginning 7/97. Coworkers, including MD DNR commander, noted impairment in patient's memory, patient had abdominal cramps and skin lesions. Patient was
referred for treatment by Case 2. Memory loss documented to be
an inability to remember a five number sequence (0/5) and a four
word list (1/4).

Treatment was initiated 9/25/97 with fading of skin lesions, improvement in memory and elimination of abdominal pain by
10/3/97.

Discussion

As our knowledge of PHIS expands, laboratory markers for the illness should become available. Neurocognitive testing, the fingerprint of the illness, is expensive and not readily available. A clinical diagnosis of PHIS can be made. While the illness can be self limited, the persistent symptoms of these five patients improved rapidly with cholestyramine treatment.

Studies of brevetoxin, a different dinoflagellate toxin, in rats (6) show prompt clearing of an IV dose, within 24 seconds, with uptake by muscle, metabolism by liver, with excretion into intestine. Drs. Sherwood Hall (4) FDA Shellfish Poisoning and Mark Poli (5) brevetoxin expert, have endorsed continuing work with cholestyramine.

The hypothesis for consideration is that the pfiesteria toxin causes an acute human illness and in some patients, a persistent human illness. The toxin, a non specific irritant of skin and mucus membranes passes quickly from alveoli into blood following aerosol or droplet inhalation. The toxin is postulated to be absorbed into muscle, with equilibration into lipid tissues such as brain and surfactant in lung. The toxin is excreted into bile with enterohepatic recirculation.

Cholestyramine may bind toxin in the small intestine, permitting excretion in stool, depleting the toxin from lipid reservoirs. The clinical symptoms fit such a proposed model (see pfiesteria symptom complex, table 1) with conjunctival irritation, and cough being early onset symptoms, followed by myalgias, headache and memory loss. Bronchospasm and abdominal symptoms are late manifestations.

Recurrence of symptoms with repeat exposure suggests a lack of protective immune response to the toxin. While cholestyramine is not a totally benign treatment, the resolution of headache, memory impairment and bronchospasm suggest strongly that treatment of the GI tract affords an opportunity to reduce the body burden of toxin.

The prompt improvement in persistent symptoms with use of cholestyramine may provide a therapeutic option for the practicing physician faced with the clinical problem of profound memory impairment and disruption of normal daily life that pfiesteria can cause.

References
1) Shoemaker R., *Maryland Medical Journal*, Vol. 46 No. 10, pp. 521–523 1997
2) Grattan, *et al.*, *Lancet* in press
3) Burkholder, *et al.*, *J. Toxicology and Environmental Health*, 46: 501-22, 1995
4) Hall, Sherwood, Personal Communications
5) Poli, Mark, Personal Communications
6) Distribution and Elimination of Brevetoxin PbTx-3 in Rats, *Poli, Toxicon*, Vol. 28, No. 8, pp. 910–903, 1996

Pfiesteria Symptom Complex
(October 1)

- IMMEDIATE EFFECTS
    Skin burning
    Conjunctival injection
    Cough
    Wheeze
    Sore throat
- THREE HOURS
    Myalgia
    Headache
    Memory impairment
- 24 HOURS
    Rash
    Headache
    Abdominal cramps
    Exercise induced asthma
- PERSISTENT
    Rash up to 2 months
    Memory loss of up to 6 months
    Neurocognitive deficits unknown duration
    Bronchospasm
    Secretory diarrhea

MCS Protocol
(October 1)

1) Upon awakening, before brushing teeth and before eating: One tsp. Milk of Magnesia (oral chole-cystagogue).

2) 30 minutes after eating, four times a day, 1 scoop or one packet cholestyramine mixed with 1 oz. 70% Sorbitol and 6 oz. juice.

3) Bloating, reflux, satiety, constipation, diarrhea respond to changing food/medication sequence.

4) For chronic exposure, occupational, 1 scoop twice a day.

5) For recurrent exposure reinstitute full program.

About the Author

Ritchie Shoemaker, M.D., is a practicing family physician in Pocomoke City, Maryland, and also a dedicated wetland ecologist. Dr. Shoemaker graduated *magna cum laude* from Duke University in 1973 with a B.S. in molecular biology and a minor in philosophy.

While attending Duke Medical School, Dr. Shoemaker concentrated on public health studies and epidemiology. He also launched a journal for medical students—*First Contact*—that achieved national distribution during his term as editor.

After graduating from medical school in 1977, Dr. Shoemaker completed his medicine residency at the Williamsport Hospital in Williamsport, Pennsylvania, where he designed a rural health care system. His interests in rural primary care medicine led him to Pocomoke City, located at the extreme southern end of Maryland's Eastern Shore.

Dr. Shoemaker has practiced in Pocomoke City since 1980. He and his friends have built award-winning nature trails in the region, along with both non-tidal wetland and tidal wetland gardens.

His wife JoAnn teaches kindergarten in the public elementary school, where she takes a nurturing approach to teaching young children. Daughter Sally trains and cares for her horses at the family home along the Pocomoke River, where her formative years have been enriched by science, photography and music.